FRONTIERS OF ASTRONOMY

Frontiers of Astronomy

FRED HOYLE

Author of *The Nature of the Universe*

ILLUSTRATED

HARPER & ROW, PUBLISHERS, NEW YORK

TO MY WIFE

It is a pleasure to thank colleagues with whom I have collaborated on various investigations mentioned in the present book: I am indebted to Mr. T. Gold in relation to Chapter Six, to Prof. Bondi and Dr. R. A. Lyttleton in relation to Chapter Seven, and to Dr. Martin Schwarzschild concerning topics discussed in Chapters Eight and Nine.

I also wish to thank those many astronomers with whom I have argued over knotty problems, and who have so often put me right (I hope!) on many points.

My debt is great to the Observatories that have supplied the photographs with which this volume is illustrated. Individual astronomers have also been most generous in making their personal photographs available to me. My thanks in this respect are due to Dr. Bart. J. Bok, Dr. Peter van de Kamp, Mr. W. Miller, Mr. M. Ryle, and Dr. Fritz Zwicky.

CONTENTS

LIST OF PLATES

Plates I–X *will be found as a complete section
between pp.* 64 *and* 65

Plates XI–XXI *will be found as a complete
section between pp.* 128 *and* 129.

ix

LINE ILLUSTRATIONS

PROLOGUE

The spin of a coin depends on chance. So do many of the things that take place in our minds: the precise moment of time when a new idea forms itself in a man's brain, for instance. But chance is a concept all too readily overworked. When at a loss to understand something, we are only too often tempted to suppose that our ignorance lies in a failure to trace some random quirk. And nowhere is this done more easily than in astronomy. Yet I think there are few studies in which chance is less important at root than it is in astronomy. The great stage where the Universe acts out its play is one on which the twin roles of coincidence and chance have scarcely any entry. From the vast expanding system of galaxies down to the humblest planet, and to the creatures that may live on it, there seems to be a strongly forged chain of cause and effect. Accidents there must be sometimes, but they matter not a jot to the march of the larger events.

The main theme of the present book lies not so much in any particular astronomical topic as in an attempt to write coincidence and chance out of the play. The first and last chapters have nothing factual in common, but they are linked by this underlying aim.

The astronomer seems at first sight to be the most helpless of all scientists. He cannot experiment with the Universe. It is a significant matter of nomenclature that whereas we speak of experimental work in other sciences we speak of *observational* work in astronomy. The astronomer cannot move around the Universe taking an especially detailed look at any object that he finds of interest, as the 'field' worker does in other sciences. He cannot tear objects such as stars to pieces when he wants to find out how they work, which is the method used by the physicists—the tough guys of science. Astronomers perforce have to accept a comparatively meek role. They cannot alter the light that comes into the telescope, although they can build larger telescopes to get more light and they can use more efficient devices to analyse the light. Yet the astronomer possesses one well-nigh overwhelming advantage. This lies in the sheer variety of the things that can be observed. The Universe is so vast, and the lengths of time that are of interest in astronomy are so long, that almost every conceivable type of astronomical process is still going on somewhere or other. The astronomer's problem is not a lack of information but an embarrassing excess of it. His is often a problem of disentanglement rather than one of synthesis: among the great wealth of detail he has to decide what is important and what is irrelevant. The light that enters the telescope contains a truly fantastic tangle of information. It is just to assist in the unwinding of the tangle that astronomical theory has been developed, the weapons of astronomical theory being derived directly from physics, chemistry, aerodynamics, and a host of other sciences in a lesser degree. Often the theories that are used are well-known and well-tried but sometimes they are less well-known and sometimes they lie at the very frontiers of knowledge.

CHAPTER ONE

Oddities About the Earth

Man's claim to have progressed far beyond his fellow animals must be supported, not by his search for food, warmth, and shelter (however ingeniously conducted) but by his penetration into the very fabric of the Universe. It is in the world of ideas and in the relation of his brain to the Universe itself, that the superiority of Man lies. The rise of Man may justly be described as an adventure in ideas.

The present book is concerned with one of the chapters of this adventure. It is in some respects the most spectacular chapter—the one in which the large scale features of the Universe are beginning to be unfolded to us in all their majesty. But we cannot seek for grandeur at the outset, rather must we begin very modestly with the Earth itself.

Let's start with the Earth, and with a very simple question about it.

Why is the length of the day 24 hours?

Half the Earth is lit by the Sun and the other half lies in shadow. Because of the rotation of the Earth we are constantly turning from shadow to Sun and from Sun to shadow: we experience the procession of night and day. The Earth is turning with respect to the Sun rather like a joint on a spit, although of course there is no material spit stuck through the Earth—we are turning freely in space, just as we are moving freely in space on our annual journey around the Sun.

In the past the Earth rotated considerably more rapidly than it does now: at the time of its origin the cycle of day and night may have been as short as 10 hours. The spin of the Earth must accordingly have been slowed down during the 4,000 million years or so that have elapsed since the early

I

period of its life. The agency responsible for the braking action is known. It is just the twice-daily tides that are raised by the Moon and the Sun. The oceanic tides cause a frictional resistance when they impinge on the continental margins. This friction produces heat at the expense of the energy of rotation of the Earth, thereby slightly slowing the Earth's spin. In return for its effect on the Earth, the Moon experiences a force that pushes it gradually farther and farther away from us.

Formerly it was thought that the spin of the Earth has been slowing down continuously ever since the time of its formation, so that on this old view it just happens that we are living at the time when the spin has been braked down to 24 hours: it was thought that in the past the cycle of night and day took less than 24 hours, and that in the future it would take more. But a very recent theory, due to E. R. R. Holmberg, disagrees with this last step, disagrees that the cycle of day and night will ever take longer than 24 hours in the future.

Now since the braking effect of the oceanic tides is un-doubtedly still operative, this view of Holmberg evidently demands that there shall be some compensating process tending to speed up the spin of the Earth. The substance of the new argument is that such a compensating speeding-up process does in fact exist. To understand how it operates let us first consider an analogy. Take a weight suspended from a spring, give the weight a pull downwards, and then let go. The system will start oscillating up and down. Now give the weight a small push downward during each oscillation. It will be found that, provided the weight is always pushed at the same stage of each oscillation, a quite violent motion will be built up. This is known as forcing an oscillation in reson-ance—'forcing' because of the pushes and 'in resonance' because the pushes are adjusted to come at the same stage of each oscillation.

Now the atmosphere of the Earth oscillates up and down like the spring and the weight, the pressure in the air taking the part of the spring and the weight of the atmosphere acting, of course, as the weight. Not only this, but the atmos-phere is pushed by the same forces as those that raise the oceanic tides. But the force due to the Moon, which is the more important in the raising of the oceanic tides, does not act in resonance with the oscillations of the atmosphere and consequently does not build up appreciable motions of the atmospheric gases. The somewhat weaker pushes due to the Sun do act in resonance with the atmosphere, however. The result is that very considerable up and down motions of the air are set up. These motions are accompanied by oscillations of pressure that can be detected on a sensitive barometer. The variations occur twice daily, just as the oceanic tides do. The pressure is found to be at a maximum about two hours before midday and about two hours before midnight. By a careful calculation it can be shown that this precedence of the atmospheric tides before midday and midnight causes the gravitational field of the Sun to put a twist on the Earth tending to speed it up. The strength of the twist can also be estimated. The very important result emerges that the twist is comparable with the slowing down effect of the oceanic tides, just as Holmberg's theory requires it to be.

It is important to realise that the speeding-up process need not exactly compensate all the time for the slowing-down effect of the oceanic tides. It is sufficient if the two processes compensate each other *on the average*, averages being calculated over say a time of 100,000 years. Indeed exact equality at all times is not to be expected for the reason that the slowing effect is likely to vary quite appreciably and quickly from one time to another. During the last ice-age for instance the slowing effect may well have been much less than it is today.

The theory is also favoured by another point, one that seems to me to be well nigh decisive; namely that the time of oscillation of the atmosphere and the time between successive pushes of the Sun on the atmosphere depend on entirely different considerations. The time for the oscillation depends on the temperature, density, and chemical nature of the air, whereas the time between successive pushes of the Sun depends on the rate of spin of the Earth. How comes it then that the two are so closely coincident?

In answering this question, Holmberg follows the older ideas to begin with. He supposes that at one time the Earth was rotating considerably faster than at present. There was then no resonance between the pushes of the Sun and the oscillations of the atmosphere. Consequently no strong oscillations were set up, so that the speeding-up process was inappreciable. The slowing-down effect of the oceanic tides therefore operated essentially unchecked, just as used to be supposed. But here now is the crucial point. As the Earth slowed to a day of 24 hours the pushes of the Sun gradually came into resonance with the oscillations of the atmosphere. So larger and larger motions of the air were built up, and the speeding-up process increased correspondingly. This went on until the speeding-up process came into average balance with the slowing effect of the oceanic tides. A state of balance has been operative ever since.

These ideas of Holmberg lead to other interesting consequences. It appears that the Earth must be spiralling very slowly inwards towards the Sun, and the Moon must be spiralling slowly outwards from the Earth. The change in the distance of the Earth from the Sun remains very small, but the change in the distance of the Moon from the Earth does not remain small. Given sufficient time the Moon will spiral so far away from the Earth that it will fall prey to the gravitational influence of the Sun. The Sun will pull it away from the Earth entirely so that it will no longer go circling around us, but will move independently around the Sun as a planet in its own right. This will happen when the slow spiralling that is going on all the time takes the Moon out from its present distance of nearly a quarter of million miles to a distance of about a million miles. Long before this stage is reached we shall unfortunately lose one of the finest of all cosmic spectacles, however: the total eclipse of the Sun. This depends on the Moon coming between us and the Sun and on it serving to block out so much of the fierce solar glare that we are able to see the delicate extensive outer atmosphere of the Sun—the corona. At present the Moon is only just able to do this: and when it has spiralled a little farther away it will not be able to produce a total eclipse at all. Conversely in earlier ages when the Moon was nearer to the Earth such eclipses must have been more frequent, more striking, and more prolonged than they now are.

The Ice-Ages

Over most of the long history of the Earth the climate throughout the world has been considerably warmer than it is at present. But during the last million years the Earth has been plunged into one of its rare transient cold epochs; epochs that are characterised by the presence of ice-sheets in the Arctic and by the frequent excursions of these ice-sheets into temperate latitudes—the so-called ice-ages. The exceptional nature of present-day conditions is shown by the temperature of the Atlantic Ocean, which is now some ten degrees centigrade lower than normal; normal being reckoned as the average situation taken over the whole existence of the Earth, over 4,000 million years.

There have been four major periods during the last million years when a glacial climate has been dominant in the northern temperate zone of the Earth (since the southern temperate zone is nearly all sea a straightforward similarity between the two hemispheres is not to be expected). At their greatest extension, the glaciers have stretched from the Arctic into N. Europe and N. America, reaching into England and Denmark, and into positions south of the great lakes in the United States. These periods of glacial dominance each occupied some 50,000 to 70,000 years. The last of them came to an end only very recently, geologically speaking—about 10,000 years ago. Partly because it was so recent, and partly because one ice-age tends to obliterate the relics left from previous ice-ages, more is known about this last of the ice-ages than about the earlier ones. Perhaps its most remarkable feature was the abruptness of its end. The ice simply melted, the water flowing away in huge rivers into the sea. Within only two or three thousand years the glaciers retreated into the Arctic, to much their present locations. The climate of the northern temperate zone changed within this short time (again geologically speaking) from a pronouncedly glacial character to being distinctly warmer than at present. The rapidity of this melting of the ice sets a challenging problem. How was it possible for such a startling change of climate to occur within such a short time (3,000 years!)?

The external theory of the ice-ages

The cause of the ice-ages is not known with any certainty, but two theories that deserve close consideration have been put forward very recently. We shall consider the first of these now, leaving the second to be discussed at the end of the present chapter. The reader may then like to make his own choice as to which of the two alternatives is to be preferred.

The first theory seeks to explain the ice-ages in terms of a cause external to the Earth. The simplest such cause would be a change in the amount of light and heat that we receive from the Sun. An increase of the Sun's radiation by several per cent would certainly have been sufficient to cause the rapid melting of the last ice-sheet. Our climate is very sensitively balanced to the amount of radiation that we receive from the Sun. Normally we pay little attention to things outside the Earth, but if the Sun were to vary a little, only a very little, we should soon be faced by a situation beside which the political crises that fill our lives would fall into entire insignificance.

There is neither theoretical nor observational evidence that changes take place in the radiation of the Sun, however. It is difficult to see how anything occurring inside the Sun could produce an appreciable fluctuation in a time as short as 3,000 years. The time for changes to become important in the Sun must be measured in millions or even in thousands of millions of years. In support of this it is certain that variations in the Sun's radiation from year to year are very small at the present time. This has been established by Harold Johnson using a new method of observation of considerable interest. Instead of attempting to measure directly the amount of heat and light that we receive from the Sun, which is difficult to do because the intensity of sunlight is too great to allow of easy measurement, Johnson measures the sunlight that is reflected by the planet Uranus. This can be done with great accuracy. Since if the Sun's radiation were to vary there would be a proportionate alteration in the amount of sunlight reflected by Uranus this method is an excellent one for keeping a watch on the Sun— if the Sun tries any monkey business we shall soon know about it.

With the Sun out of court, we are left to search for a more

subtle external cause of climatic variation. Instead of describing the many unsuccessful attempts that have in the past been made to discover such a cause, let us come straight away to some recent ideas that seem far preferable to the older suggestions. Perhaps the best way to approach these ideas is from a direction that you would least expect. Let us think for the moment about the ordinary horticultural greenhouse. Even without an internal supply of heat the temperature will be found to be higher inside a greenhouse than it is outside. Why? Let us try first to answer this everyday question.

The glass roof of a greenhouse allows much of the incident light and heat from the Sun to pass freely into the interior, where it is mostly absorbed by the contents of the greenhouse, by plants and other materials, causing them to become heated. Now as more and more sunlight streams through the roof why do the plants not become steadily hotter and hotter? Because sooner or later they begin to lose as much energy as they are receiving from the sunlight. This loss of energy happens in a not very obvious way. It takes place because the plants emit infra-red radiation.

Possibly it may come as a surprise to realise that every object we handle in our daily lives emits radiation. But the radiation is invisible infra-red and does not enable us to see everyday objects. We see everyday objects because they reflect sunlight. During the day every object becomes heated by constantly absorbing light and simultaneously becomes cooled by constantly emitting infra-red radiation, the two processes working in opposite directions, tending to compensate each other. This is the situation for the plants inside a greenhouse.

Let us now come quickly to the crucial point. The glass roof of a greenhouse allows sunlight to stream freely in but it does not allow the infra-red radiation emitted by the plants and the other contents to stream freely out. It is just because sunlight can come freely in but the infra-red cannot go easily out that the temperature is raised inside a greenhouse.

Now our atmosphere acts like the roof of a greenhouse. Thus while it allows sunlight to come more or less freely in, it tends to trap the radiation that is constantly being emitted by the surface material of the Earth. The temperature is thereby raised very appreciably, just as it is in a greenhouse. This rise of temperature is very crucial to our existence, for without it the whole Earth would be plunged into a permanent glacial condition.

Evidently then an ice-age would arise if the greenhouse effect of our atmosphere were destroyed or seriously weakened. This would happen if the concentrations of those gases of the atmosphere that are responsible for blocking the infra-red radiation were appreciably reduced. The gas of main importance in this respect is water vapour. The question therefore arises as to how the amount of water vapour in the atmosphere might be systematically reduced, especially the amount at a height of some 20,000 feet above the ground. In this, may lie the answer to the riddle of the ice-ages.

The water vapour in the atmosphere sometimes condenses into liquid droplets that fall to the ground as rain. This process tends to decrease the water vapour content of the atmosphere. Evaporation from the oceans works in the opposite direction tending to increase the water vapour content. Thus the amount of water vapour in the atmosphere represents a balance between these two opposing processes. Evidently the balance can be altered, in the sense of decreasing the amount of water vapour, either if the evaporation rate is reduced or if the tendency for the water to fall as rain is increased. Of these two possibilities the former can be dismissed, since a general reduction of evaporation would only occur if there was a decrease in the amount of light and heat that we receive from the Sun; and we have already seen that this is not a likely possibility.

How then can the tendency for the water to fall out of the atmosphere as rain be increased? Possibly through the entry into the atmosphere of swarms of the tiny particles known as meteors. Such particles do actually exist in great numbers in the realms of space between the planets. As the Earth moves around the Sun particles are constantly being swept into our atmosphere. The entry of exceptionally large meteors, of about the size of a small pea, can often be seen at night: they are the well-known shooting stars (the trail of a shooting star can be seen on Plate I). But a normal meteor, with a size of

8

perhaps one thousandth part of a centimetre, is too small to be seen in this way. Their motions are largely checked when they are about 60 miles up in the atmosphere, where they are sometimes observed as the famous noctilucent clouds. After this they fall slowly downwards, taking a number of days to reach the surface of the Earth.

Now conditions are often operative in the atmosphere, say at a height of about 20,000 feet, where a considerable concentration of water vapour exists that does not fall as rain because there is no way of forming large water drops out of the vapour—and only drops of an appreciable size can fall as rain. The arrival from above of a large number of meteoric particles might well produce a drastic change in such a situation, since water drops would immediately tend to condense around the particles. If the concentration of the water vapour were large enough, rain would probably fall.

The tendency of meteoric particles to bring down water vapour as rain must weaken the greenhouse effect, and the possibility exists that for a sufficiently large number of meteoric particles entering the atmosphere the greenhouse effect might be weakened to the point of onset of a glacial climate.

The recent work of E. G. Bowen gives support to these ideas. By analysing records for the last fifty years it has become apparent that there is a world-wide tendency for exceptionally heavy falls of rain to take place on specific days in the year, on January 12th to 13th for instance. Bowen's explanation is that at some time prior to these exceptional dates the Earth on its journey round the Sun passes across the track of an exceptionally dense swarm of meteors—meteors that for the most part are much too small to show as shooting stars when they enter our atmosphere. The meteors fall through the atmosphere and are available to produce rain in the manner we have just discussed.

Comets and Meteors

Meteors become distributed throughout the solar system when a comet breaks up, as comets are observed to do from time to time. According to the theory of Lyttleton, comets

9

are nothing but swarms of tiny particles probably composed of ice.* The break-up of a comet accordingly consists of the break-up of a swarm, not of the break-up of a few large chunks of solid material. We can think of the break-up of a cloud of birds as an analogy. The comets break up not through any internal influence, but through the external action of the Sun. Usually comets break up rather slowly, but sometimes if one comes too close to the Sun the break-up may be very sudden.

It might seem from this that the density of interplanetary particles must be steadily increasing, since further comets are being broken up all the time. But this is not so, because two other processes are working in an opposite direction by causing the meteors to fall steadily towards the Sun. Of these probably the more important arises from a flow of gas within the whole solar system. (Evidence will be presented in Chapter 7 showing that a flow of gas is actually taking place at the present time.) Whereas a large body like the Earth is scarcely affected at all by the gas, a tiny meteoric particle must experience a strong dragging influence; a tiny particle instead of moving indefinitely round and round the Sun, as the Earth does, will be caused to spiral inwards towards the Sun until eventually it is brought in close enough to become entirely vaporised by the scorching heat.

We see therefore that the meteors in the solar system form a reservoir with an input and an output. The break-up of comets supplies the input, while the dragging effect of gas within the solar system supplies the output. The situation is therefore similar to an ordinary reservoir, the capacity of which can be increased either by stepping up the inflow or by decreasing the output, or of course by both of these. The sudden break-up of an exceptionally large comet might conceivably increase the reservoir of meteors to the point at which glacial conditions would return to the Earth. But such an occurrence would probably cause the glacial conditions to have a sudden beginning and a slow end—which is just the opposite from what happened at the end of the last ice-age. A sudden end to an ice-age demands a sharp increase in the outflow from the

* For a thorough discussion of this theory, see Lyttleton's book, *The Comets and Their Origin*, Cambridge, 1952.

reservoir, and this requires a sudden increase in the flow of gas within the solar system. It seems more likely, therefore, that if the variations of climate of the last ten thousand years or so are to be explained in terms of the present theory they must come from changes in the flow of gas rather from changes in the rate of break-up of comets.

We are now following a different trail. We started by considering the greenhouse effect. Then we moved on to meteors and comets. Now we have come to a flow of gas within the solar system. Next we must ask: where does this flow of gas come from? Although there is a fairly general agreement among astronomers that the flow exists, there is a divergence of opinion on its origin. Some maintain that the flow comes outwards from the Sun, others take the view that it comes inwards from the vast cloud of diffuse gas that fills the space between the stars—the interstellar gas. On this second view the Sun is constantly scooping up quantities of the interstellar gas, and this produces a flow into, not out of, the Sun.

Perhaps before we go on to more argument it is as well to take a look at the villain of the piece—the comet. One of them is shown in Plate II. It is an old superstition that the appearance of comets in the sky presages disaster. Perhaps the old superstition was right.

It has been estimated that the break-up of many comets is taking place at such a rate that they will be entirely disrupted within a million years. It is an immediate inference that these comets cannot have been moving around the Sun as they are at present for much longer than a million years, since otherwise they would already have been broken up.

Now the theory of the ice-ages discussed in the previous section requires the last million years to have a special significance in the history of the comets. If this were not so, it would be difficult to understand why the Earth's climate during the last million years has been so different from the preceding 100 million years—no ice-ages occurred at all during the whole of this long period. Indeed for over 100 million years, up to the last million years, the climate of the Earth was considerably warmer than it is now. This would be entirely explicable in terms of our theory if the break-up of

11

comets were an abnormal process belonging to the last million years, a process that scarcely occurred at all during the preceding 100 million years.

The toppling over of the Earth

Not all evidence of glaciation can be explained completely in the manner discussed above. Several hundred million years ago glaciations of a very strange sort occurred. The glaciated areas did not occur at all in the present arctic zones, but in an arc stretching from Western Australia to India, then to Madagascar and the central African plateau, and thence to the western part of Brazil. It would indeed be difficult to explain this except on the basis that the arctics, tropics, and the temperate zones were differently situated in the distant past from what they are today. We need to suppose that some 200 or 300 million years ago one of the poles, probably the south pole, was moving around very considerably from place to place in the Indian Ocean.

This idea can be subjected to a test. If regions now in the tropics were once in the arctic it is necessary that land at present in the two arctic zones must formerly have enjoyed a considerably warmer climate than they do now. Was this so? Evidence from fossilised plants shows that this was indeed the case. Plants that require a warm climate once grew in Spitzbergen, Greenland, and on the antarctic continent. The idea gains further credence from this evidence.

How then could this have happened? Not I think through the continents floating around on the surface of the Earth, being sometimes in one place and sometimes in another. How a continent composed of rock some 35 kilometres thick could contrive to move is something that has never been explained, and until some plausible reason is offered in its support we need scarcely take the notion of 'drifting continents' at all seriously. Nor can we accept the idea that the Earth's axis of rotation, the axis that determines the climatic zones, was differently aligned in the past to what it is now. The Earth's axis of rotation is tilted at an angle of about 67° to the plane of the orbit in which the Earth moves around the Sun. The climatic zones would indeed be altered if this angle were changed, but a careful analysis by G. H. Darwin showed many years ago that such a change is quite out of the question. The tilt of the axis of rotation cannot have altered by any appreciable margin since the time of formation of the Earth.

There remains the more subtle idea that the Earth may have turned relative to its axis of rotation. Imagine a metal skewer stuck through a sphere of butter. Evidently the sphere could be turned even though the skewer stayed fixed—the skewer would simply cut through the butter as the sphere turned. We could describe this by saying that the sphere had turned relative to the skewer. Now replace the butter by the Earth, and the skewer by the axis around which the Earth is spinning. A turning of the Earth relative to its axis of rotation implies the same idea as the turning of the butter relative to the skewer. But we have still to explain how such a reorientation might happen to the Earth.

Suppose to begin with that the Earth were entirely uniform in composition. Then suppose a mountain range to develop in some part of the surface. According to a recent suggestion of T. Gold the Earth must turn slowly relative to its axis of rotation until the mountain range comes to lie on the equator. Formerly it was thought that the equatorial bulge of the Earth acts as a stabilising influence to prevent such a toppling-over from occurring. It is well known that as a consequence of its rotation the equatorial diameter of the Earth exceeds the polar diameter by about 27 miles—the Earth is slightly squashed at its poles in other words. The bulge at the equator would certainly prevent toppling-over from occurring if the material of the Earth were rigid. But the material of the Earth is not rigid; even rocks can move slowly when subjected to large forces. According to Gold it is just this lack of complete rigidity that allows the toppling-over to occur. What happens is that the bulge adjusts itself in such a way as the Earth turns that it is always maintained at the equator, irrespective of what parts of the surface happen to lie at the equator at any moment. This is the new aspect of the problem that was not realised by previous investigators.

Of course in actuality the Earth is not entirely uniform

apart from one mountain range. The interior of the Earth is not uniform, as we shall see in the following chapter. Nor is there just one irregularity on the surface. But a similar argument must be applicable in the actual case. The Earth must take up such a position that all its irregularities are placed in a suitably disposed position with respect to the equator. And if for any reason the irregularities should alter, the Earth will turn relative to its axis of rotation until the new irregularities arrive at a new position of stability in which they again become suitably averaged with respect to the equator.

We see therefore that the question of why the Earth is differently orientated today from what it was about 200 million years ago can be answered by saying that the present irregularities are different to what they formerly were. Such a suggestion is entirely plausible. It is especially possible that the internal irregularities of the Earth have altered during the last 200 million years.

It is perhaps a little curious that no one in the past seems to have given serious consideration to the question of why the Earth is orientated as we find it: why is Greenland near the north pole? Why is Ceylon near the equator? I suppose that if I had been asked these questions a few years ago I would have answered that the way the Earth happens to be orientated is a matter of chance, depending on the way that the Earth happened to be spinning at the time it was formed. But according to these new ideas no chance enters the issue. The Earth must be orientated as we find it because of the present distribution of its irregularities—change these and the orientation will be changed. Even if a cosmic giant were to turn the Earth relative to its axis of rotation, as we might turn a model globe, the Earth given time—a few millions of years—would come back to its present position. We are balanced in our present orientation.

It is perhaps a pity that the Earth would take many thousands of years to heel over, otherwise a novel method of warfare could be suggested. Instead of blowing our enemies to perdition we could simply turn them up into the Arctic—a much more elegant procedure. This might be done by spending our resources on the creation of vast inland seas into which we could pump water from the oceans. Instead of building tanks, bombs, planes, and battleships, we should concentrate on building bigger and bigger pumps. Hydraulics would become the science of the day. High honours would come to those who invented better and better pumps, and international espionage would devote its sinister activities to the winkling out of the other fellows' watery secrets (which would become a very serious matter indeed).

The internal theory of the ice-ages

We introduced the subject of the toppling of the Earth by pointing out that ice once lay on strange regions of the Earth—Australia, India, Africa, and Brazil. Now if we explain the glaciation of such regions by a movement of the Earth relative to its polar axis, why should we not explain the recent ice-ages of the last million years in a similar fashion? Such ice-sheets would undoubtedly sweep over N. America and N. Europe if the Earth were to turn so that the North pole were to fall in Greenland. This theory would be highly satisfactory if two difficulties could be overcome.

One difficulty is to make the Earth topple fast enough. To fit the rapid changes of climate that are known to have taken place, it would be necessary for the poles to move appreciably over the surface of the Earth in 10,000 years, or perhaps in even less time than this. Until recently it seemed most unlikely that changes so sudden could come about, but recent calculations by Gold have suggested that perhaps this difficulty is not so serious as it was once thought to be.

There is a second awkward point. Some thirty million years ago there were marked disturbances in the contours of the Earth's surface. During this epoch the great mountain ranges were thrust up—the Himalayas, Rockies, and Alps, among others. Such changes in the irregularities of the surface might perhaps have been expected to topple the Earth to an appreciable degree. Yet no appreciable polar-wander took place, and there were no ice-ages. This can only be explained on the basis that the present orientation of the Earth possesses a large measure of stability and some quite exceptional disturbance is apparently required to shift it. Hence we see that, if polar-wander has been responsible for the ice-ages of the last million years, then the disturbing agent must have been of outstanding potency—it must have been stronger and more effective than the process of uplift of the great mountain ranges. The question then arises: what was the disturbing agent? It is here that the difficulty emerges, because no disturbance of the required magnitude and of the required rapidity of change is known to have occurred. Certainly no such disturbance has occurred at the Earth's surface. Indeed the theory can only be saved from annihilation on this point if marked changes have taken place in irregularities that are situated deep *inside* the Earth. The discussion of the next chapter will show that this hypothesis is perhaps not so wild as it might at first sight be thought to be.

Let us turn now to the outstanding merit of the theory. If the North pole were once in Greenland then Siberia must have lain nearer the equator than it is at present. Consequently there should have been no glaciation of Siberia. In fact there was no glaciation of Siberia.

It has been customary to explain this by saying that precipitation was inadequate to build ice-fields in N. Asia. A very cold climate is not by itself a guarantee that glaciers will form on the land—there must also be sufficient snowfall. For myself I have always been a little suspicious of this argument. It is true that precipitation in Siberia was probably less than in N. America and N. Europe, but I have always felt that ice-sheets would nevertheless be formed if the temperature was low enough.

Here then we have a notable difference between the two theories described in the present chapter. If the meteoric theory is correct the lowering of temperature during an ice-age must have operated over the whole Earth, and in particular in Siberia. If on the other hand the polar-wander theory is correct the temperature in Siberia must have been higher, not lower, during an ice-age than it is now. Similar differences apply to other parts of the Earth. The polar-wander theory requires the N. Atlantic to have been colder during an ice-age, but the N. Pacific should have been warmer. Australia on the other hand should have been colder. It will eventually be possible to check these different predictions. For instance, the ocean temperatures of the past can be ascertained in various ways. By carrying out measurements of ocean temperatures systematically over the whole Earth it is likely that enough information can be obtained for a clear-cut decision to be made between the two theories. On which do you put your money?

CHAPTER TWO

The Working Earth

It has often been supposed that we possess a ready perception of the three dimensions of space. But this is not really so. Every student of geometry knows that it is much easier to think about problems in two dimensions, problems that can be completely represented on a sheet of paper, than it is to think about problems in three dimensions. Intuition cannot be trusted in three dimensions, as it can in two. Engineers and architects recognise this in their use of drawings and plans, which ingeniously seek to represent three dimensional objects—machines and buildings, in a two dimensional way. Yet we are not wholly lacking in our perception of a third spacial dimension. Perhaps we should say that our perception extends to two and a half dimensions.

The reason for this somewhat curious state of affairs lies in the way we live, and in a past evolution that has equipped us with rather defective sense organs. We judge distances and directions over the surface of the Earth with commendable accuracy, and it is no doubt from this that we derive our geometrical abilities in two dimensions. But our idea of the third dimension, up and down, is woefully inaccurate. Look out over an impressive landscape, and you get the idea that distances upwards through the air are as great as distances over the land. This gives us the notion that the atmosphere is a big place. Yet the atmosphere is no more than a thin skin surrounding the Earth like a single thickness of paper pasted on a billiard ball. Our whole existence lies in this skin and all our intuitive notions about the Earth are derived from it. Creatures that move in the air probably have a better intuitive grasp of the three dimensions of space than we have. But such creatures do not possess the powers of analysis to find out the things that they do not intuitively perceive. Herein lies our special

18

strength. From our studies of two dimensions we have developed methods that can be extended with complete precision, if not with intuition, to three dimensions and even to four or more dimensions. And by analysis we can probe into the Earth, and can find out what it is made of, and about the things that are happening inside it.

What the interior of the Earth is like

The planet we live on is not just a ball of inert material. During past ages dramatic changes have taken place inside the Earth. Indeed it is likely that without these changes life could never have originated on the Earth. And changes are still going on today. They show themselves in the occurrence of earthquakes, in the outbursts of volcanoes, and in the uplift of mountain ranges.

In outward appearance the Earth is a nearly spherical ball with a radius of about 6,350 kilometres. Internally the Earth consists of two parts, a core and a mantle. An essential distinction is that the core consists mainly of liquid and the mantle mainly of solid rock. The core extends outwards from the centre to a distance of some 3,450 kilometres. The mantle as its name implies is an outer covering extending from the core to the surface of the Earth.

Judged by ordinary standards the core is made of rather dense stuff. Bulk for bulk the material at the centre of the Earth is at least 13 times as heavy as ordinary water, while in the outer parts of the core the material is about 10 times as heavy as ordinary water.

The mantle possesses a thin outer crust that is exceptional in being composed of a particularly light kind of rock, with a density about 2.7 times that of water (compare this with a density of 13 at the centre of the Earth). Over the continents of the world this crustal rock is about 35 kilometres thick, while over the oceans it is at most only two or three kilometres thick. Below the crustal layer comes a different, denser rock, probably of a basic silicate variety. Indeed it seems likely that apart from the thin outer crust the rocks of the whole mantle are of a basic silicate variety right down to the junction

19

with the core, at a depth below the surface of about 2,900 kilometres. The general disposition of material inside the Earth is sketched in Fig. 1.

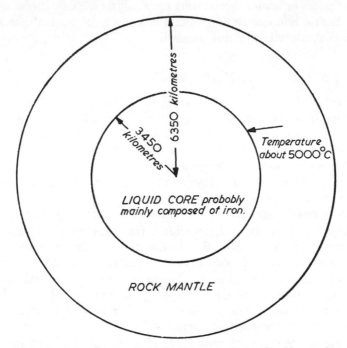

FIG. 1. The Earth's interior. K. E. Bullen suggests that liquid may give place to solid near the extreme centre.

We must now introduce the idea that the pressures occurring inside the Earth are very considerable. It is well known that at sea-level our atmosphere exerts a pressure of about 15 lbs. per square inch. This in itself is no mean pressure as we all soon come to realise if we have to pump up an automobile tyre. But the pressure inside the Earth is vastly greater than this, amounting to tens of millions of lbs. per square inch. At such enormous pressures ordinary rock becomes appreciably squashed. This is why the density of the rocks of the Earth's mantle increases as we go inwards to greater and greater depths. The density immediately below the outer crust is about 3.3 times that of water. We may compare this with a density 4.0 at a depth of 500 kilometres, 4.5 at 1,000 kilometres, about 5.0 at 2,000 kilometres, and with about 5.6 at the surface of the core at a depth of 2,900 kilometres.

The last of these values raises an important question. We are now saying that the density in the part of the mantle immediately outside the core is about 5.6 times that of water. On the other hand immediately inside the core the density is about 9.7. This means that at the surface of the core there is not only a change from liquid on the inside to solid on the outside, but there is also a very considerable change in the density of the material, from 9.7 on the inside to 5.6 on the outside. This change gives an important clue to the nature of the material that constitutes the core, and the next main step in our argument will be to consider this question.

Before doing this, however, it may be of interest to say a little about how the results so far mentioned have been obtained. At first sight it might seem impossible to obtain experimental evidence about the situation inside the Earth. We shall now see that this is not so, that perhaps surprisingly the above results are all soundly based on experiment.

By good fortune the Earth itself goes a long way towards revealing its own secrets. This it does through the earthquake. Earthquakes are caused by a fracturing and slipping of rocks inside the Earth. This happens at all depths down to about 700 kilometres, but not at greater depths. How the rocks come to fracture, and why apparently they do not do so at depths greater than 700 kilometres is a problem that we shall take up at a later stage.

When an earthquake occurs vibrations travel away from the centre of fracture in all directions. Vibrations come vertically upwards from the fracture to the surface of the Earth often causing loss of life and damage to property, but they also go inwards towards the centre of the Earth. Such vibrations can go right through the central regions of the Earth and emerge at the surface on the far side of the world. The effects of an earthquake occurring in California can be studied in Singapore, for instance. Indeed the effects of an earthquake occurring in California can be studied all over the world, although very sensitive instruments may be required since the vibrations naturally become very feeble when they have spread out through the whole Earth.

The behaviour of the vibrations depends on the nature of the material through which they travel. The behaviour depends on the density of the material, and very critically indeed on whether the material is liquid or solid. Vibrations that have passed through the core of the Earth always show that they have passed through liquid. This is why we can be so sure that the core is largely composed of liquid. The dependence of the vibrations on density also shows how the density varies inside the Earth, yielding the estimates that were quoted above. It was in this way that the jump of density at the surface of the core was discovered, a jump from a value of 9.7 on the inside to about 5.6 on the outside. Much of our knowledge derived from this source is due to the work of K. E. Bullen.

What is the core made of?

The simplest explanation of why there should be such a decisive jump of density at the surface of the core is that the surface of the core marks the boundary of separation between two entirely different materials. We have seen that the material of the mantle is probably mainly a basic silicate rock. We must now consider what the material of the core is likely to be.

This problem is best tackled by considering what sort of material would give about the right density for the core. Taking account of the squashing effect of the very high pressure in the core, we have to decide what material would give densities ranging from about 13 at the centre to 9.7 at the surface of the core. Allowance for the effect of squashing suggests that such material under ordinary laboratory conditions would have a density of about 8. This places it rather definitely in what is known as the 'iron group' of elements; that is to say, material composed mainly of the following elements: chromium, manganese, iron, cobalt and nickel. The material might also contain moderate concentrations of titanium, copper, and zinc.

The density argument will not take us any further than this, however. It will not tell us which of the 'iron group' is likely to be present in the greatest abundance. For this step we must appeal to astronomy. The Earth belongs to the Universe. So we may expect its composition to bear some relation to the composition of other cosmic bodies with the exception that the Earth being very small fry as cosmic bodies go has been unable to hang on to the light gases, hydrogen and helium, both of which are very abundant indeed in the stars, but which are in only low abundance on the Earth. Particularly we expect that if the core of the Earth is composed of elements in the 'iron group' then these elements will bear the same proportions to one another as they do in the stars. On this argument the composition of the core comes out to be about 89 per cent iron, 10 per cent nickel, and about 1 per cent of titanium, chromium, manganese, cobalt, copper and zinc.

It is possible to test the present conclusion. If we neglect any small amount of iron that there may be outside the core our result requires 30 per cent of the Earth to consist of iron. The remainder is largely basic silicate rock, of which the main elements are oxygen, magnesium, and silicon. Reckoning the oxygen at some 30 per cent, magnesium and silicon together therefore make up about 40 per cent of the mass of the whole Earth. This means that the ratio in the Earth of iron to magnesium and silicon is about 3/4. The searching question that we can now pose is: do the stars show the same ratio? If they do we can feel a considerable confidence in our cosmic comparison of the Earth with the stars, and as a corollary we can feel considerable confidence in our identification of the Earth's core as an iron-nickel alloy, with iron the greatly dominating component.

Fortunately the compositions of the stars are well enough known for the present question to be answered. It turns out that in the stars the ratio of the mass of iron to the combined contributions of magnesium and silicon is indeed so close to 3/4 as to pretty well clinch our identification of the Earth's core as an iron core.

An interesting supporting argument is worth mentioning. Chunks of matter, known as meteorites, sometimes plunge into the atmosphere from outer space and manage to penetrate right through to the surface of the Earth. They are of two types, a 'stony' silicate variety, and an iron variety. Since the meteorites are thought to have compositions that are representative of bits of a planet like the Earth, it is natural to suppose that just as the meteorites are of two types so the material of the Earth falls into two categories; the material of the rocky mantle and the material of the iron core.

Care should be taken not to confuse meteorites with meteors. Meteors are much smaller particles that also enter the atmosphere from outside. But whereas the incidence of meteorites is rare, meteors enter our atmosphere constantly and in quite large numbers. Meteorites are thought to either represent debris left over from the process of formation of the planets themselves, or to be products of the break-up of a small planet. Meteors, on the other hand, represent debris left over from the break-up of comets.

The temperature inside the Earth

At the surface of the core the temperature must satisfy two conditions. It must be high enough to melt the iron of the core but it must not be high enough to melt the rock of the solid mantle. This means that the temperature at the surface of the core must lie between two definite limits: it must lie above the melting point of iron and it must lie below the melting point of the rocky mantle. If we are fortunate and these two limits turn out to be fairly close together, then the temperature at the surface of the core becomes contained to within a close margin.

Geophysicists have been aware of this possibility for a long time, but no one could make effective use of it because the melting point of iron at high pressure was unknown. Very recently, however, F. E. Simon has estimated the melting point of iron at the surface of the core as about 4,000° C. Reckoning the melting point of the rocky mantle at about 6,000° C, we see that the temperature at the surface of the core must be greater than about 4,000° C. but less than 6,000° C. Evidently if we estimate 5,000° C. the margin of error cannot be very appreciable.

We must now add one further idea in order to complete the

argument. The iron of the core being a metal is a good conductor of heat. It can be shown by a rather technical discussion, of a sort that will come up again in a later chapter, that there cannot in such a case be much of a variation of temperature within the core. The core must everywhere be at very nearly the same temperature. This means that the temperature we have just determined, about 5,000° C., must be regarded as a quite typical value for the whole core.

The thermal history of the Earth

In the days when it was thought that the Earth originated in a high temperature molten condition an internal temperature of 5,000° C. would have seemed rather low. But according to modern views the Earth was aggregated out of a large number of small, cold bodies; and in such a theory an internal temperature of 5,000° C. does not seem at all low—rather is there a difficulty in explaining how the temperature comes to be so high.

The most obvious possibility is that the Earth is growing hotter due to the heat that is constantly being released by radioactive substances, of which uranium and potassium are the most important. That the Earth must be heated in this way is undoubted. The question is to what degree. How much heating can we expect the radioactive processes have produced? On the supposition that the Earth was originally cold, and that none of the heat released has been lost, how hot should the interior now be? This evidently depends on how much radioactive material was present in the Earth at the time of its formation. An answer has been worked out by Harold Urey on the very reasonable supposition that the proportion of radioactive material originally present in the Earth was the same as the proportion originally present in the meteorites. The latter can be inferred from the observed composition of meteorites (when this is taken together with an estimate of their age, about 4,000 million years). The result obtained by Urey contains an element of surprise. It turns out that the main heating comes from radioactive potassium, not from uranium as was at one time believed. But even including

25

the effect of potassium, the degree of heating is rather small. It amounts to only about 1,500° C.

It was this result that led me to suggest a few years ago that the temperature inside the Earth might be not very high. ". . . We see that there is no direct evidence in favour of an Earth that is really hot inside. What indirect evidence there is points in the opposite direction and suggests that the centre may be no warmer than a wood fire."*

But some pretty direct evidence has since become available to show that this view was incorrect. We have seen that the recent work of Simon on the melting point of iron suggests that the temperature of the core is about 5,000° C. This is much hotter than a wood fire. It is even hotter than an electric furnace, but not quite as hot as the surface of the Sun. Nor is it at all hot when compared to the inside of the Sun, where the temperature exceeds 10,000,000° C. But it is quite hot enough to demand an explanation!

An interesting further possibility has been suggested by Harold Urey. It would be very artificial to assume that the iron of the Earth's core all happened to lie in the central regions at the time that the Earth was formed. This would require a highly implausible mode of coagulation of the bodies that went to form the Earth. It would require chunks of material made largely of iron to coagulate first, and chunks of material made largely of rock to be added only after an iron nucleus had thus been built up. Quite apart from there being no certainty that the originally separate bodies were sharply differentiated into iron-bodies and rock-bodies, such a preferential coagulation clearly cannot be accepted. But if the iron now in the Earth's core was not there originally it must have sunk to the centre since the Earth was formed. And it turns out that a sinking of the iron releases energy, thereby heating the interior of the Earth to an appreciable degree, over and above the heating due to radioactive substances.

Yet ingenious as this suggestion undoubtedly is I suspect that it is not likely to be the sought-for explanation. The difficulty is that until the iron has sunk to the centre the temperature ought to be no more than about 1,500° C., and at

* Quotation from *The Nature of the Universe.*

26

this temperature the deep interior of the Earth would be quite solid. And it seems most doubtful whether the iron could sink through a solid matrix of rock: the deposits of iron ore on the surface of the Earth are certainly not sinking inwards. My suspicion is that the iron would simply stay put, embedded in the rock, and that no core would be formed. But if this suggestion does not succeed in solving our problem it does have interest in raising an important new question, the question of how the Earth's core came to be formed. This also demands an answer.

The following argument gives what I now personally believe to be the correct solution to the problem of the interior temperature of the Earth. I do this rather diffidently, because the results of my own calculations in this respect seem to disagree with those that I can find by other authors. I will indicate where the difference lies at the relevant stage.

We imagine that the formation of the Earth consisted in the gradual accumulation of a large number of comparatively small cold chunks of material. Even after an agglomeration of appreciable size was formed we may think of a rain of small bodies continuing to fall on to the surface of the primitive planet. When a particle hit the surface its motion was destroyed and heat was produced. But this only succeeded in warming up the surface, not the interior. And any heat released at the surface was simply radiated away into space. The heating of the interior had to come about in a different way. As the primitive Earth grew in size the pressure inside it increased accordingly. And as the internal pressure increased the material became squashed, at first very little, and then more and more. This squashing caused heat to be released, and the heat caused the internal temperature to rise.

That this process must have occurred is undoubted. The only issue in doubt is its efficacy. Estimates that I have consulted suggest that the resulting rise of temperature would be comparatively unimportant, but my own recent calculations yield a very different result. Perhaps it would be as well to be specific. Just outside the core, rock has been squashed from a normal density of about 3.3 (times that of ordinary water) to a density of about 5.6. This has occurred at a pressure of about

27

20 million lbs. per square inch. Under these conditions I find that the heat released must have been sufficient to raise the temperature of an equal mixture of rock and iron to a value somewhat in excess of 4,000° C. This agrees almost exactly with our requirements. It seems natural therefore to suggest that the present temperature inside the Earth is mainly a survival from the heating that occurred during the accumulation of the Earth, the heating being due to the compression of material produced by high pressure.

The inclusion of the effects of compression would accordingly seem to solve the temperature problem. It still remains, however, to consider the manner of formation of the core. At first sight it would seem easy to understand how the iron came to fall towards the inner regions. With the internal temperature near 5,000° C. material must have been close to a liquid condition; and if the material were liquid the iron would certainly settle to the centre. Yet such a dismissal of the problem glosses over subtleties. The iron it is true was probably heated sufficiently for it to assume a molten condition (except of course in the outermost surface layers). But since the rock is not molten at the present time it would be unsafe to assume that the melting point of the rocks was also reached at the time of formation of the Earth. So the problem is not one of a heavy liquid (iron) falling through a less dense liquid (rock). It is the problem of liquid iron embedded in solid rock. How in such circumstances did the iron manage to work its way towards the centre of the Earth? So far as I am aware the only attempt that has been made to answer the question in this form is a theory due to T. Gold. This is a topic suited to a separate discussion.

Gold's pore theory

We may expect that to begin with the Earth was a heterogeneous jumble of different sorts of material. Not only this, but since we are regarding the Earth as being assembled from small particles there may have been very appreciable initial differences of composition between places that were quite close together. We do not expect the iron to be distributed in a few large pools, but in a multitude of small pores. Sometimes one pore would be connected with another, and when this happened liquid would usually flow between them, rather as air is found to rush between two balloons placed neck to neck. In this way there must have been a tendency for increasingly large pores to be formed.

An important question now arises. When two pores become thus connected what decides which way the liquid flows between them? What decides which pore grows at the expense of the other? The answer is determined by the distances of the two pores from the centre of the Earth. When the liquid is denser than the surrounding rock, as molten iron is denser than the surrounding rock, the pore nearer the centre grows at the expense of the other one. (When there happens to be equality of distance no flow occurs, however.) In this way the iron has a marked tendency to flow inwards to the centre of the Earth. It is squeezed inwards by the surrounding rock whenever any radial channel of communication is opened from one volume of liquid to another. According to Gold this represents the manner of formation of the core of the Earth.

There is an extension of these considerations of special interest to us who live on the surface. Indeed it seems that this extension may provide us with an explanation of the outburst of volcanoes, the incidence of earthquakes, the origin of the oceans, the formation of mineral deposits, and perhaps even of the origin of the continents.

Other substances besides iron must have become liquid during the compression that accompanied the formation of the Earth. Although iron and magnesium silicates were almost certainly the dominant materials in the swarm of small bodies that went to form the Earth, other substances must equally certainly have been present to a minor degree. Among them would be many materials that are far more readily liquifiable than iron is: water, sulphur, tin and lead are examples. Such materials would also form liquid pores inside the Earth and would be subject to the same sort of behaviour as the pores of liquid iron but with one important difference in some of the cases. When a liquid is less dense than the surrounding rocks the flow from pore to pore is upwards towards the surface,

29

not down towards the centre as in the case of liquid iron. Now what happens to the light liquids that are thus squeezed upwards? When does the squeezing stop? If the outermost rocks contained no fissures even very light liquids would be unable to penetrate through them to the surface of the Earth. This would mean that the light liquids would be trapped beneath the outermost rocks. Suppose that such a situation has arisen; that in the first few hundred kilometres of depth below the surface a quantity of light liquid has been squeezed up from the inner regions of the Earth. The quantity is of course nothing like so great as the amount of heavy liquid that has been squeezed inwards because the materials of the light liquids were present only in low concentrations in the bodies that went to construct the Earth. Even so the light liquids may perhaps come to occupy a few per cent of the volume of the subcrustal rocks. The liquid is distributed in pores some of which will be connected by veins and channels. Let a fissure now develop in the overlying rock and let the fissure be such as to establish a connection from the surface down to one of the pores. What happens? Evidently the pressure of the surrounding rocks forces the liquid in the pore to gush to the surface. This phenomenon is observed in the outburst of a volcano.

Unless an obstruction develops in the upward vent the whole pore-full of liquid will rise to the surface. Indeed the liquid in every pore to which there happens to be a channel of communication will also burst through to the surface. But if a block develops in the vent this will not happen. Now a block may develop simply through the liquid solidifying as it cools on approaching the surface. Whether this happens or not depends on the melting point of the liquid. Some volcanoes exude lavas of rather low melting point, about 900° C. At this melting point there is very little solidification in the vent. For this reason these volcanoes are capable of ejecting enormous quantities of lava in quite a short time—a whole pore, or even a whole system of pores, being drained in one outburst. Cases where the lava flow has been immense are known. On the Deccan plateau of India for instance, there is a lava flow with a depth of about 2 kilometres and a surface area of some 500,000 square kilometres.

Some volcanoes, on the other hand, emit lavas of higher melting point which have a pronounced tendency to form obstructive plugs in the output vent. This prevents very extensive quantities of lava from being spouted out but it leads to another dangerous phenomenon. Sometimes after a plug has been formed the movement of liquid in the subcrustal regions leads to a rise of pressure in the liquid below the solid plug. If the pressure should become greater than the plug can withstand a further outburst can no longer be prevented. In such cases the outburst occurs with extraordinary violence because of the exceptionally high pressure that the plug has allowed to build up. This was the process that presumably caused the tremendous explosion of Krakatoa in 1883.

Fissures of the type required to promote volcanism are most likely to be found along the chains of the great folded mountains. This is no doubt the reason why volcanoes are so intimately associated with the folded mountains, especially with young folded mountains, the old folded mountains, such as the Scottish Highlands, having presumably had all their fissures thoroughly plugged up by now. It is an interesting thought that it is possibly only the absence of connecting vents that saves the Eastern United States and the British Isles from a whole rash of volcanoes.

It may have come as something of a surprise that our first application of the upward squeezing of light liquids should have been to the rocky material exuded by volcanoes since we have always spoken of the rock inside the Earth as being in a solid condition. Yet if the Earth originally contained a light, comparatively easily melted, type of rock this would probably become the most abundant of the light liquids. The existence of volcanic lavas goes far towards establishing the existence of such a type of rock. Volcanic lava is the least dense of all rocks, so that from the present point of view it can certainly be considered as a 'light' liquid. Moreover lava, even the lava of a volcano of the Krakatoa type, has a distinctly lower melting point than the magnesium silicates, of which most of the rock of the mantle is probably composed.

It seems therefore that we must admit the presence of a low density fluid rock inside the Earth at the time of its formation.

Now it seems rather unlikely that this exceptional sort of rock was present only in the very minute quantity that is necessary to explain the lava flows from known volcanoes, active and extinct. Rather would we expect that a lightweight fluid rock, if it were present at all would be present in a concentration of at least a per cent or two. The rising of the lightweight fluid would then lead to the Earth developing an outer zone of low density rock.

But the Earth does in fact possess a covering of particularly low density rock, the rocks of the crust, especially the rocks of the continents. It was previously something of a mystery how the continental rocks managed to get on the outside of the Earth. The explanation now seems obvious. The continents, being composed of low density rock of low melting point, were simply squeezed outwards from the interior of the Earth by the denser solid rock of the mantle.

This does not mean that the material of the continents was all poured out by a vast number of unknown volcanoes in the distant past. In the case of a volcano liquid rock of low density reaches the surface of the Earth. This is an unnecessarily stringent condition so far as the building of the continents is concerned, for all that is required in order to increase the continents is that additional rock should be added at their base—there is evidently no need for the rock to burst through to the surface, except in order to establish some initial thickness of the crustal rocks.

Now once we come to think that the continents were squeezed out from the deep interior of the Earth it puts no strain on the imagination to think that the water of the oceans was also squeezed out of the deep interior. It would indeed be difficult to deny that the Earth's interior must have been an important source of surface water, except on the supposition that the bodies out of which the Earth accumulated did not contain any water.

It is of interest to notice some of the evidence that seems to favour the theory developed above. The evidence is perhaps best discussed as a separate topic.

The internal origin of the continents and oceans

It appears likely that the crustal rocks contain a much higher concentration of uranium than the normal rock of the mantle does. Certainly the rocks of the crust contain a very much higher concentration of uranium than the meteorites do, and the rocks of the mantle are likely to be much more similar to the meteorites than they are to the crustal rocks.

Part of the explanation of this curious situation comes from the exceptionally large size of the uranium atom. It is easier for a large atom to fit itself into the interstices between the atoms of a light kind of rock than between the atoms of a dense form of rock. This is simply because the atoms that form a light rock are farther apart than the atoms of a dense rock. Thus a uranium atom, if it is given its choice, will prefer to make its home in the rocks of the crust rather than in the interior rocks of the mantle. But how does the uranium atom come to be given its choice? The answer to this forms the second part of the problem.

We must, I think, regard the uranium as being initially distributed pretty well uniformly throughout the Earth. How then did the uranium manage to get concentrated in the surface rocks? The only plausible explanation for this, of which I am aware, is that the uranium was brought to the surface by the crustal rock itself. We can readily visualise in terms of the pore theory how this happened. Consider a pore of light liquid rock initially deep inside the Earth but subsequently to be squeezed outwards to join the rocks of the crust. At the surface of the pore, where the liquid meets the solid denser rock of the mantle, uranium will tend to pass from the dense rock to the light rock for just the reason explained above. Now the liquid does not stay permanently in contact with the same piece of solid rock. On its journey outward it is constantly coming in contact with new samples of the dense rock of the mantle and uranium constantly passes to the liquid rock. In this way the pores act as collectors of uranium. They tend to sweep the interior clean of uranium and to carry it out to the surface. This it would seem is the explanation of the excess concentration of uranium in the crustal rocks. A similar process must

33

operate to concentrate other atoms of large size, for example the elements lead, gold, platinum, and mercury.

Let us next consider the problem of the formation of submarine canyons, reminiscent of the canyons cut by rivers on land (the Grand Canyon for instance). The submarine canyons are often located in places where existing rivers, or formerly existing rivers, would have extended their flow if the level of the oceans were once much lower than at present. It is natural therefore to suggest that the oceans were once appreciably lower than they are now, and that the canyons were then cut by the rivers. The Hudson is a river that possesses one of these great offshore canyons.

An internal origin for the oceans provides an immediate answer as to why the sea was at one time much lower than at present—because in the past less water had been squeezed out of the Earth's interior. But a difficulty arises, a difficulty so serious that many geologists have abandoned the straightforward theory that the canyons were cut by rivers and have come to prefer the notion that the cutting has been done by submarine mud chutes. Since many of the canyons have been fashioned out of rather hard rock this suggestion seems somewhat absurd—try to punch someone when you are under water and the absurdity becomes obvious.

The argument against the view that the now submerged canyons were once cut by rivers arises from the fact that their beds are very much steeper than the river bed of any known canyon on the land. The floor of the Hudson canyon is about ten times steeper than the river bed of the Grand Canyon, for instance. Not only this, but it is pointed out that if by some magic the level of the sea were to fall and the rivers were to flow down the now submerged canyons the resulting tremendous cascades of water would very soon lead to drastic changes in the forms of the canyons. As this argument is almost certainly correct, how can we suppose that the canyons were ever cut by rivers? If they had been cut by rivers, would not their beds have been much less steep than they are observed to be?

This argument depends for its force on the assumption that over the time since the canyons were cut the continents have

34

remained substantially unchanged. But if the continents have been considerably augmented by further additions of light rock arriving at their bases from the interior of the Earth then the difference of level between the continents and the ocean bottoms must have been increasing steadily all the time. This means that the drop between the continental edges and the ocean depths must have been steadily steepening. And any canyons that were cut in this slope by the action of ancient rivers must have steepened correspondingly. In this way it is possible to reconcile the cutting of the canyons by river action with the present steepness of their beds. That the dilemma could be resolved by such a steepening of the continental margins was pointed out some years ago by F. P. Shepard. Mud chutes probably do enter the problem in one respect. They may well operate to prevent the canyons from becoming silted up.

More about the pore theory

The idea that the light fluid rock responsible for the formation of the crustal rocks may have carried the water of the oceans with it is capable ⌐f extension. Quantities of other readily liquifiable materials must also have mixed with the molten rock, and must thereby have been carried outwards to the crust by the squeezing process. In cases where the molten rock managed to gush to the extreme surface these materials would also reach the surface. It was almost certainly in this way that the highly volatile substances that we find on the Earth managed to reach the surface—the compounds of arsenic, and of mercury, the deposits of almost pure sulphur, and so forth.

Sometimes a pore filled with light fluid rock must have become connected to a pore filled with heavy liquid; the heavy liquid being composed mainly of iron, to a lesser extent of nickel, and in a minor degree of titanium, chromium, manganese, cobalt, copper, zinc, lead, etc. If the pore containing the rock should happen to be nearer the centre of the Earth, the light liquid would rise into the upper pore, and the heavy liquid would drain downwards. The two liquids would thus stream past each other, and in so doing some of the heavy liquid would become dissolved in the light liquid, since it is known that molten rock dissolves small quantities of the metals quite readily. Such dissolved metals do not increase the density of the liquid rock significantly, however, and therefore would not prevent it from being squeezed outwards in the manner we have already discussed. The effect of this process is to cause small quantities of the core-forming metals to be carried upwards to the outer crust.

If the rock carrying these metals should manage to spout to the extreme surface then the metals would be carried to the surface, but their concentration in the outward streaming lava would not be high. To explain the high concentration found in many ore deposits it is necessary to appeal to a rather different process.

Suppose liquid rock manages to come close to the surface but without a complete break-through occurring. We expect that the rock will circulate around in a fine network of thin veins, located at a depth of perhaps a few miles. Owing to the comparatively low temperature of the outermost parts of the Earth there will be a pronounced tendency for these liquid rocks to solidify; and given sufficient time they will certainly do so, unless a circulatory connection is maintained with material at significantly greater depths where the temperatures are much higher. Such a connection requires the network of veins to possess roots that extend downwards to the base of the crustal rocks at least.

Evidently there will be cases where the circulating rocks almost solidify. It is in such cases that the deposition of mineral ores is likely to occur. For if the main body of the rock only just escapes solidification any material dissolved in it that happens to have a higher melting point will indeed solidify at some place in the circulatory system. The place where this happens will depend on the temperature distribution within the circulating rock and on the melting point of the material in question, and will be quite critically located. So as the rock circulates the dissolved material will always solidify out at approximately the same definite place. A high concentration of the material will therefore be built up at this place.

In such a way rich deposits of iron and other metallic ores can be formed. It is of course the situation that such ore deposits must always be formed below the extreme surface. But subsequent folding, buckling, and erosion of the outermost rocks can lead to the veins being brought to the surface.

Gold considers this explanation of the origin of metallic ores to be one of the strongest points in favour of the pore theory. He also believes that the occurrence of another important sort of deposit may possibly be explained in terms of the pore theory, namely the deposits of oil.

The idea that oil, so important to our modern civilisation, has been squeezed out of the Earth's interior derives an immediate plausibility from Urey's discovery that the meteorites contain small concentrations of hydrocarbons. The presence of hydrocarbons in the bodies out of which the Earth is formed would certainly make the Earth's interior contain vastly more oil than could ever be produced from decayed fish—a strange theory that has been in vogue for many years.

Among the many remaining aspects of the pore theory we have just space to discuss one more. To end with I have reserved what is perhaps the simplest and most striking consequence of the theory. This is the explanation that it affords of the origin of earthquakes. We have seen that liquid flows from one pore to another. When this occurs an unoccupied space develops in the pore that happens to lose liquid. Then owing to the pressure in the surrounding solid material the unoccupied space tends to get filled in with rock. If the pore empties quickly enough the filling-in process can lead to a catastrophic collapse of the surrounding wall of rock—and this is exactly the sort of event that would manifest itself as an earthquake. It is clear that we should expect just the close connection that is actually found to occur between volcanoes and earthquakes.

Now why do earthquakes not occur at depths greater than about 700 kilometres? Perhaps because all the liquid that was originally present in the deeper parts of the mantle has by now either been squeezed down into the core or into the outer parts of the mantle. Perhaps there are no pores of liquid still remaining in the mantle at depths greater than 700 kilometres.

37

The simplicity of this explanation contrasts with the difficulty that is otherwise encountered. Without the pore theory one would have to argue that a change in the composition of the solid rock occurred at a depth of about 700 kilometres—above 700 kilometres the rock being liable to fracture, but below 700 kilometres the rock being such as will not permit fracture. Such a change if it occurred ought to be accompanied by some major change in the density of the rock. Yet no such major change exists.

The future changes of the Earth's interior

The theory we have considered suggests that down to a depth of several hundred kilometres the Earth is probably honeycombed with a network of pores and interconnecting channels containing 'light' liquids that are constantly trying to force themselves outwards to the surface. Since the amount of liquid so contained may amount to as much as a few per cent of the amount of solid surrounding rock, it is clear that the amount of liquid if it were all to break through to the crustal rocks would be sufficient to produce profound modifications in the surface features of the Earth.

It seems likely that the continents will continue to grow and will continue to lift themselves above the ocean bottoms. The seas will likewise continue to acquire more and more water. The addition of further quantities of light rock to the bases of the continents may well be a somewhat patchy process: more rock may be added in one part of a continent than in another. If so one part of a continent will be elevated more than another. Unevenness of this sort will produce lowlands and highland plateaus, and may even be an important component in the origin of mountain ranges.

If our prognostication that the oil deposits have also been squeezed out from the interior of the Earth is correct, then we must I think accept the view that the amount of oil still present at great depths vastly exceeds the comparatively tiny quantities that man has been able to recover. Whether it will ever be possible to gain access to these vast supplies is an entertaining speculation.

It has sometimes been said that our civilisation is gobbling up the mineral resources of the world, and that when they are exhausted the conditions that we are now enjoying will never again be experienced. This view is probably incorrect. New mineral deposits will be laid down by the processes we have discussed and new reserves of oil will be squeezed up from inside the Earth. Conditions will again become suited to an industrial civilisation. Yes, but when?—several hundred million years hence.

CHAPTER THREE

The Tap Root

The four revolutions of physics

It is not only the smallest features of the Universe that are controlled by the laws of physics. The behaviour of matter on the very large scale that concerns us in astronomy is also determined by physics. The heavenly bodies dance like puppets on strings. If we are to understand why they dance as they do, it is necessary to find out how the strings are manipulated.

Physics has developed in three major steps, or if we include the revolution of thought that is taking place at the present time, in four major steps. The first era was concerned with the study of gravitation and with the dynamics of massive moving bodies, an era overwhelmingly associated with the work of Newton. The outstanding achievement of this first phase was the demonstration that the properties of the physical world can be described and *predicted* with a precision that had previously been unexpected and unhoped-for. Science did better than even its warmest protagonists had anticipated. The further development of the Newtonian era is associated with the names of the Bernoullis, Euler, Lagrange, and Laplace. But in spite of the impetus added by these outstanding men, the first great scientific revolution had largely lost its momentum by the middle of the nineteenth century, and physics in order to come alive again had to enter its second era.

The second era was concerned with the electrical and magnetic properties of matter in bulk, and with the nature of radiation. The establishment of the experimental basis of this second phase is notably associated with the name of Faraday, and its theoretical description with that of Maxwell. It was this revolution that ushered in the age of electricity. Modern industry is now entirely dominated by the discoveries of this era: the modern science of electronics stems directly from it.

This is an opportune moment to say something about the properties of radiation. Radiation is composed of individual units, known as quanta. When there are enough of them the quanta arrange themselves in wave patterns. Each pattern possesses a wavelength, and it is by wavelengths that we usually describe radiation. For instance radiation with 'long' wavelengths, from several thousand metres down to about one-tenth of a centimetre is just the radio wave-band. From a wavelength of one-tenth of a centimetre down to 8 hundred-thousandths of a centimetre we have the range of the infra-red. Then from 8 hundred-thousandths to 4 hundred-thousandths comes ordinary visible light. The ultra-violet comprises the range from 4 hundred-thousandths down to a millionth of a centimetre; from a millionth to a thousand-millionth is the range of X-rays; while radiation of still shorter wavelengths is known as γ-rays, now unfortunately only too well known from its presence in atomic explosions. All this is summarised as follows:

CLASS OF RADIATION	WAVELENGTH RANGE
Radio-waves	Several thousand metres down to a tenth of a centimetre.
Infra-red	One-tenth down to 8 hundred-thou-sandths of a centimetre.
Visible light	8 hundred-thousandths of a centi-metre down to 4 hundred-thousandths
Ultra-violet light	4 hundred-thousandths down to one millionth of a centimetre.
X-rays	One millionth down to one thousand-millionth of a centimetre.
γ-rays	Wavelengths shorter than one thou-sand-millionth of a centimetre.

It is worth noting that the shorter the wavelength the more energetic the individual quanta become. It is because of this that γ-rays, X-rays, and even ultra-violet light are so destructive of animal tissue, and why radio-waves are so harmless.

A further interesting point is that of the vast range of wavelength from radio-waves to γ-rays only the narrow band from 8 hundred-thousandths to 4 hundred-thousandths of a centimetre can be detected by the human senses with reasonable precision (other wavelengths can sometimes be crudely detected by a heating effect on the skin). This confinement of human vision is not an accident, however, because this is just the range in which most of the Sun's radiation is emitted. It is true that the Sun does emit some ultra-violet and even some X-rays, but the Earth's atmosphere absorbs such destructive radiation quite strongly, thereby preventing it from reaching the ground. Consequently there has never been an opportunity for creatures on the Earth to develop senses receptive to these wavelengths. Similarly most of the infra-red from the Sun is absorbed by the water vapour in the Earth's atmosphere—you may remember the greenhouse effect discussed in the first chapter. Yet there are narrow bands of infra-red that do succeed in penetrating through the atmosphere (these bands do not affect the operation of the greenhouse effect), so that the failure of our eyes to accept these bands cannot be explained by a similar argument of biological evolution. Plate III shows two photographs of the same scene one taken in visible light and the other in infra-red (photographic plates sensitive to a limited range of the infra-red from about a wavelength of 12 hundred-thousandths of a centimetre down to 8 hundred-thousandths can be made—as can plates sensitive to ultra-violet light, X-rays, and γ-rays). Evidently the infra-red gives a far greater penetration in distance. This is because of small water droplets that are always present in the lower parts of our atmosphere. In contrast to water vapour these droplets absorb visible light much more readily than they absorb infra-red. Hence in the lower atmosphere, where droplets are a dominating influence, penetration is always less in visible light. Clearly it would be a great advantage to possess eyes that were sensitive to infra-red, as indeed I suspect that birds may. This would go far towards explaining the amazing eyesight that birds seem to possess.

Even though this diversion is now becoming somewhat long,

we may notice that a similar situation occurs with sound waves. Sound can be described in terms of wavelengths, as radiation can, but sound—ordinary sound—is a disturbance of the air, whereas radiation is an electric oscillation in space: radiation can travel across a vacuum but sound cannot. The pitch of a note of sound is an indication of wavelength, while colour is an indication of the wavelength of visible light—the whole range of colours, violet, indigo, blue, green, yellow, orange, and red lie in the range of wavelengths from 8 hundred-thousandths of a centimetre down to 4 hundred-thousandths, red at 8 hundred-thousandths and violet at 4 hundred-thousandths.

The wave nature of light was an important discovery of the second phase of physics. Before the second phase had been allowed to run its course, physics was already in the throes of its third revolution. This opened quietly enough, at the beginning of the present century, with Planck's discovery of the quantum nature of light. But soon with the coming of Einstein's theory of relativity, Rutherford's work on the atom, Bohr's quantum theory, and later the new quantum theory, scientists were plunged into an intellectual maelstrom out of which it seemed that they had come unscathed by the early nineteen-thirties.

Much of the present chapter will be concerned with a very brief description of some of the knowledge that has been won in this third phase, knowledge that has led to almost explosive progress in astronomy. It is interesting in this connection to notice that physics in its first phase was very largely concerned with astronomy. Then during the second phase interest swung away from the heavens to the terrestrial laboratory. Now something of a reversal of this trend has come about, but it has only come about through the knowledge that has been won in the laboratory. Astronomy could never have climbed to its present height if it had been obliged to remain in the Newtonian era.

It seemed at one time in the middle nineteen-thirties as if physics was destined for a rather lengthy period of comparatively tranquil development. It seemed as if the calm after the storm had been reached. But appearances were deceptive.

43

The calm presaged the bursting of another storm, a storm that seems to be even more violent than before, a storm that does not yet seem to have reached its height.

The fourth revolution of physics started in 1938 with the discovery of a new type of material particle by C. Anderson. This turned out to be typical of later discoveries. By now about 14 new sorts of particles have been found. All are evanescent. All change either directly or by a series of intermediate steps into previously known particles (whose nature will be discussed later in this chapter). What lies behind this plethora of evanescent particles is still quite unknown, and how physical theory will develop in the future is still quite uncertain. It is to be expected that the patient accumulation of new data must precede any startlingly new theoretical developments, much as happened in the three preceding phases of physics.

The discoveries of the last few years have come rather as a shock. In the middle thirties physicists were beginning to think that they had at last dug through to bedrock. To have such a pleasant dream so rudely shattered in a few short years was naturally a somewhat disturbing experience. But now that the worst of the shock is over most physicists, I think, are coming to the view that the present situation is really a very healthy one. Looking back it is becoming clear that without the new developments physics must soon have found itself at a dead-end.

It is still far too early to offer any opinion as to how the fourth revolution in physics will affect astronomy. Astronomers seem fairly confident that most of their problems are not likely to be concerned with anything more than the third phase of physics. There is one important problem, however, where this may not be so. This is the problem of cosmology. When in the last chapters we come to speak about the origin of matter (and a consideration of this problem can be shown to be unavoidable) it is difficult to resist the impression that new physical knowledge may turn out to be of overriding importance at just this point. When we come to examine the ultra-small we find that our present knowledge peters out in shifting sands. When we come to examine the ultra-large we find that it does likewise. It is tempting to suppose that ignorance in the one field bears a relation to ignorance in the other. Certainly it would be quite astonishing if radically new physical knowledge of the nature of matter should have no application to the Universe in the large.

Building out of atoms

Everyone is familiar with a child's constructional toy in which certain basic components are purchased that can then be built into a variety of structures. A vitally important concept underlies the use of such toys, a concept that has applications that are anything but toylike. Let us take one or two important examples. The electronic computer, a great modern invention almost certainly destined to have a decisive influence on human history, is built out of what are in themselves quite simple units. All animals and plants are also built out of basic units. Our interest in both these cases can be divided into separate parts: a consideration of the units by themselves, and a consideration of the structures that can be built out of the units. The structural element must not be overlooked. The unit out of which a human is made is not in itself, when taken alone, more interesting or remarkable than the unit out of which a cabbage is made: the added interest comes only when we go on to consider the structural organisation into which the human unit can be built. A fine building is something more than the pile of bricks out of which it is assembled.

On a still smaller scale matter is constructed in a similar way, out of units called atoms. There are 90 different sorts of atoms occurring naturally on the Earth, while an additional half-dozen or so can be prepared artificially in the laboratory. Physics is conveniently divided into two parts—a study of the atoms themselves and a study of the structures that can be built out of them. We shall begin with the second of these, although most of what is to follow in this chapter will be concerned with the first.

Matter in bulk is constructed out of atoms, either as a single stage process, or in two stages. In the single stage process a particular type of atom forms the building unit—this is the situation with most of the metals, for instance. In the two stage

45

process a number of atoms, often of several different kinds, are first combined into a molecule and it is the molecule that then acts as the building unit. A water droplet is a structure built out of a simple molecule, consisting of two atoms of hydrogen and one of oxygen (hydrogen and oxygen being different atoms whose internal properties we shall discuss later). Water vapour, on the other hand, consists of separate molecules uncombined into any structure. While the molecule out of which sugar is built is much more complex than the molecule of water, the structure of sugar is simpler than that of liquid water: from which we see that a simple molecule does not necessarily build into a simple structure, nor does a complex molecule necessarily give rise to a complex structure.

It may be remarked as an aside that simple molecules are sometimes found in the atmospheres of stars—of those stars with particularly cool atmospheres, cooler than that of the Sun; but molecules are too fragile to exist in the fiercely hot interiors of the stars. Molecules are present to an important degree in the gases that lie between the stars where their presence leads to considerable astronomical complexities.

We may add a note on how small atoms and molecules are when judged by ordinary standards. Even a pin's head contains considerably more than a million, million, million atoms of iron, while a pig's head contains more than a million, million, million, million molecules of water.

Solids, liquids, and gases

When in an assembly with a large number of atoms or molecules the individuals can move freely around among their neighbours the bulk material is said to behave as a gas. But when the behaviour of one particle is appreciably influenced by its neighbours the material has either the properties of a liquid or of a solid. In a solid this interaction is sufficiently strong to entirely prevent the individuals from wandering around in a nomad existence: they stay put in definite positions, like the average worker in a modern industrial community. Liquids are intermediate between gases and solids. In a liquid the interaction between neighbouring individuals

46

is neither so small as it is in a gas nor is it so large as to prevent the molecules from wandering around, as in a solid.

It is the interactions of molecules with their neighbours that produce the well-known properties of materials in everyday life: the difference between the fluidity of water and the stickiness of molasses, the tensile strength of solids, and so forth. Indeed the cohesive strength of a material comes from the interactions of atoms or molecules with their neighbours, rather as the strength of a human community comes from the extent to which the individuals co-operate with each other.

Atoms

It is now appropriate to consider the inner structure of the atoms themselves. An account of this inner structure was first given by Rutherford, according to whom the main substance is contained within a tiny central nucleus that is surrounded by a comparatively extensive diaphanous cloud of particles known as electrons—a name derived from their electric properties. It is these electron clouds that become associated when a molecule is formed out of separate atoms. It is also the electron clouds that are responsible for the interactions that occur in solids and liquids.

Sometimes electrons get knocked out of an atom. When this happens the atom is said to be ionised, the degree of ionisation being determined by the number of electrons that have thus been knocked out. Such knocked-out electrons were indeed discovered by J. J. Thomson some years before the work of Rutherford.

There are many ways of knocking electrons out of atoms. The simplest is to rub two surfaces together. The shock that you may get from sliding on the plastic seating of an automobile is due to electric effects that arise from the knocking-out of electrons; so is the crackling that you may hear when a nylon or a silk garment is taken off on a day of low humidity; so is the lightning in a thunderstorm—knocking-out occurs in this case when large water-drops fragment into smaller ones.

The rubbing of surfaces is not the only way that atoms may

47

become ionised. When light falls on an atom, electrons may be knocked out. This is known as the photo-electric effect. It forms the basis of many technological processes. When a door opens, apparently by itself, as you approach it, you can be pretty sure that the photo-electric effect is being used. More important, electric effects produced by light form the physiological basis of human sight.

But important as the photo-electric processes occurring in everyday life undoubtedly are, they are still very weak compared with the situation inside the stars, where the intensity of radiation is so great that the knocking-out process is extremely powerful. Nowhere in the Universe is the photo-electric effect as strong as it is inside stars.

When one or more electrons have been knocked out of an atom, the atom develops the property of attracting electrons towards itself. Sometimes an electron from outside such an atom may come so close that it is pulled into the electron cloud of the atom itself, in which case there is a good chance that it will remain permanently within the cloud, instead of moving out again. When this happens radiation is emitted. This process is just the reverse of the photo-electric effect. Most of the light and heat that we now receive from the Sun and the stars was emitted by atoms that managed to capture wandering electrons in this way.

We see therefore that there are two contrary processes in nature, one a knocking-out process that removes electrons from atoms, and the other a recombination process in which atoms capture electrons. What happens in any particular physical environment depends on the balance between these processes. On the Earth knocking-out processes are for the most part comparatively weak, with the result that the great majority of terrestrial atoms are not ionised. Inside the stars, on the other hand, the photo-electric effect is so strong that nearly all the electrons are stripped out of the atoms.

Protons

A vitally important problem remains from the previous discussion; namely to decide what the nucleus of the atom is composed of. We may start with the simplest of the chemical elements, hydrogen. Hydrogen is the simplest element because it has but one electron in its outer cloud, whereas all other elements have more: the helium atom has 2 cloud electrons, the lithium atom 3, beryllium 4, boron 5, carbon 6, nitrogen has 7, oxygen 8, iron has 26 electrons, lead has 82, uranium 92; and of the new elements, recently artificially produced in the laboratory, neptunium has 93, plutonium has 94, americium 95, and californium 96.

The nucleus of a hydrogen atom has an electric charge but of a different sort from that of the electron. To distinguish between the two kinds of charges we notice that two particles with the same type of charge tend to push away from each other. On the other hand two particles with opposite kinds of charge pull towards each other. So while two electrons push away from each other, the nucleus of the hydrogen atom and its surrounding electron pull together. This cohesion explains how the hydrogen atom holds together. The nucleus of the hydrogen atom has been given a special name; it is called a proton.

The concept of electric charge has a simple numerical property. Let us write $+ 1$ for the charge of the proton, and $- 1$ for the charge of the electron. Then the total charge of 7 protons is $+ 7$, and the total charge of 5 electrons is $- 5$. Now what is the total charge of 7 protons and 5 electrons when taken together? The answer is

$$+ 7 - 5 = + 2$$

This means that a group of 7 protons and 5 electrons has the same total charge as 2 protons. What is the total charge of the hydrogen atom with 1 proton and 1 electron? The answer is

$$+ 1 - 1 = 0$$

The hydrogen atom has zero total charge, the electron and the proton just compensate each other. We say, in such a case, that the atom is neutral.

Electric compensation also occurs in all other un-ionised atoms. In the un-ionised oxygen atom, for instance, the nucleus has the same electric charge that 8 protons would have, while

49

in the surrounding cloud there are 8 electrons. Now how does the nucleus of the oxygen atom contrive to have the same charge as 8 protons? The answer given by physics is simple and straightforward: because the nucleus of the oxygen atom contains 8 protons. And in a like manner the nuclei of other atoms are regarded as containing a number of protons, a number that for neutral atoms is always equal to the number of electrons in the surrounding cloud. The element helium accordingly has 2 protons in its nucleus, lithium has 3, beryllium 4, boron 5, carbon 6, nitrogen 7, . . . iron has 26, and uranium 92.

We are now in a position to describe the answer given by modern physics to one of the great classical problems of science; what decides the chemical properties that an atom possesses? The number of protons contained in the nucleus determines the number of electrons in the surrounding cloud. This fixes all the building properties of the atom. Hence we reach the simple and elegant conclusion that the chemistry of an atom is determined by the number of protons in its nucleus.

The co-existence of more than one proton in all nuclei except that of hydrogen shows us that an entirely new type of cohesive force must operate in the nucleus, a cohesive force that is not electrical in origin. We have seen that particles with the same sort of electric charge tend to push away from each other. Clearly then the protons in a nucleus, the 8 protons in the oxygen nucleus, for instance, would simply push apart from each other unless they were held together by some new force more powerful than the electric forces. This new force is called the nuclear force. It is thought to be intensely strong so long as the protons are very close together. This is indeed why the atomic nuclei are so small in size, for it is only if the nucleus is very tightly packed that the nuclear forces can prevent the electric forces from dispersing it.

As the number of protons in the nucleus increases, the electric force tending towards disruption grows more rapidly than the cohesive effect of the nuclear forces. This means that if we were to go on increasing the number of protons sooner or later the electric forces would become dominant. Parts of the nucleus would then be forced to break away from the main body under the repulsive action of the electric forces. The nucleus would no longer be stable; in the usual terminology it would be radioactive (a terminology that has nothing to do with radio-waves!) This explains why the elements do not go on indefinitely, why there is a largest nucleus found in nature—that of the element uranium. Even if larger nuclei were present in the Earth at the time of its origin they would all have disappeared by now. Indeed uranium itself is unstable, but not in a sufficient degree for it all to have yet disappeared. But the margin in the case of uranium is not very great: the electric forces are nearly able to push the nucleus apart—they will in fact do so if the nucleus is suitably jostled. This is just what happens in the fission of uranium, the process on which atomic energy is based.

The neutron

It is now necessary to introduce the idea that there is something else inside the atomic nuclei besides protons (except in the case of ordinary hydrogen, where the nucleus contains nothing but a single proton). If the oxygen atom, for instance, consisted only of a nucleus with 8 protons surrounded by a cloud with 8 electrons, the oxygen atom would have a weight about 8 times greater than the hydrogen atom. Actually the weight of the oxygen atom is about 16 times that of the hydrogen atom. Remembering that the weight of the electron cloud is quite negligible, we see that an additional contribution to the weight must come from some new component present in the nucleus. Chadwick's discovery of the neutron resolved the puzzle as to what this component might be. The neutron was found to be a particle without electric charge, and with weight nearly equal, but a little greater than that of the proton. The nucleus of the ordinary oxygen atom contains 8 protons and 8 neutrons—the neutrons add weight but do not affect the electric charge. The whole aggregate of neutrons and protons is bound together by the self-same nuclear forces that were mentioned above.

Now suppose that we had 8 protons and 9 neutrons bound together in a nucleus. What would be the properties of the

51

resulting atom? Since the neutrons themselves possess no electric charge the addition of one extra neutron does not affect the number of electrons that must be present in the surrounding cloud in order to compensate for the charge of the nucleus. Since moreover the building properties of an atom are determined by the electron cloud it follows that the chemistry of the new atom is no different from that of an ordinary oxygen atom with 8 protons and 8 neutrons in its nucleus. Therefore we must still regard the new atom as an atom of oxygen. To distinguish the two cases we refer to the ordinary oxygen atom as O^{16} and to the other as O^{17}, the index 16 telling us that in the one case there are 16 particles in the nucleus and in the other case 17.

In a similar way we could consider a nucleus with 8 protons and 10 neutrons. From what has been said the resulting atom would still possess the chemical properties of oxygen, and would be denoted by O^{18}. When atoms differ as O^{16}, O^{17}, and O^{18} differ, in possessing nuclei with different numbers of neutrons, they are said to be *isotopes* of the same element. The notion of an element is derived from chemistry, in other words from the molecule-building properties of an atom: we get a different element when we change the number of protons in the nucleus; we get a different isotope when we change the number of neutrons.

Of the elements found in nature many possess isotopes. When a chemist obtains what he regards as a chemically pure sample of an element it is often found to contain a mixture of different isotopes. These can be separated by the physicist using a method that depends on differences of weight, not on differences in chemical behaviour. Generally speaking chemical separation—separation according to the number of protons in the nucleus—is a much easier job than the separation of isotopes.

This suggests an aside on atomic energy. Only one naturally occurring nucleus possesses the particular fission properties that are of importance in atomic energy projects. This is one of the isotopes of uranium, U^{235}, containing 92 protons and 143 neutrons. The natural abundance of U^{235} is less than one per cent of the natural abundance of U^{238} (92 protons, 146 neutrons). It will therefore be realised that to separate pure U^{235} from the naturally occurring mixture of U^{235} and U^{238} is an awkward problem. This explains the difficulties that were encountered in setting up the first plant at Oakridge for obtaining supplies of fissionable material. In later developments it was found possible to prepare artificially an element with the required fission properties. This is an isotope of plutonium, the nucleus possessing 94 protons and 145 neutrons. Because plutonium is a different element it can be separated from uranium by chemical processes. This greatly simplifies the problem of obtaining supplies of fissionable material, and explains why this is so much easier to do today than it was ten years ago.

The elements and their isotopes are very queerly distributed in nature. An understanding of how the observed abundances came about cannot be answered by physics alone. To solve this problem astronomy must also be called upon. In a later chapter we shall see how it is plausible to suppose that the simplest of the elements—hydrogen—forms the base out of which all the other nuclei have been fashioned. We shall see how conditions inside stars lead to the building of complex nuclei, and that the abundances of the nuclei as we find them on the Earth can be explained in these terms.

β-disintegration and the neutrino

Now what limits the number of isotopes that a particular element can have? If we built an atom with a nucleus of 8 protons and 11 neutrons we should still have an atom of oxygen—O^{19}. Is O^{19} found in nature? The answer is that O^{19} is not found in nature, but O^{19} can be prepared artificially in the laboratory. A study of its properties shows immediately why O^{19} is not found in nature. It is unstable. One of the neutrons changes spontaneously into a proton emitting an electron as it does so, the electron being disgorged by the nucleus. This is the process known as $β$-disintegration. The reason for this behaviour lies, not in the electrical forces as in the fission of uranium, but in the nuclear forces themselves which act in such a way as to prevent the disparity in the

53

numbers of neutrons and protons from becoming too large. In the case of oxygen a disparity of 2 is allowable (O^{18} is stable), but a disparity of 3 induces instability. When one of the neutrons in O^{19} changes to a proton, the element is changed since the number of protons is increased to 9. The new element is fluorine.

Nuclear forces are similarly able to change a proton into a neutron. In this case the nucleus disgorges, not an ordinary electron, but a positron, a particle otherwise similar to an electron but possessing the opposite sort of charge. The positron was discovered experimentally by C. Anderson and by P. M. S. Blackett, but theoretical reasons for its existence had been given earlier by P. A. M. Dirac. A positron and an electron can combine together, the result being not a material particle but a quantum of radiation.

A nucleus with 8 protons and 7 neutrons—O^{15}, another isotope of oxygen, can also be prepared artificially. It is also unstable, with one of the protons changing into a neutron, the result being the isotope N^{15} of nitrogen with 7 protons and 8 neutrons. The dream of the alchemists—the transmutation of one element into another, has become a commonplace reality of modern physics.

We now see that the answer to our question as to what limits the number of stable isotopes of a given element is that the nuclear forces prevent the difference between the number of neutrons and the number of protons from being varied by more than a small margin. There is no absolute prohibition on the existence of other isotopes, but they are unstable, they change by β-disintegration into other elements.

Now when an electron is thrown out of a nucleus by β-disintegration (a neutron changing into a proton) the speed of emission is not fixed. The electrons emitted when O^{19} decays into fluorine, for instance, have variable speeds, even though the initial state of the nucleus before decay and the final state after decay are the same in all cases.

The explanation of this remarkable fact is that a second particle is emitted by the decaying nucleus at the same time as the electron. The neutrino, as this particle is called, takes some of the energy released by the decay of the nucleus. This enables us to say that although the electron alone does not always receive the same energy the electron and the neutrino together always receive the same energy. When the electron takes less energy the neutrino takes more, and vice versa. In this way an energy balance can be maintained in all cases. The neutrino possesses no electric charge being in this respect like the neutron, and it apparently possesses no mass being in this respect like a quantum of radiation. These properties make the neutrino very difficult to observe.

In astronomy neutrinos act as a sink of energy. Neutrinos produced inside the stars escape out into space carrying energy with them. In the Sun the loss of energy by this process is small compared to the loss through the escape of radiation from the surface, but in some exceptional stars energy loss through the escape of neutrinos is a much more powerful process than it is in the Sun. Indeed it can on occasion greatly exceed the loss of energy through the escape of radiation from the surface of the star, as was first pointed out by G. Gamow. Stars can collapse catastrophically due to this cause, as we shall later see.

The fourth revolution of physics

Several questions arise out of the above discussion that go beyond the scope of the third phase of physics. Does the neutrino have a connection with gravitation? What is the relationship between gravitational, electrical, and nuclear forces? Why is there only one unit of electric charge (proton + 1, electron − 1)? Why are the weights of the proton and neutron so nearly equal, and yet not exactly equal? It is the hope that answers to questions such as these will eventually be forthcoming when the fourth phase of physics comes to be better understood. Much remains to be done.

It was remarked at the outset that it is also the hope that by the new developments the ultra-large aspects of the Universe may become closely related to the ultra-small. It may be of interest, by way of ending the present chapter to give a more precise idea of what is meant by ultra-large and ultra-small. Atoms are small: 10,000,000,000 of them placed end to end along a line would cover a distance comparable to the height of a human: an adult human contains about 7,000,000,000, 000,000,000,000,000,000 atoms. The nuclei of atoms are ultrasmall: only about one million millionth of the space within an atom is occupied by the nucleus. Turning to the ultra-large, the problems to be considered in the last chapters concern the distribution of matter on a scale that is almost incredibly vast compared with the size of the atomic nucleus. The ultralarge exceeds the ultra-small by the fantastic number 10,000, 000,000,000,000,000,000,000,000,000,000,000,000. The problems of science cover this range.

CHAPTER FOUR

Some Varied Applications of Physics

Let us consider a few applications of the ideas of the previous chapter.

Physics invades history

As an outcome of the work of W. F. Libby, the nucleus C^{14} with 6 protons and 8 neutrons is now of great importance in historical and archæological studies. This nucleus has a 'half-life' close to 5,550 years. If we start with a large number of C^{14} nuclei, then after 5,550 years one-half of them will have changed into the isotope N^{14} of nitrogen (7 protons, 7 neutrons) in accordance with a β-disintegration in which a neutron changes into a proton. After a further interval of 5,550 years one-half of those C^{14} nuclei still remaining will then also have decayed; so that after 11,100 years one-quarter of the nuclei initial present will still remain as C^{14}. After a further 5,550 years one-half of this residue will again have decayed into nitrogen—and so forth. All this can be seen by consulting Fig. 2 where a plot is given of the fraction of C^{14} that remains after various lengths of time.

The curve shown in Fig. 2 can be made use of in several ways. If we are given a sample of C^{14}, then we can read off how much of it will remain after any specified length of time. If we are given a sample of C^{14} and we are told that its age is such-and-such, then we can use Fig. 2 to tell us how much C^{14} there must have been originally. Thirdly, if we are given a sample of C^{14} and we are also told how much C^{14} there was originally, then Fig. 2 allows us to determine the age of the sample (since the prescribed information tells us what fraction of C^{14} remains). It is this third use of Fig. 2 that is important in the present instance.

57

The nucleus C^{14} enters history through the action of the cosmic rays. Cosmic rays are highly energetic particles, mostly protons, that enter the Earth's atmosphere from outside space. Their nature and origin forms an important topic to be discussed in a later chapter.

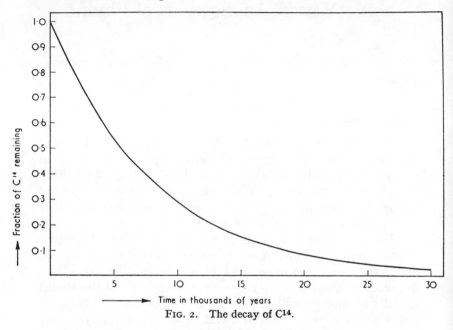

FIG. 2.   The decay of C^{14}.

The incoming cosmic rays collide with the nuclei of the atoms in the Earth's atmosphere. These collisions are the most violent of any yet known to physics. They produce a whole lot of debris, of which wandering 'free' neutrons is one constituent ('free' neutrons are neutrons that are not locked away inside nuclei). These free neutrons move around until they collide with the nuclei of other atoms in the atmosphere. Sometimes they enter the nuclei of atoms of nitrogen. When this happens the nitrogen nucleus may disgorge a proton, thereby yielding C^{14}: thus

$$N^{14} \ (n, \ p) \ C^{14}$$

This means that a nucleus of nitrogen (7 protons, 7 neutrons)

58

absorbs a neutron (n), emits a proton (p), and thereby becomes a nucleus of C^{14} (6 protons, 8 neutrons). In this way C^{14} is produced in small quantities in our atmosphere. The atmospheric concentration strikes a balance between the rate at which C^{14} is thus formed and the rate at which it decays.

Living creatures take in carbon from the atmosphere. Most of the carbon absorbed is C^{12}, the common stable isotope of carbon with 6 protons and 6 neutrons; but a tiny fraction of the carbon taken in is C^{14}, the unstable C^{14} formed through the action of the cosmic rays. The ratio of C^{14} to C^{12} in living tissue, whether animal or vegetable, therefore depends on the ratio of C^{14} to C^{12} in the atmosphere, and this depends on the balance between the rate of formation of C^{14} and its decay. Now the half-life for decay is a fixed quantity; and the formation rate is not likely to change much over many thousands of years. Consequently we may expect the ratio of C^{14} to C^{12} in the atmosphere and hence in living tissue, to be a definite determinable quantity that does not change appreciably with time, at any rate over an interval of many millennia.

Next we notice that when an animal or a plant dies there is no longer an intake of carbon from the atmosphere. Consequently as the C^{14} in the tissue of the animal or plant decays there is no renewal from the atmosphere. This means that the C^{14} must gradually disappear from dead tissue.

Suppose now that we are given a piece of dead tissue, say a piece of wood. Then by careful analysis the fraction of the carbon in the tissue that remains as C^{14} can be found. The fraction of the carbon that is present as C^{14} in living tissue can also be found. These items of information enable the curve of Fig. 2 to be used in the third of the ways described above. That is to say, the age of the piece of wood can be read off from the curve, the age since the tree of which it formed a part died. In this way Libby has dated pieces of sequoia that are up to about 1,500 years old, and the results have been checked against an independent age determination based on the counting of tree rings. The agreement is highly satisfactory.

But this is not all, for pieces of wood can be recovered from ancient tombs and the same method used. Not only this, but the method really only comes into its own when specimens

59

that are as old as 5,000 years, or even older, are examined. This takes us back to the days of the earliest civilisations of Mesopotamia and Egypt. It has been estimated, for instance, that the age of the tomb of *Hemaka* is about 4,900 years. Estimates based on historical data, by Braidwood, suggested an age between 4,700 years and 5,100 years.

This remarkable agreement should give us pause for thought. When we reflect on the long chain of reasoning that is necessary to connect the documentary evidence on which an historian's assessment of the past is based on the one hand, with the physicist's development of the theory of the atomic nucleus on the other, it is a matter for astonishment that the whole intricate mental operation, involving the thoughts of not one individual but of many, should have been carried out with such sustained accuracy.

When the last of the great ice-sheets from the Arctic thrust its way into N. America and into N. West Europe an advancing tongue of ice somewhere tore down and buried a tree. When the ice retreated bits of the tree were left buried among the general rubble that had been accumulated by the ice. Many thousands of years later men dug up the pieces of the tree. The bits were taken to a laboratory to have their C^{14} content measured. And so the age of the bits of wood was found. And so the men came to know how long ago it was since the advancing tongue of ice tore down the tree.

In such a fashion the date of the last great ice-age has been discovered to have been only 10,000 years ago, much more recent than had previously been supposed by many geologists. All human habitation in N. America seems to have been later than this. In Europe, on the other hand, men lived in caves to the south of the ice. The cave of Lascaux in France, with its famous wall paintings, was occupied some 15,500 years ago. This is known from the analysis of a piece of charcoal found in the cave.

What was the temperature of the Atlantic Ocean 200 million years ago?

At first sight this question might seem impossible to answer. Yet it turns out, most remarkably, to be susceptible of attack by an ingenious method invented by Harold Urey. This depends on the isotopes of oxygen. It will be recalled that three isotopes of oxygen are found in nature—O^{16} the main isotope with a nucleus containing 8 protons and 8 neutrons, O^{17} containing 8 protons and 9 neutrons, and O^{18} with 8 protons and 10 neutrons. Water is a molecule containing two atoms of hydrogen and one of oxygen. The oxygen atom normally has an O^{16} nucleus, but in a small proportion of water molecules the oxygen atom has an O^{17} nucleus or an O^{18} nucleus. In sea-water about one molecule in 2,000 contains O^{17}, and about one in 300 contains O^{18}.

Now certain small animals living in the sea take in oxygen from the water in order to build up the carbonates of which their shells are formed. It is therefore to be expected that the shells of these animals will contain all three isotopes of oxygen. But here is the point—the relative proportions of the three isotopes in the shells are not exactly the same as they are in the water. Their proportions are slightly altered by the chemical processes that lead to the deposition of the carbonates, and they are altered by amounts that depend on the temperature of the water. Hence if we examine the shell of some animal that lived in the distant past the proportions of the oxygen isotopes in the shell will tell us the temperature of the ocean in which the animal lived. The shell serves as a fossil thermometer.

This plan is rather awkward to operate in practice since very small concentrations of the isotopes have to be measured. Indeed it has only proved possible to use the O^{18} and O^{16} isotopes, for the reason that the concentration of O^{17} is too low for effective measurement. Care has to be taken that the shells have not altered since the deaths of the animals themselves. It is moreover essential to use only the shells of animals that lived in sea water of full salinity, because fresh water possesses different isotope ratios from sea water. In spite of these and other difficulties, measurements have been carried through by Urey, Lowenstam, Epstein, and McKinney. They have discovered, for instance, that the temperature over a wide belt of ocean ranging from latitude 33° in the Mississippi basin over the N. Atlantic to England and Denmark was remarkably constant at about 15° C. This was 200 million years ago.

One other point may be mentioned. The building of the shell of a sea animal may take several years. By examining the isotopic composition of different bits of the shell it is possible to find out how the sea temperature changed during the life of the animal. This has been done by the authors already mentioned. They find a systematic oscillation of temperature through a range of about 6° C., which is considered to reflect the change of sea temperature between summer and winter. This is an astonishing result. To be able to measure the seasonal changes of ocean temperature that occurred some 200 million years ago seems quite fantastic.

The age of the Earth

We have spoken several times of the Earth being some 4,000 million years old. It is of interest to say a little about how this estimate has been arrived at. The method used is in principle the same as that employed in the dating of historical and archæological remains. But the decay of the C^{14} nucleus is useless for the purpose of dating the Earth—the Earth is so old that any C^{14} initially present inside it would have disappeared long ago. Evidently to avoid this difficulty we require a nucleus that decays in a half-life of 1,000 million years or more. This greatly limits our choice of radioactive substance, since only a very few nuclei possess such long half-lives. In fact only two types of nuclei have been extensively used for this purpose. They are the two isotopes of uranium, U^{238} (92 protons, 146 neutrons) with a half-life of 4,510 million years, and the isotope U^{235} (92 protons, 143 neutrons) with a half-life of 707 million years.

The uranium isotopes are unstable because of large electrical forces within their nuclei, the electrical forces causing bits to be shot out of the nuclei from time to time. Once one bit (actually a nucleus of helium with 2 protons and 2 neutrons) has been fired out of a uranium nucleus other bits are ejected in comparatively quick succession, the process going on until a stable nucleus is eventually reached. This happens when the electrical forces have been reduced sufficiently for the nuclear forces to gain complete control of the situation. Uranium ultimately ends as lead. The isotope U^{238} decays eventually into the isotope of lead Pb^{206} (82 protons, 124 neutrons), and U^{235} decays into the isotope Pb^{207} (82 protons, 125 neutrons).

It is particularly to be noticed that this is not the process of fission that occurs in the atomic bomb. We are now referring to what is known as the natural radioactivity of uranium— what uranium will do if left to itself for a sufficiently long time. The fission of uranium has to be induced artificially. This is done by stirring up the uranium nucleus by adding a neutron to it. When a uranium nucleus undergoes fission it does not simply eject small pieces but splits into two comparable portions. The processes are similar, however, in the sense that they are both caused by the intensity of the electrical forces in the uranium nucleus.

Coming back now to our problem of determining the age of the Earth, this might appear from what has been said to be a rather simple matter. Suppose that we analyse a sample of rock and determine its present content of U^{238} (for instance). Suppose further that we determine the content of Pb^{206}. Cannot we argue that both the original and the present U^{238} content are thereby determined, since the Pb^{206} has come from the uranium that has decayed since the rock was formed? Knowing the half-life of U^{238} a simple calculation would then give the age of the piece of rock. But such an argument assumes that there was no Pb^{206} in the rock at the time it formed. If there was, the calculation is vitiated. This uncertainty has proved a serious obstacle to the use of uranium for determining the age of the Earth—a similar difficulty evidently arises also for the other isotope of uranium U^{235}. Only very recently has it been found possible to use the method in a way that seems free from objection. This has been done by C. Patterson and R. Hayden working at the California Institute of Technology. The new step consists in the analysis of a meteorite that contains no uranium, and which apparently never did contain uranium. The object of this step is to determine the lead content as it was originally, for the lead content of this particular meteorite has certainly not been altered by the decay of uranium. If then we take a second meteorite that does contain uranium, the difference of lead content in the two cases can

63

validly be regarded as due to the uranium. The age of the latter meteorite can then be deduced by a simple calculation. Moreover, provided we assume that the lead isotopes were originally distributed in the same proportions in the Earth as in the meteorites, the ages of the rocks of the Earth can also readily be determined. The results both for the ages of meteorites and for the age of the Earth turn out at about 4,000 million years (it may be mentioned that the commonest isotope of lead Pb^{204} is not affected in any way by the decay of uranium so that measurements of Pb^{206} and Pb^{207} are always referred to the content of Pb^{204} as a standard of reference).

The estimate of 4,000 million years for the age of the Earth, and presumably for the age of the solar system, is about twice as great as the estimates that were widely quoted a few years ago. It may be wondered where the error in the former estimates lay. The answer is in erroneous allowances for the initial concentrations of Pb^{206} and Pb^{207}. The antiquity of the Earth seems considerably greater than was formerly believed by most scientists—a notable exception being that of Holmes, who made estimates many years ago that were close to 4,000 million years.

The energy of the Sun

A great mystery has been solved during the last few years, the mystery of the source of the vast amount of energy that the Sun constantly pours out into space: in one second of time the Sun emits more energy than men have consumed in the whole of their history.

The energy is now known to come very largely from nuclear processes that occur deep inside the Sun. These processes are:

$$H^1 \ (p, \ \beta) \ H^2 \qquad \text{(i)}$$
$$H^2 \ (p, \ \gamma) \ He^3 \qquad \text{(ii)}$$
$$He^3 \ (He^3, \ 2p) \ He^4 \quad \text{(iii)}$$

The discovery of (i) and (ii) was due to H. Bethe and C. L. Critchfield, and (iii) to C. Lauritsen. The operation of the whole set of processes has recently been investigated by E. Salpeter.

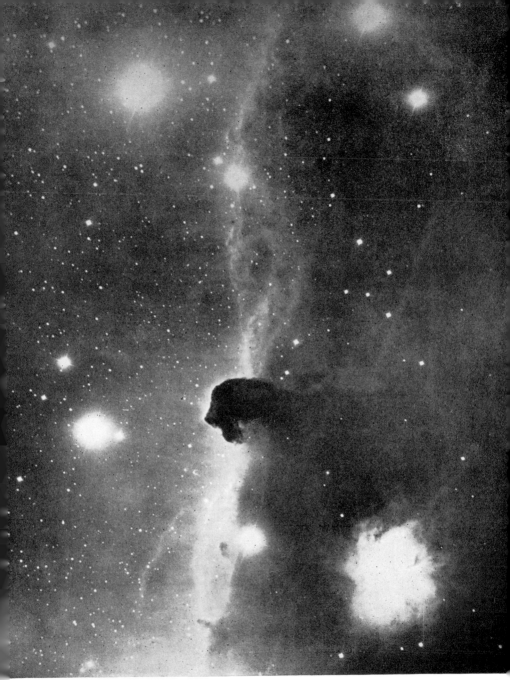

Mt. Wilson and Palomar Observatories

I—THE HORSE-HEAD NEBULA

The 'horse's head' is a cold cloud of gas and opaque dust that is being squeezed by hot surrounding gas. The hot gas is being illuminated by radiation from the near-by stars. Notice the straight trail of a meteor crossing the right-hand half of the photograph. Nebulae like this have dimensions that are measured in tens of millions of millions of miles.

Helwan Observatory

II—HALLEY'S COMET

Comets are very largely, if not wholly, composed of tiny particles that move together around the Sun in a great swarm. Comets break up from time to time. When they do so their particles become spread through vast tracts of space within the solar system. Such particles, known as meteors, sometimes come into the Earth's atmosphere. The larger ones then show up as 'shooting stars'. These apparently insignificant meteors may have an important connection with the climate of the Earth.

III—Two photographs of the same scene taken from the Lick Observatory. The picture on the left was taken in violet light, that on the right in infra-red light. Water droplets in the lower atmosphere have a smaller effect on the infra-red light. This accounts for the far greater penetration shown in the infra-red photograph.

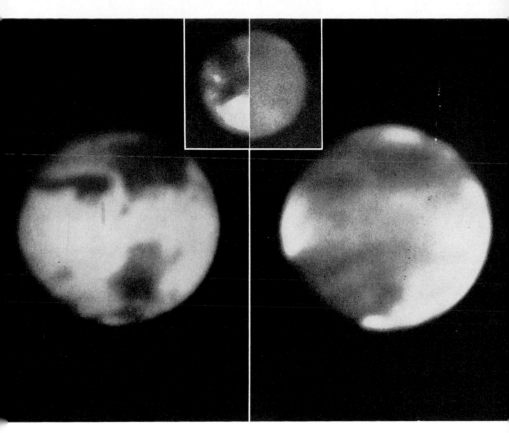

IV—Mars

Photographed in blue and red light, red to the left and blue to the right. The inset shows the difference in the apparent size of the planet according to the colour of the light used. The inset was obtained by the Lick Observatory, while the larger pictures were obtained with the 200-inch Hale telescope. The diameter of Mars is about half that of the Earth.

V—THE PLANET VENUS

Not the Moon, but the planet Venus photographed with the 200-inch telescope.
Venus is covered in white clouds, but not, it seems, clouds of water drops.
Perhaps the clouds consist of oil droplets. The dimensions of Venus are nearly
the same as those of the Earth.

VI—THE PLANET SATURN

Photographed with the 100-inch telescope on Mt. Wilson. Saturn is largely
made of hydrogen, but the outer rings seem to be mainly composed of fine ice
crystals. The dark gap in the ring is probably due to the influence of one of
Saturn's satellites, the satellite Mimas, not shown in this picture. Saturn is
95 times more massive than the Earth, and has about 9 times the dimensions.
The length of the 'day' on Saturn is only a little more than 10·hours.

VII—THE PLANET JUPITER

A beautiful photograph of Jupiter taken with the 200-inch telescope. The dimensions of Jupiter are some 10 times those of the Earth. The satellite Ganymede can be seen in the upper right-hand quadrant. Notice the circular shadow cast by Ganymede. Places in this shadow are experiencing an eclipse of the Sun. The large oval marking is the famous Red Spot.

VIII—THE MOON AT THIRD QUARTER
A dead world. The Moon at third quarter, taken with the 100-inch telescope.

IX—Full Moon

The full Moon photographed with the 100-inch telescope. The Moon looks what it is, a huge ball of stone, 2,160 miles in diameter. Notice the dark maria, and crater Tycho on the right hand side of the picture. Notice also the brilliant streaks radiating outwards from Tycho.

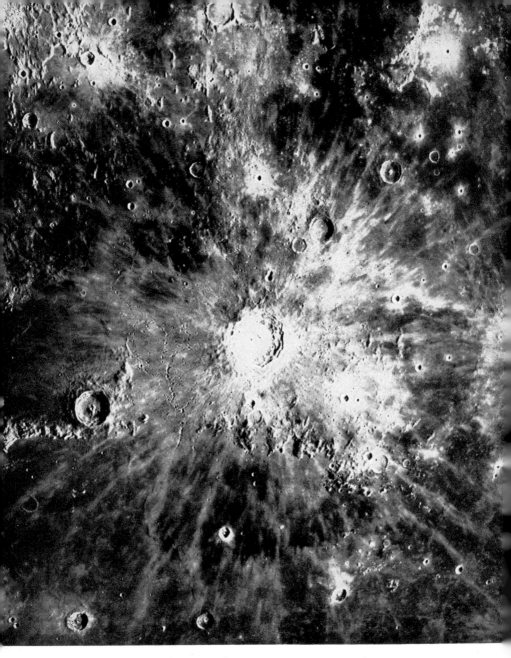

X—The Crater Copernicus and its Environs

The environs of the crater Copernicus photographed again with the 100-inch
telescope. Here you can see some of the fine details of the lunar surface.
Copernicus has a diameter of about 55 miles; the small craterlets that can be
seen are only some two or three miles in diameter.

These reactions are not so difficult to understand as one might think at first sight. In reaction (i) H^1 is hydrogen, ordinary hydrogen with a nucleus containing one particle, a proton. The H symbol in H^2 signifies hydrogen, and the 2 signifies a nucleus with two particles. Since the chemical element hydrogen has 1 proton this implies a nucleus with 1 proton and 1 neutron. Such a nucleus is known, and is called the deuteron. The symbolism of reaction (i) tells us that a proton added to H^1 makes H^2—a proton plus a proton makes a nucleus with 1 proton and 1 neutron. This requires a proton to change into a neutron during the process and this is indicated by the symbol β. Reaction (ii) implies that a proton added to H^2 (1 proton, 1 neutron) gives the isotope He^3 (2 protons, 1 neutron) of helium, radiation being emitted in the reaction. Reaction (iii) implies that He^3 (2 protons, 1 neutron) when added to He^3 (2 protons, 1 neutron) gives the isotope He^4 (2 protons, 2 neutrons) of helium and that 2 protons are ejected in the reaction.

The net effect of the three reactions is that hydrogen is converted to helium. Energy appears as an electron of positive character (positron) emitted in the β process of reaction (i), in the radiation emitted in (ii), and in the energy of motion of the two protons that are ejected in reaction (iii). These add their energy to the material of the star. A neutrino emitted in the β process carries its energy away from the star, however, and this is irretrievably lost.

The processes that we have just discussed make life possible on the Earth; for without the energy derived from the conversion of hydrogen to helium the Sun would have become a dead star several thousands of millions of years ago. Men have worshipped things more foolish than reactions (i), (ii), and (iii).

CHAPTER FIVE

Generalities About the Moon and Planets

The four inner planets

The first four planets in the order of their distances from the Sun—Mercury, Venus, Earth, and Mars, seem to be closely similar in their compositions. This can be judged from the information given in the following table:

Planet	Average distance from the Sun	Mass	Average density	Average density without compression
Mercury	0.3871	0.0543	4.5 to 5.0	4.5 to 5.0
Venus	0.7233	0.8136	4.87	4.4
Earth	1.0000	1.0000	5.52	4.4
Mars	1.5237	0.1080	4.0 to 4.2	3.8 to 4.0

Some explanation of the different columns of this table is necessary.

The Earth moves around the Sun in a nearly circular path at an average distance from the Sun of about 150 million kilometres. The distances of the planets from the Sun are given in our table in terms of this distance as unit—which explains, of course, why the distance of the Earth is given as 1.0000. Like the Earth the other planets also follow paths around the Sun that are nearly circles, all the orbits fitting very nearly into one plane, the whole solar system forming a flat distribution. To allow for the small deviation from circular motions, the distance in each case is given as an average of the greatest and least distances of the planet from the Sun.

The mass of a body is a measure of how much material it contains. The table shows that the amount of material in Mars is 10.8 per cent of the amount in the Earth. Of the four

66

planets the Earth evidently has most material. Venus comes second with 81.36 per cent of the amount in the Earth and Mercury is last with only 5.43 per cent.

The third column of the table gives the average densities of the planets in terms of the density of water (1 gram per c.c.). It will be noticed that there are uncertainties in the values for Mercury and Mars. This is due to the difficulty of measuring the sizes of these small planets with great accuracy, in the case of Mercury because it lies so far towards the Sun and in the case of Mars because the presence of an atmosphere causes us to misjudge the size: the effect of the Martian atmosphere can be seen in Plate IV, especially in the comparison of photographs taken in red and blue light.

The densities given in the third column cannot as they stand be used as indicators of composition because densities are affected by compression and the compression is different inside the different planets. The compression inside the Earth is much greater than that inside Mars, for instance. To allow for this the effects of compression have been removed from the last column, where estimates are given for what the average densities of the planets would be if there were no compression occurring inside them.

Two features are immediately noteworthy from the entries in this last column. One is that the densities of the Earth and Venus become closely comparable, indicating that these planets are probably built out of almost identical material. The other is the progressive shift of density from the innermost planet, Mercury, to the outermost planet, Mars. This would suggest that the relative proportions of rock and iron change systematically from perhaps 40 per cent of iron in the case of Mercury, to 30 per cent for Venus and the Earth, and to about 20 per cent in the case of Mars.

The similarity of Venus and the Earth suggests that in Venus an iron core has probably also been formed by the processes that were discussed in the second chapter. With Mercury and Mars the situation is somewhat uncertain, however. It is true that compressional heating, so important in the case of the Earth, must have been very much less in these planets. But even if compressional heating is ignored in the cases of

67

Mercury and Mars, it is still possible that iron has liquified in their interiors. The point here is that because of the much lower pressures inside Mercury and Mars the melting point of iron, even in the deep interiors, cannot be much greater than 1,500° C., and this is within the possible range of heating that might be produced by radioactivity. Evidently a determination of whether Mercury and Mars do or do not possess high density cores would be of great importance, since it would provide information on the degree of heating of the four inner planets that has been generated by radioactivity (always assuming that the concentration of radioactive substances is much the same in one planet as another). Unfortunately present-day observations are scarcely accurate enough to decide this question.

Let us turn now from a consideration of the formation of high density cores to the opposite process in which 'light' liquids are squeezed outwards to the surface of a planet. The internal temperatures in all cases must be adequate for the squeezing out of water. Yet on only one of the inner planets, other than the Earth, has water been detected. This is on Mars. And even on Mars there is only a very small quantity of water.

The failure to find water on Mercury is not surprising, for any water that was squeezed out of the interior of Mercury must have evaporated rapidly away into outside space, thereby leaving the planet altogether. Such an evaporation of water does not happen to any appreciable extent on the Earth, because the Earth being much more massive than Mercury has a gravitational field that is strong enough to hold water in check.

So the main problem concerns the case of Venus, and here we encounter an acute situation. Venus has a gravitational field almost as strong as that of the Earth. Accordingly we cannot argue that Venus has lost water through evaporation into space. Why then, if Venus is so similar to the Earth, is no water found on Venus? It scarcely seems plausible to suppose that the bodies out of which Venus accumulated contained no water. Because of their greater proximity to the Sun we might perhaps claim that these bodies contained less water than the bodies out of which the Earth accumulated, but that they should contain no water at all seems scarcely feasible. It appears necessary therefore to consider what might have happened if water was indeed contained in Venus at the time of its formation.

As in the case of the Earth, water would be squeezed out of the interior of Venus to the surface, where some of it would evaporate into a gaseous atmosphere—but not off the planet altogether as in the case of Mercury. Once in the atmosphere, molecules of water would probably become dissociated into their constituent atoms of hydrogen and oxygen through the action of ultra-violet light from the Sun. This process does not happen very much in our own atmosphere for a reason that would almost certainly not have been operative on Venus. In the atmosphere of the Earth oxygen rises higher than the water vapour and oxygen has the property of absorbing ultra-violet light, thereby preventing it from attacking the underlying water vapour. On Venus, oxygen would probably not have risen higher than the water vapour, so that no protective shielding of the water vapour from the solar ultra-violet light would be operative. The difference between the two cases depends simply on the higher temperature that the atmosphere of Venus must have, on account of closer proximity to the Sun. In the Earth's atmosphere water vapour, if it tries to rise high, becomes cooled and condenses into droplets which fall back to the surface as rain. The same prevention of the rise of water vapour would not occur at the higher temperature on Venus.

We arrive then at the conclusion that a steady dissociation of water molecules into hydrogen and oxygen atoms must have gone on in the atmosphere of Venus. At first thought it might seem that this process would be just balanced by a recombination of the hydrogen and oxygen atoms back into water molecules. But this ignores the point that hydrogen atoms can escape completely from the atmosphere of Venus—the gravitational field of Venus is strong enough to hold water vapour in check, but not to hold on to hydrogen. Thus the hydrogen of the water would steadily be lost into space, leaving an atmosphere of oxygen instead of water.

All this would be very fine if Venus were observed to have

an extensive atmosphere of oxygen. Venus does have quite an atmosphere, but it is an atmosphere of carbon dioxide. No free oxygen at all can be detected. The situation is not entirely without hope, however, because oxygen is extremely active in its chemical properties, so that oxygen may have combined with some other substance. It seems possible in particular that the oxygen that is present in the carbon dioxide molecules (each molecule with one atom of carbon and two of oxygen) may be just the residual oxygen that we are seeking.

The considerations of the next chapter are important in the present connection in that they suggest that carbon was much more likely to be initially present in combination with hydrogen, not with oxygen. If this is correct then we may be in sight of the solution of the water problem of Venus. For if all the carbon was initially locked away in the higher hydrocarbons, aи oxidation process was necessary in order to produce the carbon dioxide that we now observe. It is possible that the oxygen derived from the dissociation of the water was all absorbed in the oxidation of hydrocarbons.

The words 'all absorbed' are important because they point the way to an understanding of a further difference between Venus and the Earth. For all the oxygen of Venus to be thus used up, there must initially have been an excess of hydrocarbons over water. The situation on the Earth seems to have been the other way round. We had an excess of water over hydrocarbons. To appreciate the consequences of these remarks we need to give some attention to the case of the Earth.

Suppose an enormous quantity of oil were to gush to the Earth's surface: what would the effect be? The oil, consisting as it does of hydrocarbons, would proceed to absorb oxygen from the air. If the amount of oil were great enough all the oxygen would be removed. When this happened the water vapour in our atmosphere would no longer be protected from the disruptive effect of ultra-violet light from the Sun. So water vapour would begin to be dissociated into separate atoms of oxygen and hydrogen. The oxygen would combine with more oil, while the hydrogen atoms would proceed to escape altogether from the Earth out into space. More and more of the water would be dissociated and more and more of the oil would become oxidised. The process would only come to an end when either the water or the oil became exhausted. On the Earth it is clear that water has been dominant over oil. On Venus the situation seems to have been the other way round, the water has become exhausted and presumably the excess of oil remains—just as the excess of water remains on the Earth.

This possibility has an interesting consequence. The surface of Venus is perpetually covered by thick white clouds. In writing previously about these clouds* I said that the only suggestion that seemed to fit the observations was that the clouds are made up of fine dust particles. To this suggestion we must now add the possibility that the clouds might consist of drops of oil—that Venus may be draped in a kind of perpetual smog. The white appearance of Venus, due possibly to this smog, can be seen in Plate V.

There is another problem that may be soluble in terms of these ideas. Venus apparently rotates very slowly on her axis. The 'day' on Venus seems to occupy more than 20 Earth-days. Since it is likely that Venus originally rotated at much the same rate as the Earth, the problem is to explain how the rotation rate of Venus came to be slowed down so much. If Venus possesses oceans the question is readily solved, because Venus being nearer the Sun would experience stronger tides than the Earth does (even with Moon's action added to that of the Sun). Not only this, but the atmosphere of Venus being of quite different composition to that of the Earth, there need be no process of the sort discussed by Holmberg to prevent the rotation rate of Venus being slowed down to a much greater degree than that of the Earth. It is thus reasonable to suppose that the slowing down of Venus can be explained by the friction of tides—if Venus possesses oceans, but not I think otherwise. Previously the difficulty was to understand what liquid the oceans were made of. Now we see that the oceans may well be oceans of oil. Venus is probably endowed beyond the dreams of the richest Texas oil-king.

One point remains. We have still to explain why Venus

* *The Nature of the Universe.*

71

apparently possessed an excess of hydrocarbons over water, while in the Earth the situation was reversed. The explanation of this reversal is presumably to be sought in the different distances of the two planets from the Sun. With water more volatile than the oil, it is probable that the relative concentration of water was decreased at the nearer distance. This is a rather important matter. If the Earth had formed somewhat nearer the Sun we might have had oceans of considerably smaller capacity. If on the other hand the Earth had formed a little farther away from the Sun we might have had more water, with the result that the whole surface of the Earth would have been entirely submerged.

The great planets

The next four planets in the order of distances from the Sun are Jupiter, Saturn, Uranus, and Neptune. Information for these planets similar to that given previously for the four inner planets is set out as follows:

Planet	Average distance from the Sun	Mass	Average density
Jupiter	5.203	318.35	1.35
Saturn	9.539	95.3	0.71
Uranus	19.191	14.58	1.56
Neptune	30.071	17.26	2.47

The units employed in this table are the same as before. The distances from the Sun are measured in terms of the average distance of the Earth from the Sun, the masses are in terms of that of the Earth, and the densities in terms of water. The values given for the densities are in accordance with recent estimates by G. P. Kuiper.

It is at once apparent that these planets differ drastically from the four inner planets. Their densities are much too low for them to be built out of a rock-iron mixture. Their masses are much greater than those of the inner planets.

The compositions of these planets is a problem that is only now within sight of solution. It was thought until about five years ago that even the very low density of Saturn could be explained on the basis that the great planets contain a rather modest proportion of the lightest of all the elements, hydrogen— not more than 40 per cent for Saturn, about 20 per cent for Jupiter and still less for Uranus and Neptune. Although this would require the great planets to contain considerably more hydrogen than the inner planets do, the concentration of hydrogen would still be very much less than it is in the material of the Sun. Indeed the great planets would be deficient in hydrogen, as compared to the material of the Sun, by a factor of about 300.

Recent work has very much altered the situation for Jupiter and Saturn, however. It has been pointed out by Harrison Brown and by W. H. Ramsey that the older work made a quite inadequate allowance for the effects of compression in Jupiter and Saturn (it will be noticed that the present densities do not allow for compression, as the last column of table on page 66 does). The work of Ramsey has shown that Jupiter and Saturn must contain at least 80 per cent hydrogen. But the situation remains as it was before for Uranus and Neptune. Water, methane, ammonia and possibly neon would give about the right densities for these planets.

The strange case of Pluto

One more planet remains to be mentioned, the last planet of the solar system, Pluto, discovered in 1930 by C. W. Tombough at the Lowell Observatory.

The orbit of Pluto differs quite appreciably from a circle. On the average Pluto is about 30 per cent farther away from the Sun than Neptune, but because its orbit is not a circle Pluto actually dips inside the orbit of Neptune when it is nearest to the Sun. This peculiarity led Lyttleton to suggest that Pluto may be an escaped satellite of Neptune. Some plausibility is attached to this suggestion because Pluto is a planet of small mass, like the four inner planets.

The mass of Pluto has been inferred from slight distortions of the orbit of Neptune that are believed to be due to the influence of Pluto. According to Dirk Brouwer the mass is nearly equal to that of the Earth. This result when combined with observations by G. P. Kuiper on the size of Pluto allows the density to be worked out. The answer is the impossible value of 50 times the density of water—impossible because no material at the pressures operative in Pluto can have a density as high as this. Where the mistake lies is not known, but there must certainly be a mistake somewhere. One might suspect that the measurement of the size of Pluto is more likely to be in error than the estimation of its mass. This is especially so, since there is one possibility that would completely vitiate any observational attempt to determine the size. If Pluto acted like a highly polished ball we should not observe the ball itself, but only a highly illuminated spot near the centre. The effect can be seen by holding a polished steel ball in sunlight. But why Pluto should behave like a polished ball remains a mystery.

The satellites

As we go outwards from the Sun, the Earth is the first planet to possess a satellite—the Moon. Then comes Mars with two, but both are extremely small compared with the Moon. Indeed the Moon is a very respectably-sized satellite even when we compare it with the satellites of the great planets. Of the 12 satellites of Jupiter only two have larger masses than the Moon. Of the 9 satellites of Saturn only one has a larger mass than the Moon. None of the 5 satellites of Uranus compares with the Moon, although one of the 2 satellites of Neptune does. The masses and densities of the larger satellites of the solar system are given as follows:

Planet	Satellite	Mass (in terms of the Moon)	Average density
Earth	Moon	1.00	3.33
Jupiter	Io	0.99	4.03
	Europa	0.64	3.78
	Ganymede	2.11	2.35
	Callisto	1.32	2.06
Saturn	Titan	1.92	2.4
Neptune	Triton	1.8	2 (?)

74

It is particularly to be noted that the masses are given here in terms of the Moon as unit, not in terms of the Earth (as in tables on pages 66 and 72). The mass of the Moon is 1.23 per cent of that of the Earth. Since the mass of the smallest planet, Mercury, is 5.43 per cent of that of the Earth it follows that the masses of the satellites fit smoothly on to the masses of the planets, although no satellite has a mass quite as great as Mercury.

The average density of the Moon suggests that the Moon is entirely made of rock, similar to the rocks of the Earth's mantle. The compositions of Io and Europa seem to be similar to Mars, about 20 per cent of iron being necessary in order to explain the densities of these satellites. In the other cases, however, it is clear that a mixture of rock and iron is quite inappropriate, for no known rock has a density low enough for these satellites. To obtain the observed densities, appreciable quantities of such substances as water, ammonia, carbon disulphide are required. An interesting feature of the present table is the tendency of the density to fall as the distance of the parent planet from the Sun increases. The significance of this trend will become clear in the next chapter.

The case of the Moon deserves detailed comment. Unless the rock of the Moon is of the light variety found in the crustal zone of the Earth the Moon can contain no iron. This raises serious issues. The Earth and the Moon were evidently formed quite close to each other. How then did the Earth come to contain iron in a proportion of about 30 per cent, while the Moon apparently possesses none? This question seems so difficult to answer that one is tempted to accept the alternative view—that the rocks of the Moon are light rocks like the rocks of the terrestrial continents with a density of about 2.7. This would allow the Moon to contain about 30 per cent iron, so that its chemical composition would then be quite similar to that of the Earth.

The idea that the Moon might be largely composed of a light sort of rock agrees with an important observed characteristic of the Moon—there is no volcanic activity on the Moon. We saw in the second chapter that volcanoes on the Earth probably arise from light molten rock that is squeezed to the surface by

75

the solid denser rock of the mantle. If the rocks of the Moon were all light rocks, squeezing could not take place.

There is, of course, an alternative explanation of the lack of volcanic activity on the Moon—the interior of the Moon may be entirely solid. If this is the case then the heating by radioactivity in the Moon must have been insufficient to raise the internal temperature much above 1,500° C., since at the pressures occurring in the Moon melting points cannot be much different from the values measured in the laboratory (1,500° C. for iron, between 900° C. and 1,800° C. for various kinds of rock). This would tend to confirm the view expressed in the third chapter, that the heating of the Earth's interior by radioactivity has probably not been a factor of great importance.

The origin of the lunar craters

The lack of volcanic activity on the Moon suggests that we abandon the old theory that the craters on the Moon were formed by lunar volcanoes. This is all to the good, since the volcanic theory never succeeded in explaining the vast dimensions of the lunar craters, the largest of which are nearly 100 miles in diameter. This is more than ten times the diameter of any terrestrial volcanic crater. The appearance of the surface of the Moon, studded with craters large and small can be judged from the photograph reproduced in Plate VIII.

The last bodies that fell into the Moon must have plunged into the surface at very considerable speeds, speeds of several miles per second. A body falling on to the surface of the Moon at such a speed (or on to the surface of the Earth) would not have its progress immediately halted at the moment it struck the surface. It would penetrate some distance below the surface, as a bullet penetrates into a block of wood. But whereas an ordinary bullet shoulders aside the wood through which it passes, it seems unlikely that this could happen in the case of a very high velocity missile which would ram impeding material in front of it—the material would not be shouldered aside because there would be no time to get out of the way! When a missile plunged into the Moon the rocks of the lunar surface at the point of impact must simply have been crushed flat. This would change the material from a solid into a high temperature gas. The gas would form a pocket driven in front of the missile. As more and more gas joined the pocket the pressure would rise until eventually it became sufficient to stop the missile. When this happened the pocket of high pressure gas might have been several miles below the surface of the Moon. The next step is obvious. A pocket of gas at high pressure situated a few miles below the surface must produce a shattering explosion, the result being a crater.

A striking confirmation of these arguments is shown in Fig. 3, which is due to R. B. Baldwin. It plots the depth of craters against their diameters. The points at the bottom of the curve refer to terrestrial craters made by shells, bombs, and other explosions. The points marked ■ are terrestrial craters that are known to have been formed by missiles that have struck the Earth from outside (the famous Arizona crater being one of them). The points at the upper end of the curve all refer to lunar craters. The excellent fit of the various sorts of crater to a common curve leaves little doubt that the lunar craters originated by explosion.

The origin of the bright rays shown on the photograph of the full Moon in Plate IX provides another point in favour of the impact theory. These are the rays that radiate outwards from the prominent craters. The bright rays from Tycho, the most notable crater showing on Plate IX, stretch in some places completely across the visible hemisphere. The bright rays are probably jets of fused glass-like material that were shot out by the explosions that produced the associated craters.

Plate IX also brings out the marked tendency of the dark patches towards a circular shape. These dark patches are the lunar seas or maria, so named before it was realised that they are not oceans. It is thought by many astronomers that even the maria were produced by impact, but by the impact of larger bodies than were responsible for the craters, by veritable planetesimals perhaps a hundred miles or so in diameter.

Often two craters intersect each other, as can be seen from an examination of Plate VIII. When they do so it is nearly always the wall of the larger crater that is broken, the smaller

77

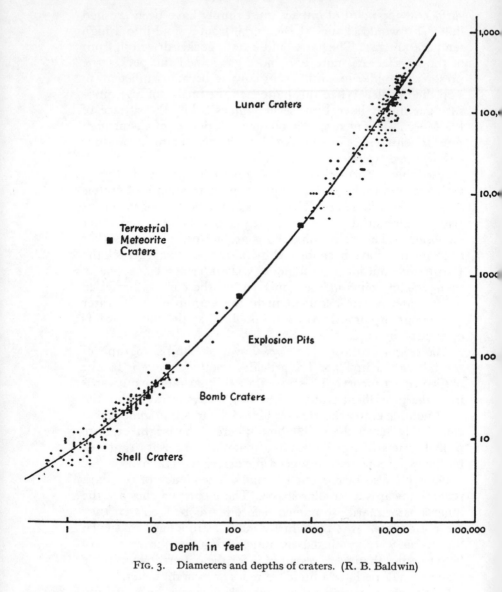

FIG. 3.   Diameters and depths of craters. (R. B. Baldwin)

crater being usually complete. This might be explained by saying that the smaller crater was produced after the larger one. But why should the larger missile fall first in almost all cases? This apparently awkward question can be partially countered by noticing that if the larger missile fell second it would in many cases simply obliterate the smaller crater. This gives a systematic tendency for the observed double craters to be the ones in which the smaller crater formed second. I find it difficult to believe that this argument is entirely adequate to explain all the facts, however. That it is an argument with considerable force is clear, but there seem to be so many cases where small craters lie absolutely squarely on the walls of a large crater, or on the central cone of a large crater, that I do not think the matter can be entirely dismissed in this way. Such cases can be found by a careful examination of the more detailed photograph shown in Plate X. These cases look as if they may have been caused by the collapse of domes of rubble. This sort of occurrence could well happen if a few bubbles of gas remained trapped for a time in the rubble after the explosion that led to the formation of the main crater.

Even a casual glance at Plate VIII shows that the maria are notably lacking in distinctive craters. One suggestion that has been put forward to account for this is that the large bodies that gave rise to the maria fell into the Moon practically last of all. This view was expressed to me by Harold Urey, who believes that the maria are great flows of molten lava produced by the heat of impact of the striking bodies. Urey considers that iron sulphide may be a notable constituent of these lava flows, and that it is this compound that gives to the maria their characteristic dark appearance.

Much as Professor Urey's arguments on this question demand respect, I have grave doubts as to whether this view can be correct, however. Quite apart from the implausible suggestion that the maria were formed by almost the last bodies to join the Moon, I do not believe that the impact of fast moving missiles with the surface of the Moon would produce any liquification. The surface of the Moon is not liquified at the point of impact, it is gasified. Even if it be argued that the velocities of the missiles that produced the maria were so low that gasification, along the lines described above did not occur, I still doubt whether any substantial liquifaction of the colliding materials would occur. A bullet fired into wood does not liquify the wood. It loses its energy in destroying the fibre structure of the wood. I suspect that a missile falling with small speed on to the surface of the Moon (if indeed this were ever to occur) would likewise lose its energy in breaking the crystal structure of the rocks of the Moon's surface, not in liquifaction. If the maria are indeed lava flows, then the molten rock must have come from the interior of the Moon.

An important clue to the understanding of the nature of the maria comes from a careful examination of their surfaces. This soon shows that although notable craters on the maria are certainly rare, there are very many places where the circular outlines of quite substantial craters can be faintly detected. In many places a part of the wall of a crater can be seen sticking out of the maria. How were these so-called 'drowned' craters formed? Certainly they could not have been formed before the maria, since then they would surely have been entirely obliterated during the formation of the maria themselves. And if we argue that they were formed after the maria then we must admit that many substantial missiles did in fact fall after those that produced the maria. So we are back at the difficulty of explaining why the drowned craters do not show up more notably. It has been suggested that the later missiles fell into the maria at a time when they were still molten. This would have no effect however on the explosive gasification process that produced the craters. All that can be argued along these lines is that the craters produced in a molten maria would have molten walls, and that the walls might proceed to flow away. But at this point the argument collapses because in those cases where portions of the walls of craters stick up above the floor of the maria the walls can be seen to be entirely normal, indistinguishable from the walls of the craters outside the maria.

As far as I am aware only one suggestion has been made that is capable of meeting this situation. This is a suggestion due to Gold, that I already described in *The Nature of the Universe*. On this view there are just as many craters on the maria as anywhere else. The 'drowned' craters are examples of these, and are regarded as being entirely normal craters. The 'drowning' agent is taken to be, not lava, but fine dust, which is supposed to have accumulated on the maria to very considerable depths. Cases where a part of the wall of a drowned crater is plainly visible are simply cases where the walls stick up above the level of the dust. It is an immediately encouraging feature that whenever an obstacle rises out of the level maria the slope does not increase gradually, the obstacle rears up abruptly like a cliff out of the sea.

The two outstanding craters on Plate IX form an interesting comparison, Tycho lying off the maria in the lunar uplands, and Copernicus lying on the maria. Tycho is cleanly sculptured in its internal form and its external ray system is bright and straight. Copernicus on the other hand has a noticeably terraced internal structure and its ray system is contorted and less marked than that of Tycho. Yet the two craters being comparable in size must have been produced by explosions of comparable violence. How do we account for these differences? The natural explanation is that the explosion that produced Tycho occurred in solid rock, whereas the explosion that produced Copernicus occurred in a mixture of dust and rock.

Gold has also considered the problem of how dust is formed on the Moon and of how it is transported from place to place. Since the Moon possesses no atmosphere the surface is constantly being bombarded with ultra-violet light and with X-rays from the Sun. This must tend to break down the crystal structure of rock at the extreme surface, allowing small bits to break away. The bits are thought to be transported to the lower parts of the lunar surface, which indeed is where the maria are found, by the combined action of electrical forces and of gravitation.

It is also worth noticing that a considerable quantity of fine dust was presumably added to the Moon during the process of its origin. Much of the dust now to be found on the lunar surface may be simply primeval dust—tiny particles that showered on to the Moon during the final phases of its formation.

The surface rocks of the Moon are not coloured like the

surface rocks of the Earth. Examination through a small telescope or with binoculars shows the Moon to be a monotonous grey. This is now thought to be also due to the incidence of ultra-violet light from the Sun, which is known to destroy colour.

The dry, dead, colourless surface of the Moon gives us a graphic picture of what the surface of the Earth was once like. Before the Earth developed its atmosphere and oceans it must have gone spinning through space the same sort of dead grey ball that we now observe the Moon to be. With the coming of the oceans and the atmosphere, wonderful transformations of the Earth's surface began. The old scars, left from the accumulation of the Earth, were soon removed by erosion. The atmosphere shielded the surface from the deadly ultra-violet rays, so that colours could arise and persist. The fall of rain quickly suppresses the once dusty surface of the planet. So was the stage gradually laid for the emergence of life.

CHAPTER SIX

The Origin of the Planets

Planets by the billion

Besides satisfying a natural curiosity as to how our particular home came into being, a study of the origin of the planets is also of great interest in suggesting how frequently places like the Earth are to be found in the Universe. In a former discussion* of this particular problem, I was led to the conclusion that there might be as many as one million planetary systems very similar to our own among the stars of the Milky Way. The arguments of the present chapter will show that this estimate is in need of revision. The new number comes out, not at a mere 1 million, but at 100,000 million.

In outline, my earlier idea was that at one time the Sun was a member of a double-star system—two stars that moved around each other. It was also supposed that the Sun's companion exploded with enormous violence, the catastrophic disintegration causing the remains to be flung away from the Sun, save for a small wisp of material that the Sun managed to hang on to. The wisp of material then spread out around the Sun as a disk, and in this disk condensations occurred that eventually grew into the planets.

The suggestion that the material of the Earth was indeed derived from an exploding star—a supernova, is supported by strong evidence, as we shall see in Chapter 12. But it now seems less likely that the supernova was a companion to the Sun in a double system. Rather does it seem that the Sun was born in a whole shower of stars and that the supernova (or supernovae) belonged to the shower. Evidence for this will be considered in Chapter 15.

Although this new view may not seem much different from

* *The Nature of the Universe.*

83

the old, it turns out that the changes of argument are far greater than might be thought at first sight. The shower of stars must have been surrounded by a cloud of gas—the cloud from which the stars had just condensed. A supernova undergoing violent disintegration must have expelled gases that went to join this cloud, the material from the supernova thereby getting mixed with the large quantity of hydrogen of which the cloud was mainly composed. Our problem is then to explain how both the Sun and planets were formed out of this mixture of materials. In particular, we have to explain how the materials of the Earth, derived from the supernova, were separated out again after they had thus become mixed with a great deal of hydrogen.

But before we deal with this question we have other more immediate difficulties to face, difficulties that confront all theories that seek to explain the origin of solar system, Sun and planets together, in terms of a condensation process from the interstellar gas. How, for instance, do we explain the wide separations of the planets from the Sun?

To appreciate the seriousness of this question, consider a model with the Sun represented by a ball 6 inches in diameter, about the size of a grapefruit. On this model the inner planets Mercury, Venus, Earth, and Mars are at the respective distances of 7, 13, 18, and 27 yards, being in themselves not more than the size of a pin's head. The great planets Jupiter, Saturn, Uranus, and Neptune are of the sizes of small peas at about 90, 170, 350 and 540 yards respectively from the Sun. Pluto is a speck of silver about 700 yards away.

The clue

It is the characteristic of a good detective story that one vital clue should reveal the solution to the mystery, but that the clue and its significance should be far from obvious. Such a clue exists in the present problem. It turns on the simple fact that the Sun takes some 26 days to spin once round on its axis—the axis being nearly perpendicular to the orbits of the planets, which lie nearly in the same plane. The importance of this fact is that the Sun has no business to be rotating in 26 days. It ought to be rotating in a fraction of a day, several hundred times faster than it is actually doing. Manifestly something has slowed the spin of the Sun. It is this something that yields the key to the mystery. But before we go on to discuss the crucial steps of the argument we ought first to understand why the Sun might have been expected to spin very much faster than it is in fact doing.

Stars are the products of condensations that occur in the dense interstellar gas clouds. A notable cloud is shown in Plate XI. This is the well-known Orion Nebula whose presence in the 'sword' of Orion can easily be seen with binoculars. It is known that stars are forming in large numbers within the Orion Nebula at the present time.

Stars forming out of the gas in such clouds must undergo a very great degree of condensation. To begin with, the material of a star must occupy a very large volume, because of the extremely small density of the interstellar gas. In order to contain as much material as the Sun does, a sphere of gas in the Orion Nebula must have a diameter of some 10,000,000,000,000 miles. Contrast this with the present diameter of the Sun, which is only about a million miles. Evidently in order to produce a star like the Sun a blob of gas with an initial diameter of some 10,000,000,000,000 miles must be shrunk down in some way to a mere million miles. This implies a shrinkage to one ten-millionth of the original size.

Now it is a consequence of the laws of dynamics, the laws discovered in the first revolution of physics, that unless some external process acts on it a blob of gas must spin more and more rapidly as it shrinks. The size of a condensation and the speed of its spin keep an inverse proportion with each other: a decrease of size to one ten-millionth of the original dimensions leads to an increase in the speed of spin by 10 million. So if the initial speed was only 1 centimetre per second the final speed would be 10 million centimetres per second—100 kilometres per second, that is (100,000 centimetres equals 1 kilometre). But the rotation speed of the Sun is only about 2 kilometres per second at the equator, and the speed is faster at the equator than anywhere else. At a speed of 100 kilometres per second the Sun would spin around once in about half a day, instead of in the observed time of 26 days.

The discrepancy cannot be evaded by saying that the original spin should not be set as high as 1 centimetre per second. Observations of the motion of the gases in the Orion Nebula lead to the opposite conclusion, that we have already set the initial speed much too low. An initial speed of 10 centimetres per second, or even of 100 centimetres per second, would agree better with the observations. These initial speeds would lead to final speeds of 1,000 kilometres per second, and of 10,000 kilometres per second respectively. Actually no star like the Sun could spin as rapidly as this—it would be torn apart by rotary forces, as a flywheel bursts if it is spun too quickly.

As a desperate measure we might feel tempted to argue that the Sun is a freak case. It is true that any calculation based on observations of the Orion Nebula refers to an average situation, to an average star. Perhaps we could set the initial speed of spin at less than 1 centimetre per second for the case of the Sun, even though the initial spin must be much more rapid for the average star? But this would require the majority of stars otherwise similar to the Sun to spin very rapidly, in flat contradiction with observation. Stars otherwise similar to the Sun are also similar in that they spin slowly. The policy of desperation fails.

Only one loophole remains. We must appeal to some external process to slow down the spin of the solar condensation. Our problem is to discover how such an external process operates.

The external process

First we must decide at what stage of the condensation the external process acts. Does it act while the condensing blob still has very large dimensions? Or does it operate only in the later stages, as the condensation reaches the compact stellar state? Or does it operate more or less equally throughout the whole shrinkage?

These questions have an obvious relevance to the origin of the planets. If the slowing down occurred while the solar condensation was still spread out through a vast volume with dimensions of some 10,000,000,000,000 miles the process would have operated much too soon. Jupiter, the largest planet, is situated some 500 million miles from the Sun, a distance much smaller than the original size of the solar condensation. Evidently unless the slowing of the rotation occurred only after the proto-Sun had shrunk to less than one-thousandth of its original size, the process could not have had any effect on the origin of the planets. It seems likely that this was so, not for any reason connected with the planets themselves, but from an entirely independent line of evidence. The point is such an important one that even at the expense of interrupting our main discussion it is worth giving a short outline of this evidence.

A strong hint that the process must act mainly in the late stages of the condensation comes from observations of the rates of spin of the stars. It is found that the rates of spin have a very curious dependence on surface temperature. Stars like the Sun, with surface temperatures less than 6,000° C. (the surface temperature of the Sun is about 5,460° C.), rotate slowly like the Sun. But stars with surface temperatures greater than 7,000° C. rotate considerably more rapidly, their equatorial speeds of rotation being usually greater than 50 kilometres per second. Although this is still much less than what we should expect if no external process were operative, it is considerably greater than the equatorial rotation speed possessed by the Sun. This shows that while the external process must be operative in all cases, it is operative to different degrees that depend on the surface temperature of the final star. Now the difference between one star and another can scarcely show at all during the early stages of the shrinkage. Certainly the difference between two condensations, one yielding a star of surface temperature 6,000° C. and the other yielding a star of surface temperature 7,000° C., must be very small indeed during the early stages, much too small for the two stars to come to have markedly different rotation speeds if the external process were of main effect during the early stages. The inference is that the process operates mainly during the late stages of condensation.

Now what was the external process? We have mentioned

87

that rotary forces must have become important during the late stages of the condensation. The effect of these forces was to cause the condensation to become more and more flattened at its poles. Eventually the flattening became sufficient for an external rotating disk to begin growing out of the equator. This sequence of events is illustrated in Fig. 4.

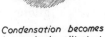

Condensation is initially of an approximately spherical shape.

Condensation becomes increasingly elliptical during shrinkage.

Eventually the condensation grows a disk.

FIG. 4. Shrinkage of solar condensation. The shrinkage reduces the dimensions ten million-fold and consequently cannot be drawn to scale. The condensation is shown edge-on.

Once the Sun had thus grown a disk the external process was able to come into operation. The word 'external' simply means 'external to the Sun', and the disk was now external to the Sun. The process consisted of a steady transference of rotational momentum from the Sun to the disk. Two birds were thereby killed with one stone. The Sun was slowed down to its present slow rate of spin and the disk, containing the material out of which the planets were subsequently to condense, was pushed farther and farther from the Sun. The solar condensation probably first grew its disk when it had shrunk to a size somewhat less than the orbit of the innermost planet, Mercury. The pushing outwards of the main bulk of the material of the disk explains why the larger planets now lie so far from the Sun.

Overcoming the first difficulty

It may be wondered why such an obvious theory was not put forward long ago. The answer is that there seemed to be such grave objections to it that not until very recently has it been examined at all seriously. And now it turns out that the objections are not so grave as was previously believed. Both the Matterhorn and Everest were climbed by routes that were at first thought to be impossible. Only after failure had attended all attempts by what were thought to be the most feasible r)utes did mountaineers turn their attention to the ways that they had first rejected. Then it was found that the difficulties were more imagined than real. A similar situation seems to exist in the problem of the origin of the planets.

If all the planets were scooped up and mixed into the Sun, the Sun would certainly rotate much faster than it does—the equatorial speed of rotation would be about 100 kilometres per second, instead of the present 2 kilometres per second. But this is not fast enough. At such a rotation speed the Sun would become somewhat flattened at its poles, but the rotary forces would not be sufficient to make the Sun grow a disk. The Sun would have about the same shape as Jupiter has (see Plate VII). The Sun would not grow a disk any more than Jupiter is growing a disk at the present time.

This would seem at first sight to dispose of the theory. If putting all the planets back into the Sun would not cause the Sun to grow a disk, how was the Sun able to grow a disk during the condensation process? If the Sun rotated fast enough in the past to grow a disk of planetary material, should not the Sun again become unstable if the material of the planets were returned to it? Unquestionably yes, *if* the present planets contain all the material that originally left the Sun. But perhaps this is not so. Perhaps only a small proportion of the material that formed the original disk is now locked away inside the planets. This would overcome the difficulty.

But where then is the missing material? It is certainly not moving around the Sun at the present time, so that our answer must be that it escaped entirely from the gravitational influence of the Sun and went back to join the clouds of inter-stellar gas (we cannot reply that the material fell back into the Sun since this would reinstate the difficulty that we are now seeking to overcome). The theory stands or falls on the correctness or otherwise of this suggestion.

Fortunately it seems probable that a great deal of hydrogen did indeed succeed in escaping from the disk out to the interstellar gas. Otherwise the scarcity of hydrogen in the planets Uranus and Neptune cannot be satisfactorily explained. Jupiter and Saturn seem to contain much the same amount of hydrogen (see Chapter 5) as the Sun does, but the more distant Uranus and Neptune have comparatively little hydrogen. To account for this, large quantities of hydrogen must have escaped from the outermost parts of the disk of planetary material—from the outermost parts presumably because the restraining pull of the Sun was at its weakest there.

If we make the very reasonable supposition that Uranus and Neptune consist mainly of carbon, nitrogen, oxygen, and neon, we can readily estimate the amount of hydrogen that must have escaped. Carbon, nitrogen, oxygen, and neon make up about 1 per cent of the mass of the material of the Sun, so that on the basis that planetary material and solar material were originally identical (a necessity in the present theory), we require the mass of hydrogen that escaped from the outer parts of the planetary disk to have been about 100 times greater than the combined mass of Uranus and Neptune which together amount to rather more than 30 times the mass of the Earth— as can be seen from the table on page 72. Hence the mass of escaping hydrogen must have been about 3,000 times the Earth. This may be compared with about 450 Earth-masses now resident in all the planets. The escaping hydrogen therefore exceeded the total mass of the present planets about sevenfold.

Our difficulty is entirely resolved by these considerations. We see that instead of having to reckon only with the mass of the planets we have to regard the original disk of material as having possessed nearly ten times as much material as is now contained in the planets. Putting back the disk into the Sun would therefore raise the speed of rotation, not to 100 kilometres per second, but to about 1,000 kilometres per second; and at this speed the Sun would certainly grow a disk. Indeed this speed is so large that the Sun must have grown its disk when it was of appreciably larger size than it is at present. The contracting solar condensation must have grown a disk when its dimensions were perhaps fifty times the present size of the Sun.

Overcoming the second difficulty

Consider the following curious situation. After the solar condensation grew its disk the condensation continued to shrink. The disk, on the other hand, was pushed farther and farther outwards. This must have caused a gap to open up between the solar condensation and the inner edge of the disk. How did rotational momentum continue to be transferred across this gap? Here we have the second major difficulty that the theory must surmount.

A suggestion was put forward some years ago by H. Alfvén that may well be capable of fitting this piece of the puzzle into place. Alfvén pointed out that rotational momentum might be carried by a magnetic field, even across a gap of the sort that must arise in the present problem. The idea that magnetic fields may play an important role in the process of origin of the planets is an important new concept deserving of close consideration. Many years ago Faraday showed that it was possible to think of a magnetic field as a collection of lines of forces, the lines of force behaving in many ways like elastic strings. The analogy of elastic strings is of particular value in the present instance as we shall soon see. To get to grips with the matter, consider a wheel with an inner hub connected to an outer rim by spokes. When the spokes are rigid the rim is forced to rotate around in exactly the same time as the hub. But if the spokes were made of elastic the rim could lag behind the hub. This would cause the spokes to become stretched in the manner shown in Fig. 5. Such a stretching of the elastic has the effect of speeding up the rim and of slowing down the hub.

For the hub of the wheel now read the Sun, for the rim read the disk of planetary material, and for the elastic spokes read the magnetic field. The magnetic field slows down the rotation of the Sun just as the elastic spokes pull back the hub of the wheel in our analogy. The magnetic field also affects the disk of planetary material, not quite by speeding up the disk, but by pushing it farther and farther away from the Sun. This is just the situation that we require.

It appears therefore that a process for coupling the rotation of the Sun to the planetary material may exist. A further encouraging feature is that the strength of the magnetic field necessary to operate the process turns out to be very moderate (in our analogy the stiffness of the elastic spokes of the wheel corresponds to the strength of the magnetic field); this is considerably less than the strengths of the magnetic fields that are known to exist on many stars, and considerably less than the magnetic fields that exist in the sunspots—of which we shall have more to say in the next chapter.

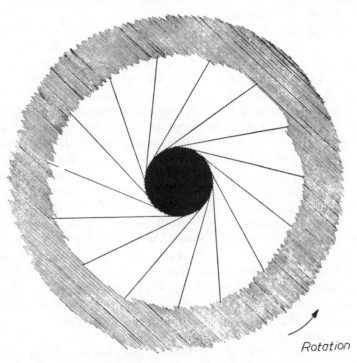

Rotation

FIG. 5. Magnetic spokes in plan, not drawn to scale.

The invoking of 'magnetic spokes' is a very new development in the study of the origin of the planets. I suspect it to be the decisive step without which no thoroughly satisfactory theory can be found. It must be admitted, however, that certain difficulties of a highly technical character still remain to be overcome.

Overcoming the third difficulty

The third and last severe difficulty concerns the compositions of the four inner planets. These are made very largely of rock and iron. Now iron and the magnesium and silicon of the rock were presumably only very minor components of the original planetary material. We can infer this because the planetary material must (on the present theory) have been exactly like solar material at one time—and the solar content of iron, magnesium, and silicon is only some ¼ per cent by weight. What process then was responsible for separating out the rock and iron? How was the iron, magnesium, and silicon separated from the main constituents of the planetary material, notably from the great mass of hydrogen?

The present difficulty is a consequence of the change from the theory advocated in *The Nature of the Universe*. Iron and the rock-forming atoms are derived from the stars, probably mainly from the exploding supernovae. The composition of the inner planets would therefore be explained immediately, if (as in the former theory) the planetary material were derived directly from a supernova. But this simple explanation is destroyed if (as in the present theory) the material from the supernovae first mixes with a large quantity of interstellar gas. The success or failure of the ideas of the present chapter depends on the outcome of a search for an alternative explanation. Actually an entirely satisfactory alternative explanation can indeed be found, as we shall now see.

Our theory requires the gases of the disk to be pushed farther and farther away from the Sun as the rotation of the Sun is slowed down. Now the magnetic coupling between the Sun and the disk depends for its functioning on the material of the disk being a gas. If solid or liquid particles of appreciable size were to condense out of the gas of the disk, rather as rain-drops condense out of the water vapour in the clouds of the terrestrial atmosphere, they would not be subjected to any appreciable magnetic effects. Solid or liquid particles of say a few yards or more in size condensing out of the gas would therefore be left behind as the main gases were pushed farther from the Sun.

Now what substances may be expected to have condensed out as solid or liquid particles? The answer depends on the temperature within the gas, and this evidently depends on the distance of the gas from the Sun—the nearer to the Sun the higher the temperature. When the temperature is comparatively high only very refractory substances such as the silicates, iron, and some other metals can condense. But with increasing distance and progressively lower temperatures substances of lower and lower boiling points condense—oil, water, ammonia.

Let us try to visualise what happened to the disk as it moved outwards from the Sun. Before the material reached the distances of the great planets, the most refractory substances became condensed out of the gas as a swarm of solid bodies. Already a great deal is explained. We see why the inner planets must represent aggregations built up out of much smaller bodies (this being the view that guided our discussion of the internal properties of the Earth in a former chapter). We also see how it came about that the inner planets were built up almost entirely of rock and iron—simply because the rock and iron were the first important materials to separate out of the gas. This is an outstanding point in favour of the theory; for quite apart from our now being able to understand how the iron and rock came to be separated out from the planetary material we also see why the inner planets must be the ones that are made of the rock and iron.

Many details remain to be understood, however. How exactly did the multitude of small bodies become agglomerated into planets? What decided the distances of Mercury, Venus, Earth, and Mars from the Sun? Only hints can at present be given as to what the answers to these questions may turn out to be. It has been suggested by Harold Urey, and independently by H. E. Suess, that liquids may have played an important part in the agglomeration process. The idea is that liquids can act as a sort of glue that sticks the solid bodies together. Two bodies coated with sticky liquids would certainly be much more likely to remain joined together after collision than would two entirely solid bodies. The identity of such sticking agents is not known with any certainty. Urey suggests water in the form of slushy snow. It is true that some water molecules may be expected to combine with the silicates as hydrates. This indeed is necessary in order to explain how water came to be present on the Earth. But slush is essentially pure water, and I doubt whether any pure water would condense from the vapour until the gases receded beyond the orbits of the inner planets. My impression is that we must look elsewhere for a sticking agent. The higher hydrocarbons would condense as oil. In itself oil is perhaps not a very suitable sticking agent, but pitch, obtained by oxidising certain hydrocarbons, would be a sticker par excellence.

The problem of deciding why the planets were formed at just their present distances from the Sun is an important one. I am inclined to believe that the distances were strictly determined by the regions in which sticking agents were particularly active. If this is correct the distance of the Earth from the Sun is not a matter of chance—and another apparently arbitrary quality disappears from the solar system.

The origin of Jupiter and Saturn

Beyond the inner planets water and ammonia were able to condense out of the gas. The agglomeration of bodies composed largely of water and ammonia presumably represented the first phase in the building of Jupiter and Saturn. Because water and ammonia must have been more important constituents of the original planetary material than either rock or iron it is only to be expected that Jupiter and Saturn should be more massive than the four inner planets. But this is not in itself sufficient to account for the very large differences of mass that actually exist. We might expect a difference perhaps by a factor 10 on this score, but not by the factor of 100 or more that we actually find. To explain factors of this order we must suppose that Jupiter and Saturn managed to add large quantities of uncondensed gas to themselves, the main component of the gas being hydrogen.

It may be wondered how it is possible for a planet to pick up gaseous substances. So far we have spoken of a planet forming through the agglomeration of solid and liquid bodies. This must be the way that the first steps of planet formation

95

occur. But once a body of considerable size has thus been built up, the gravitational field of the body itself may begin to play an important role in the condensation. This will be especially so if the newly forming planet happens to be immersed in gas, as the young Jupiter and the young Saturn presumably were. In the cases of the inner planets, the gases must have been pushed out beyond their orbits by the time that the first bodies of a sufficient size to be able to pull in gaseous material were built up. In this way it is possible to understand why the inner planets picked up so little water, neon, ammonia, etc. The necessity for giving a satisfactory explanation of this point has been emphasised by Harold Urey.

Now was this an accident? Was it an accident that the inner planets did not aggregate until after the gases had been pushed out beyond their orbits? I suspect that there was no accident at all. In keeping with the general theme of this book, I believe that nothing arbitrary entered the chain of incident that connected the origin of the Earth, and of living creatures on the Earth, with the general march of cosmic events. Rather do I suspect that no suitable sticking agent was available while the swarm of small bodies out of which the inner planets were later to agglomerate were still immersed in the hydrogen gas: that it was only after the gases had moved farther outwards, to the orbits of Jupiter and Saturn, that chemical changes leading to the presence of sticking agents occurred among the swarm of small rock and iron bodies.

The origin of Uranus and Neptune

Four problems have to be solved to give a satisfactory theory of the origin of Uranus and Neptune. The first is to discover the nature of the substances that remain to be condensed out of the gas. Water and ammonia must have been already lost when the gases moved out past the orbits of Jupiter and Saturn. Perhaps one of the lower hydrocarbons initiated the condensation from the gas. The second problem is the identity of the sticking agent responsible for the building up of bodies of considerable size. The third problem is to show why bodies of considerable size were not built up until after the hydrogen had escaped from the region of Uranus and Neptune out again to the interstellar gas clouds. The fourth problem is to find out why the hydrogen escaped from the outer parts of the solar system. Several proposals have been put forward to explain why the hydrogen escaped. Some astronomers regard the heating effect of ultra-violet light from the Sun as the cause. Others attribute importance to friction between the planetary material and the interstellar gas, while a third idea is that a very hot luminous star happened at one time to be in the vicinity of the solar system and that it was the heating effect of this neighbouring star that caused the hydrogen to escape. Of these possibilities only the third seems to me to be certainly workable; and since there are reasons why a star of the necessary type might indeed have been quite close to the solar system at the time the Sun was formed, this idea may well turn out to be the correct one. We shall return to it in a later chapter.

The third problem, of explaining why aggregations of appreciable size were not formed before the hydrogen was lost, raises a very pertinent issue. For if aggregations that were large enough to pull in gas by their gravitational fields had formed first, then Uranus and Neptune would have contained large quantities of hydrogen—just as Jupiter and Saturn contain large quantities of hydrogen. A very satisfactory solution to this problem would be obtained if, as in the case of the inner planets, it could be shown that no sticking agent was available *so long as the hydrogen remained,* but that a sticking agent could arise from chemical changes once the hydrogen was lost. This would solve the problem without any appeal to chance effects.

It may be noted that gases such as methane and neon would not be evaporated away from the solar system like the hydrogen. These gases would remain to be picked up by gravitational action once appreciable aggregation had taken place. Neon and methane are probably major constituents of Uranus and Neptune.

Further problems

It will be clear from what has been said above that the solar system, for all its tininess when viewed on a cosmic scale

97

abounds in intricate problems. It is no wonder that these problems have teased the wits of many generations of astronomers. It is also clear that a great deal of thought will still have to be expended before the subject reaches the rather uninteresting stage of being 'worked out'. But in science the excitement lies in the chase, not in the kill.

The issues discussed above are indeed only a selection of the problems that will have to be solved before the understanding of our system becomes reasonably complete. To discuss all problems in any appreciable detail would go far beyond the resources of the present chapter. It will therefore be understood that what is now to be said about further problems must necessarily be very brief.

The picture of how small solid bodies become aggregated into larger bodies needs a great deal of development. The recognition that a sticking agent is probably necessary for aggregation to take place may well turn out to be a most important step. But it is not the whole story of the aggregation process. We can ask the further question, for instance: did every major aggregation form a separate planet? In the case of the Earth was there just one major aggregation that grew steadily through the addition of small bodies, or was the Earth formed by the addition of several major agglomerations, agglomerations of the size of the Moon, say? A clue to the answers to these questions can be got by considering the orientations of the axes of spin of the planets.

The axis about which the Earth spins is inclined at an angle of about 67° to the plane of the Earth's orbit around the Sun. The corresponding inclinations for the other planets are given here.

Planet	Inclination of the axis of spin to the plane of the planets' orbits around the Sun. (G. P. Kuiper)
Mercury	87° (?)
Venus	80° (?)
Earth	66.5°
Mars	65°
Jupiter	89°
Saturn	62°
Uranus	−7°
Neptune	70°

The relevance of these values to the problem under discussion is that we should expect an inclination close to 90° for a planet that was formed as just one major aggregation. Mercury, Venus, and Jupiter are the only planets that fall into this category. The other planets seem as if they must have formed by the coagulation of two or more agglomerations of comparable sizes. This must almost certainly have been the case for Uranus whose axis of spin lies nearly in the plane of its orbit around the Sun. Uranus was probably formed by the coagulation of just two bodies of about the same size. Only in this way does it seem possible to explain the astonishing direction of the axis of spin. On Uranus the 'seasons of the year' must be odd in the extreme. Instead of the Sun being only overhead at points near the equator, as on the Earth, at any point on Uranus the Sun must be overhead or nearly overhead at some appropriate time in the year. When the Sun is overhead (or nearly so) at one of the poles it stays continuously overhead for several Earth-years on end!

Another problem whose solution demands a more precise knowledge of the details of the aggregation process is that of the origin of the satellites of the planets. It is easy enough to say that the satellites are simply fragments left over from the aggregation process, but this is not sufficient. The difficulty is not so much to see why a number of fragments should be left over, but why more fragments were not left over. Why did the Earth not have a dozen satellites? Why have Mercury and Venus no satellites? I suspect that questions such as these will not be easy to answer. The problem may turn out to require an extremely intricate piece of dynamical analysis. No solution is yet in sight.

A satisfactory feature of the present theory is that it explains the tendency shown in the table on page 74 for the densities of the satellites to decrease as the distance of the parent planet from the Sun increases. The Moon was formed in the rock-iron zone. The satellites Io and Europa of Jupiter mark the end of this zone. Already the other two large satellites of Jupiter, Ganymede and Callisto, must contain appreciable quantities of a less dense material, presumably of water. The satellites of Saturn probably consist mainly of water and ammonia.

99

But it is something of a difficulty that the density of Titan should be as high as 2. A density close to 1 would correspond better to a satellite composed mainly of water and ammonia.

Mention has just been made of the end of the rock-iron zone. It is tempting to suppose that this zone petered out, not at Jupiter, but already in the region between Mars and Jupiter. This would give a rock-iron zone that stretched from just inside the orbit of Mercury to just outside the orbit of Mars. This view has the advantage that it gives some indication of the order of size among the inner planets. Mercury and Mars lying near the inner and outer boundaries of the rock-iron zone are the two small members of the group: Venus and the Earth lying towards the central regions of the zone acquired most of the rock and iron.

This view is supported by the bodies that are actually found between Mars and Jupiter. It is estimated that about 30,000 small bodies lie in this region. These bodies, known as asteroids or minor planets, are made of rock and iron, like the inner planets. All lumped together they would scarcely make up an aggregation as large as the Moon. The asteroids seem to represent the very last of the rock and iron, when there was so little left that no reasonable sized planet could be made. The existence of this swarm of comparatively tiny bodies also gives confirmation of the view developed above, that the first step in planet-formation is the condensation of a multitude of small bodies. I suspect that in some way Jupiter managed to capture the material of the satellites Io and Europa from the asteroid zone.

The origin of life

Although this is a problem for the biologist and the biochemist rather than for an astronomer there is one feature that may be important and which might tend to be overlooked if the astronomer should keep himself entirely out of the problem.

The principle on which life is based seems to be fairly clear. Under the action of ultra-violet light from the Sun a mixture of simple substances such as water, methane, ammonia can be built into molecules of moderate complexity, molecules that contain up to perhaps 20 or 30 separate atoms, such as the amino acids. These molecules contain considerable stores of internal energy supplied to them by the ultra-violet light. Now it is a general rule that molecules with internal stores of energy tend to undergo chemical changes that get rid of the energy. Normally we should expect that a break-back into the original materials would occur, the stored energy being thereby released again. But owing to a chemical freak this does not happen in the present case provided the molecules are kept at the comparatively low temperature occurring on the Earth. It is on this freak that life is based. The lack of a straightforward process of break-down forces the molecules to dispose of their energy by adding themselves together into more and more complex molecules, small quantities of energy being released at each step. It is to be noticed that ultra-violet light is not necessary to this adding process, only to the building up of the molecules with the energy reservoir.

Ultimately the molecules become so large, and the aggregations of molecules develop to such a degree, that at last a collapse back to the primary substances becomes possible. In this way a chemical cycle based on the generating influence of ultra-violet light becomes set up. The cycle is illustrated in Fig. 6. The main interest in this cycle lies in the complex molecules and structures that precede the break-back into the primary chemicals. The nature of these structures probably depends rather sensitively on environmental factors such as the temperature, the intensity of ultra-violet light, the concentrations of the primary chemicals, and so on.

At what stage may life be said to appear? This depends on what we mean by life. As more becomes known about life it is increasingly clear that there is no hard and fast dividing line between what is alive and what is not alive. It is to a considerable extent a matter of choice where the line is drawn. This does not mean that the ordinary terminology whereby we say that a dog is alive and a stone is not alive loses its value. We can speak about rich men and poor men without implying that there is a sharp dividing line between wealth and poverty. We say that a dog is alive to denote the fact that the material of the dog is in a special condition, differing markedly from that of the material of the stone. But the properties of both the dog and the stone are different manifestations of the behaviour of matter.

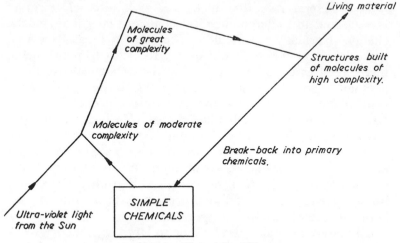

FIG. 6.   The origin of life.

Perhaps the most convenient definition of the origin of life is at the stage where some structure (built out of the highly complex molecules) becomes capable of using itself as a blueprint for the building of similar structures. Even here subtleties arise. Sometimes a structure may be able to reproduce itself in the presence of certain other complex structures, but not in the presence of the molecules produced by the solar radiation alone. The virus is a case in point. A virus can only act as a blueprint in the presence of other complex structures. Is a virus alive? It all depends on what you mean by alive.

The final break-back into the primary chemicals plays an important part in the processes of life. Certain structures have developed that possess the property of being able to break down other structures without being broken down themselves. These substances, known as enzymes, release the supplies of energy required by plants and animals.

But our present object is not to enter into a discussion of the chemistry of life, except in so far as our considerations may have an astronomical connotation. It has always been supposed that life originated on the Earth. The physical and chemical requirements must, however, have been far more favourable for the building of complex molecules *before* the Earth was aggregated. The Earth intercepts only a tiny fraction of the ultra-violet light emitted by the Sun, whereas the gases out of which the planets condensed intercepted a large fraction of the ultra-violet. The energy source was therefore much greater before the planets were aggregated than it was afterwards.

Another point in favour of a pre-planetary origin of life appears when we consider in a little more detail how the complex molecules were built up. This requires the addition together of many much smaller molecules. Now how did the smaller molecules manage to come in contact with each other? If the molecules were dissolved in the sea, for instance, the chance of enough of the right kinds of molecules coming together would be negligible (this would seem to rule out the sca as the original source of life). Bernal has called attention to the necessity for solving this problem of association, and has suggested that favourable conditions would probably occur if the molecules were coated as a film on the surface of a solid particle. Such a condition would undoubtedly best be satisfied before the planets were aggregated, while the planetary material was still distributed as a swarm of small bodies.

An interplanetary origin of life would have seemed impossible in the days when it was believed that the Earth was formed in an entirely molten state, for the associated high temperature would have destroyed all complex organic molecules. Now that we realise that the Earth must have accumulated from a multitude of cold bodies it is no longer possible to be so sure of this. It is true that the temperature deep inside the Earth became high due to compression, but the temperature at, and near the surface probably was quite low especially during the last phases of the aggregation process. I do not see why already complicated chemical structures should not have been added to the Earth in this phase.

It is important to realise that all our present considerations refer to stages in the process of origin of life that preceded the stages that are studied by the biologist. Evolution from amœba to man is only a part of the story of life. From a chemical point of view amœba is already an extremely complex structure. The crux of the origin of life had already been passed by the time that amœba had evolved. It is to such earlier phases that all the above remarks apply. There is no suggestion that animals and plants as we know them originated in interplanetary space. But the vital steps on which life is based may have occurred there.

More about other planetary systems

To end the present chapter, it is desirable to stress the importance of the part played by the magnetic field in the theory described above. The action of the magnetic field in slowing down the spin of the Sun and in pushing the gaseous disk away from the Sun is the pivot on which the whole theory turns. This may be seen by thinking about what would happen if there were no magnetic field to produce these effects.

We saw that the solar condensation probably began to grow a disk when it had shrunk to a size somewhat less than the orbit of Mercury. This would also occur in the absence of a magnetic field. But the Sun would then grow a much more substantial disk: it would go on growing a disk throughout the remainder of its contraction. The amount of material that would thus come to reside in the disk can be estimated, and it turns out to be comparable with the mass of the Sun itself. The implication is that when the disk condensed it would condense, not into comparatively tiny planets, but into a veritable star, a star that shone by its own light and which was comparable with, although probably somewhat smaller than, the Sun.

In the absence of a magnetic field the solar condensation would therefore have evolved into a double-star system. The two stars would have been quite close together, their separation being less than the radius of the orbit of Mercury, and they would have revolved around each other in orbits that were nearly circles. Both components instead of spinning slowly as the Sun does would have rotated with considerable rapidity, since no magnetic slowing down was operative.

It is a matter for considerable satisfaction that double-star systems with these characteristics are actually observed. They

are known as the W Ursa Majoris stars, named after the prototype star W Ursa Majoris (the star with catalogue designation
W in the constellation of the Great Bear). It is tempting to
ascribe them to cases where the magnetic process was very
weak or entirely absent. They comprise less than one per cent
of all cases, indicating that the solar case is normal.

The great majority of stars are indeed slowly spinning stars
like the Sun, stars that presumably have undergone the same
process of slowing down that occurred in the case of the Sun.
Accordingly we may expect planetary systems to have developed
around the majority of the stars. This requires the number
of planetary systems existing in the Milky Way to be about
100,000 million, since the number of ordinary slowly spinning
stars is of this order.

It has been stated by some that only as a result of a series of
prodigious accidents were conditions made suitable for the
development of life on the Earth. The present theory is in
opposition to this view at every point. It was not an accident
that the small planets were formed nearest the Sun. Nor do
the compositions of the planets seem in the least to be a matter
of chance. Rather do I think it would be somewhat surprising
if anything very different had occurred in any of the other
planetary systems. Even the origin of life is beginning to look
as if it was no accident.

Living creatures must it seems be rather common in the
Universe. It is something of a cosmic tragedy that the distances from one star to another are so vast by ordinary standards that there seems no prospect of one group of creatures
being able to establish communication with another. This is a
pity, because the supporters of various ideologies after attempting to impress the superior merits of their views on each other
(through the aid of fusion bombardment and other massive
activities), could proceed to impress themselves on the rest of
the Milky Way. Not only this, but the opportunity for tax-
collectors would be enormous. With taxes levied on say
250,000,000,000,000,000,000 individuals instead of on a mere
2,500 million it would be possible to whack up the defence
programme for the Milky Way to something like reasonable
proportions.

CHAPTER SEVEN

The Mystery of the Solar Atmosphere

In the previous chapter we attempted to follow a trail that had gone cold. We were following on some 4,000 million years after the event. In the present chapter we shall see that problems can also be difficult even when the trail is very hot, even when everything is happening in front of our noses. No problem shows this better than the tantalising mystery of the solar atmosphere. Let us first come to the atmosphere before we come to the mystery.

If you should look at the Sun through a piece of dark cellophane paper (to cut down the glare) you will find that the limb of the Sun looks sharp, as if the Sun ended at a definite place. This place is the photosphere, so called because this is where most of the Sun's light comes from. But the Sun does not end completely at the photosphere. It also possesses a faint outer atmosphere. Something of this atmosphere can be seen in Plate XII, which was obtained during a total eclipse of the Sun when the Moon came between the Sun and the Earth in such a way as to block out the fierce glare from the photosphere. The lower part of the solar atmosphere up to a height of 10,000 kilometres above the photosphere (for comparison, the radius of the photosphere is some 700,000 kilometres) is called the *chromosphere*. The higher portion of the atmosphere is called the *corona*.

To understand why this atmosphere sets such a serious problem consider what our expectations would be if we had never actually seen it! We should expect on the basis of a straightforward calculation that the Sun would 'end' itself in a simple and rather prosaic way; that with increasing height above the photosphere the density of the solar material would decrease quite rapidly, until it became pretty well negligible only two or three thousand kilometres up. Since the radius of the photosphere is very much greater than this—about 700,000 kilometres—we should accordingly expect the atmosphere to be confined to a very thin skin. Reference to Plate XII shows that the solar atmosphere is certainly not confined to a thin skin. The atmosphere is a huge bloated envelope. The problem is to explain why this envelope exists.

The problem is all the more strange because the atmosphere begins as if it were going to do the expected thing. In the first one or two thousand kilometres of height above the photosphere the density of the material does indeed fall very rapidly, as we anticipate; but then the rapid fall is suddenly halted, and thereafter the decline with increasing height becomes very slow. This marked change is accompanied by an astonishing situation concerning the temperature of the material.

In the first 2,000 kilometres of height the temperature is not very different from that of the photosphere. But above this height the temperature, instead of decreasing slightly as we might expect, begins to increase. At a height of 3,000 kilometres the temperature is probably as high as 7,000° C.; at a height of 4,000 kilometres, temperatures in excess of 20,000° C. are probably attained in some parts of the atmosphere; while at the top of the chromosphere at a height of 10,000 kilometres, the temperature rises quite steeply to 100,000° C. The rise continues at still greater heights, and at a height of 100,000 kilometres in the corona the temperature approaches a million degrees. Why should the temperature increase in this almost incredible fashion?

Before we attempt to answer this question it may be useful to insert a diversion on the meaning of temperature. In the present sense, temperature is a measure of the average random motion of the particles of the solar atmosphere. The designation 'kinetic temperature' is often used to denote this particular way of using the concept of temperature. The statements of the previous paragraph imply that the average speed of motion of the particles increases as we go upwards from the photosphere. The atoms contained in the gases shown in Plate XII mostly have speeds of nearly a million miles an hour.

The word temperature is sometimes used in a different way, as a measure of the intensity and quality of the radiation emitted by matter. When we speak of the temperature of material deep inside the Sun we can use the word with this significance. But it cannot be so used in the case of the solar atmosphere. If the solar atmosphere were at a 'radiation temperature' of 1,000,000° C. the atmosphere would be very much brighter than the photosphere: indeed the atmosphere would emit so much radiation that Pluto would be vaporised. It is fortunate for us that the temperature of the solar atmosphere is only a kinetic temperature.

This is not to say that the solar atmosphere emits no radiation at all, however. It not only emits some radiation, but it emits a very peculiar kind. The high part of the atmosphere emits X-rays as well as visible light, and the low part emits ultra-violet light. This is the radiation responsible for producing the well-known ionised layers of the Earth's atmosphere.

Now quite apart from the radiation that is thus being emitted by the solar atmosphere, scattering of light also occurs. We can easily understand what this means by thinking about the tiny particles of dust that are sometimes seen scintillating in a beam of light, as when a shaft of sunlight comes through a gap in a curtain. These particles of dust are scattering light, not emitting it: the scattering of light is simply a deflecting process. In a similar way the particles in the Sun's atmosphere scatter a small proportion of the light that is emitted by the photosphere. When the solar atmosphere is photographed at a total eclipse of the Sun, much of the light that enters the camera is simply photospheric light that has been deflected by the particles of the atmosphere. The photograph shown in Plate XII was taken in this scattered light, not in the ultra-violet or X-rays discussed in the previous paragraph. The latter radiation cannot be observed at sea-level since it is absorbed in the upper parts of our atmosphere, the parts where the ionised layers occur. But it can be detected with the cameras that are carried by high flying rockets. This is one of the more important uses to which recent military work on long distance rockets can be put.

After this diversion on temperature and radiation we must come back to the central problem of the present chapter: why does the Sun possess such a bloated atmosphere? What is the cause of the high kinetic temperature in the corona? Unfortunately there is no agreed opinion among astronomers about the answers to these questions. It will therefore be necessary to describe separately the three different theories that are at present under discussion. I think that it would generally be agreed that the correct explanation is to be found in one or other of these theories—the disagreements are over which theory.

We may conveniently describe the three theories as the 'magnetic theory', the 'sound-wave theory', and the 'infall theory'. I shall try to discuss them as impartially as I can, although I must admit that my own preference is for the 'infall theory', so that I cannot claim any neutrality in this matter.

Of these the first is the most unusual, depending as it does on the existence of magnetic fields on the Sun. This is such an uncommon concept that before embarking on a discussion of the magnetic theory itself it seems worthwhile describing some of the evidence that shows magnetic fields to be indeed present on the Sun. The association of magnetic fields with the Sun is also a matter of importance in relation to the theory that was put forward in the preceding chapter. It will be recalled that the suggested origin of the planets was dependent on magnetic fields in a very crucial way.

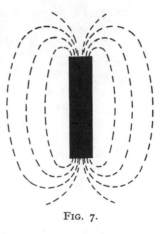

FIG. 7.

Magnetic fields on the Sun

Fig. 7 shows the pattern in which iron filings arrange themselves around an ordinary magnet. The iron filings are arranged along the lines of force of the magnetic field, the run of the lines of force being clearly shown in the figure. Now compare Fig. 7 with the photograph of the corona shown in Plate XII. It is difficult to resist the impression that the material near the poles of the Sun is arranged along the lines of force of a magnetic field, lines of force that emerge from the Sun rather like the lines of force emerge from the ends of the magnet in Fig. 7. The correctness of this view has recently been demonstrated by H. D. and H. W. Babcock, who have shown by observation that a magnetic field does indeed emerge from the poles of the Sun.

But the problem of the Sun's field is not as simple as that of an ordinary magnet. It will be noticed in Fig. 7 that the lines of force emerging from one end of the magnet curve round and enter the other end of the magnet. No evidence for such a connection between the two poles of the Sun can be seen in Plate XII. Indeed a careful examination of the polar plumes of the corona suggests that the lines of force emerging from the poles of the Sun show the behaviour indicated in Fig. 8. The lines of force apparently make a bee-line dead away from the Sun, and the farther they go the less indication there seems to be that they are ever going to curve round and join up with the lines of force from the other pole. Where do these lines of force go to? This question raises a puzzle to which there is no agreed answer. It certainly looks as though the lines of force either must go out to join the interstellar gas or they must join up at a distance far outside the Sun.

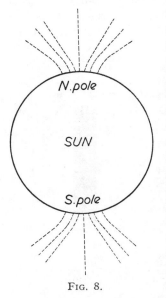

Fig. 8.

Two other lines of evidence show magnetic fields to be present on the Sun, one from prominences and the other from sunspots. Prominences are local condensations of cool material that occur from time to time in the corona. The cool material emits ordinary light, instead of ultra-violet light and X-rays as the hot material of the normal corona does. A photograph of a large prominence taken in this ordinary light is shown in

Plate XIV. It will be seen that this prominence has a curious arch-like structure.

The comparatively dense, cool material of such a prominence does not stay entirely fixed in position. It often plunges down the arches into the Sun. Indeed there is such a preponderance of downward motions in most prominences that apparently there must be a steady condensation of material from the corona, in order to provide a continuous supply of falling material. Queer problems arise. When material plunges downward it scarcely ever falls as it would if gravitational forces alone were acting on it. Some other force must also be operative, and without doubt the force must be of a magnetic nature. Another problem is to explain how the hot material of the corona manages to condense into a cool prominence. One would suppose that this is another effect of a magnetic field, although exactly how the condensation occurs is far from being fully understood.

The magnetic fields associated with prominences produce local modifications in the structure of the corona. These are of the same general arch-like form that is shown by the prominences themselves. This can be seen quite clearly in Plate XIII.

The strongest magnetic fields observed on the Sun are found in sunspots. In a terrestrial laboratory magnetic fields as large as those of sunspots can be made artificially, but it is only possible to maintain them over a distance of a few metres, in contrast with a sunspot which maintains its field over distances of many thousands of kilometres. But large as they are, sunspots are a good deal smaller than the Sun itself, so that we must think of the magnetic field of a sunspot as being a localised solar phenomenon. It is true that the field may spread out from the sunspot into a larger volume but it becomes much weakened when it does so.

An appreciable sized sunspot is shown in Plate XV. It is now generally believed that the darkening of such a spot arises from processes that are associated with its magnetic field. A few remarks concerning why the sunspots are dark may be of interest.

There is a flow of energy outwards from the deep interior of the Sun to the surface. In the inner two-thirds of the Sun this flow of energy is carried by radiation but in the outer third of the Sun the flow is mainly carried by convection, by a general stirring or boiling of the gases of the Sun in fact: it is carried in the same sort of way as heat is carried in a boiling pan of water. At the extreme photosphere, however, the convection is much reduced, and the flow changes back to a flow by radiation. This change-back is not just a matter of chance. The Sun carefully adjusts itself so that it can do this, otherwise it would not be possible to radiate away the outflow of energy steadily into space.

Returning now to the sunspots, it seems that the magnetic fields of the sunspots interfere with the flow of energy in the underlying convection zone by preventing the material from boiling. This produces a serious reduction in the outflow of energy, so that there is less available for radiation out into space from the photosphere. The surface of the sunspot therefore looks dark compared with other parts of the photosphere.

Arguments in favour of the magnetic origin of the solar atmosphere

The magnetic theory seeks to explain the high random speeds of motion of the particles of the solar atmosphere in terms of continuous magnetic disturbances, of which sunspots and prominences are exceptional examples. There are several facts and arguments that can be put forward in support of this theory. The emission of light by the ionised atoms of the corona suggests that the hottest spots in the corona are generally found in the neighbourhood of sunspots, and W. O. Roberts tells me that there seems to be a tendency for these hot spots to diffuse outwards from the sunspot areas. According to J. H. Pidding-ton and R. D. Davies measurements of the radio-waves emitted by the corona suggest the same conclusion.

Another point in favour of the magnetic theory comes from a different source; from the phenomenon known as a flare. A flare is a localised region of the lower atmosphere that becomes heated, often quite suddenly, to an unusual degree. A large flare might cover as much as one-tenth of a per cent of the whole solar surface. The probable explanation of the sudden heating is that rapidly moving particles are first produced in some magnetic disturbance and that these particles then collide with the ordinary material of the solar atmosphere. Certainly at times of solar flares fast particles are often shot out of the Sun in wide-angled jets. These jets of particles are readily recognised whenever they impinge on the Earth. They push the Earth's magnetic field around to a degree that can readily be detected. These are the so-called geomagnetic storms. Intense displays of the aurora borealis are also associated with these solar jets of particles. The work of the Australian radiophysicists has shown that the powerful bursts of radio-waves sometimes emitted by the Sun are also produced by these same jets of particles. It is found that the sources of the bursts travel outwards through the corona with a speed of about 1,000 kilometres per second, and this is just about the speed that the particles are known to have. At this speed they take about 40 hours to reach the Earth.

As an aside, it may be mentioned that some evidence has recently been obtained by the Australian radiophysicists to show that the main jet of particles may be preceded by a group of particles moving at much higher speeds, at speeds approaching that of light itself—300,000 kilometres per second. Slight disturbances of the intensity of the cosmic ray particles that hit the Earth sometimes occur about half an hour after onset of intense solar flares. This phenomenon is probably connected with these groups of very high speed particles.

All this evidence of the origin of high speed particles, pre-sumably produced by a magnetic agency, adds plausibility to the idea that the high random motions of the particles of the solar atmosphere arise from magnetic processes. And since flares are strongly associated with sunspot areas this would tend to confirm the view that the high temperature material originates near sunspots. Another pointer in the same direction is that the temperature of the corona seems to be higher in the equatorial regions of the Sun than it is at the poles; for sunspots are confined to an equatorial belt around the Sun, none are found at the poles.

Arguments against the magnetic theory

The evidence that the chromosphere and corona are affected by magnetic fields is overwhelmingly strong. But this does not prove that the existence of the chromosphere and corona is due to magnetic processes as a primary agent. The solar atmosphere might owe its origin to a quite different process and yet undergo disturbances by magnetic fields. The issue is not whether magnetic disturbances occur—this is undoubted, the issue is whether or not the magnetic effects are primary. The arguments developed in the preceding section represent an extreme view, the view that the magnetic fields are basic. It is now necessary to consider the arguments that go in the contrary direction. These seem so strong that it is difficult to believe that the whole story of the origin of the solar atmosphere lies in the magnetic theory.

It is well known that the number of spots found on the Sun waxes and wanes periodically in an 11-year cycle, the sunspot cycle. At the maximum phase, the incidence of spots may be as much as a hundred times greater than at minimum phase. If then the heating of the solar atmosphere is due to sunspots, we should expect a corresponding fluctuation in the size and temperature of the atmosphere to occur. We should expect moreover that at the maximum phase of sunspots the corona should be particularly strongly developed in the equatorial zone of the Sun since the spots are confined to the equatorial regions.

These predictions do not agree with observation. It is true that the solar atmosphere does change with the sunspot cycle but the changes are much smaller than the magnetic theory would lead us to expect. Moreover the changes that actually occur are in the wrong direction. Instead of the corona being enhanced in equatorial regions at times of maximum sunspot numbers, it is enhanced at times of minimum numbers!

Another equally grave objection can be brought against the magnetic theory. If the heated coronal gases are formed over sunspot areas we should expect a horizontal flow of material to occur away from these areas. No indication of any such general flow can be detected. An examination of Plates XII and XIII shows that the structure of the corona is predominantly *radial* not horizontal.

And this brings us to a point that seems to have caused a good deal of misunderstanding. Every photographer knows how to print from a negative in such a way as to bring out wanted features of a photograph and to suppress unwanted features. This is often a very useful procedure in astronomy. It has been used in Plate XIII to bring out the arch-like structures in the corona, and in Plate XII to bring out the polar plumes. But we must be on our guard against regarding such prints as normal: when a print is distorted to bring out some detail, we must always remember that it is distorted and how it is distorted. Plate XVI is perhaps a less interesting photograph because the structural details of the corona are not so evident. But Plate XVI is really a more accurate representation of the situation. It is certainly true that some features of the corona have a structure that can only be explained through the agency of magnetic fields. These features are only details however. The dominant features of the corona are its radial structure and its general globular form, and neither of these features is plausibly explained by the magnetic theory. It is therefore a reasonable judgment to say that magnetic fields exist in the solar atmosphere but their importance is secondary not primary. In our search for an explanation of the origin of the solar atmosphere we must I think look elsewhere.

The sound-wave theory

We have seen that below the photosphere down to a considerable depth the Sun is boiling. Indeed the boiling gas breaks right through to the photosphere. This can be seen from actual observations of the Sun. The gas boils up in cells about 1,000 kilometres in size. These are called granules. Now according to a suggestion of M. Schwarzschild sound waves are generated by the moving gases: the granules make a noise! Sound waves then travel upwards from the photosphere into the solar atmosphere. As they do so they pass through more and more tenuous gas and this causes them to become more and more violent, until by the time the corona is reached the particularly violent sort of wave known as a shock wave becomes generated. It is these shock waves that are supposed to cause the high kinetic temperature of the corona.

The process will perhaps be better understood by considering a mechanical analogue. A whip is made from a piece of tapered cord. Energy is fed into the whip at the thick end of the cord in such a way that a wave is made to travel along the cord towards the tip. Owing to the taper the wave becomes more and more violent as it moves along, until by the time that the extreme tip is reached the motion becomes very rapid indeed. The crack of a whip is caused by a violent agitation of the air produced by the fast moving tip. In the solar case the decreasing density of the material of the solar atmosphere as the waves move upwards is the analogue of the taper of the whip, and the high kinetic temperature of the corona is the analogue of the rapid motion of the tip.

How far the corona should extend outwards from the Sun on this theory is uncertain. The consequences of the propagation of shock-waves in the corona have not yet been thoroughly investigated, so that it is not known whether the corona should end at some more or less definite distance from the Sun, or whether it should extend with a slowly decreasing density indefinitely outwards into space.

Now to what extent do observations support this picture? Is there evidence of increasingly violent motions at greater and greater heights in the corona? Up to a point there is. The speeds of the granules as they boil up to the photosphere are about 0.5 kilometres per second. Compare this with speeds of about 20 kilometres per second in the material of the chromosphere and with probable speeds of about 100 kilometres per second in the corona. Here is a marked increase with height. So far so good.

But when we look into details the situation is less favourable. The main decrease of density as we go outwards from the photosphere occurs in the first 2,000 kilometres of height, in which the density falls to about one-millionth of its photospheric value. Hence we should expect that there should be a very rapid increase in the violence of the motions of material in these first 2,000 kilometres. So far no evidence has been obtained to show that this is so. Indeed the observations at present available indicate that there is no increase at all in the first 1,000 kilometres although some small increase may perhaps occur in the second thousand. Unless for some reason the present observations can be shown to be in error, this must be counted a very serious point against the theory. To this we may add that the motions that undoubtedly exist at heights above this bottom layer of the solar atmosphere (at heights of more than 2,000 kilometres above the photosphere, that is) are not really the sort of motion contemplated by the theory. The motions that actually occur are of the nature of a general streaming of the material rather than of a wave motion. These difficulties suggest that we turn our attention to the third theory.

The infall theory

The Sun and the other stars do not move around in a vacuum. A highly diffuse gas fills the space between the stars. This gas has a tendency to condense into clouds. Plate XI shows an exceptionally dense cloud of this interstellar gas—'exceptionally dense' means that one cubic centimetre of space may contain 1,000 atoms. Clouds less dense than that shown in Plate XI occur, some containing no more than 10 atoms to the cubic centimetre. The gas still persists between the clouds but with an even lower density, mainly less than one atom to the cubic centimetre. Most of the atoms are known to be hydrogen.

The normal kinetic temperature of the gas in the dense clouds is about −170° C. But sometimes the clouds become heated to a temperature of 20,000° C. or more when there is a hot bright star nearby. What happens is that the atoms of hydrogen absorb ultra-violet light emitted by the star, electrons often getting knocked out of the atoms by the photo-electric effect. The resulting heating causes the pressure in the gas to rise, thereby tending to expand the cloud. A group of such hot bright stars are shown in Plate XVII. This is the famous group known as Pleiades.

Stars like the Sun do not emit enough ultra-violet light to produce much heating of the gas clouds, however. So if the

Sun moves into a cloud the main effect that occurs is not one of heating the gas and of causing the cloud to expand. Rather does the gravitational field of the Sun produce a compression in the gas, a compression that leads to the Sun capturing gas from the cloud. This is the process of scooping-up that was mentioned in Chapter 1. The Sun drills out a tube or tunnel of material as it goes along, the material that was initially present in the tube being captured by the Sun. As might be anticipated the tube follows the direction of the Sun's motion through the gas. Its diameter, the question of whether it is fat or thin, depends on the Sun's speed of motion through the gas. A small speed gives a thick tube and a large speed gives a thin tube. A typical speed for the Sun would be 10 kilometres per second, and at this speed the diameter of the tube would be about the same as the diameter of the orbit of the planet Saturn. On a model with the Sun represented by a ball 6 inches in diameter, this would give a tube with a diameter of about 350 yards, so it will be realised that the size of the tube quite dwarfs that of the Sun. The Sun's power of sweeping up interstellar gas is therefore very considerable.

The captured gases accordingly fill a region with dimensions of the order of the size of the orbit of Saturn and they come in towards the Sun from all directions. As the gases stream inwards they accelerate due to the pull of the Sun's gravitational field. The velocity of infall increases greatly; initially it is only about 10 kilometres per second but by the time the material reaches the Earth's orbit its speed has increased to about 40 kilometres per second, at Mercury's orbit the speed is about 70 kilometres per second, and by the time the gases reach the Sun the inward motion has risen to a speed approaching 600 kilometres per second.

According to the infall theory the captured gases produce a splash when they strike the Sun. This splash, which is illustrated in Fig. 9, is regarded as comprising the chromosphere and the inner part of the corona. The infalling gases themselves comprise the outer part of the corona. The splash may be thought of as a protective shield of hot gas that the Sun erects around itself in order to take up the shock of the impact of the infalling material.

We must now consider how this third theory compares with observation. The first question that evidently arises is whether anything corresponding to a boundary of the splash region can be detected. Of course we cannot expect the splash region

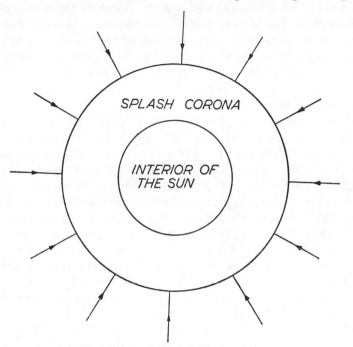

FIG. 9. Infalling material and splash corona.

to have an exact sharp boundary but there should be some distance away from the Sun where the splash region fades away quite rapidly. Actually such a region does exist, at about twice the photospheric radius from the centre of the Sun (the circle in Fig. 9). The density of the material of the solar atmosphere falls off steeply at this distance. Observation therefore confirms the requirement that the splash region must end rather abruptly.

It is not easy to observe the part of the corona beyond the splash region. The further extension of the corona is very faint and accordingly is difficult to separate from the general glow of light that arises from the scattering of sunlight by fine particles of dust. It will be recalled from our discussion in Chapter 1 of the terrestrial ice-ages that a reservoir of dust particles exists in interplanetary space as an outcome of the break-up of comets. The scattering of sunlight by those particles that happen to lie more or less along the line from the Earth to the Sun causes a faint glow of light to appear around the Sun. This gets mixed up with the genuine corona. So long as the genuine corona is comparatively bright, as it is in the splash region, the dust glow does not matter much but the dust glow becomes a nuisance as soon as the genuine corona becomes faint, as it does outside the splash region.

A word of caution is necessary. Radially directed irregularities, or streamers as they are called, can often be detected outside the splash region. There has never been any question but that these irregularities belong to the genuine corona. What is difficult to decide by direct observation is whether or not the corona has a general extension beyond the splash region. This difficulty led many astronomers, only a few years ago, to assert that apart from the streamers no general far corona exists, a view that has been abandoned in the face of new evidence that has come to light in the last two or three years. This is just as well for the infall theory which would certainly have had to be abandoned if the corona had indeed 'ended' in the way that was formerly believed by many scientists.

We may begin our consideration of this new evidence by noticing an important item of information given by a close study of photographs of the corona. These show that the material at the outer boundary of the splash region (the circle in Fig. 9) has a density of about 1 million atoms per cubic centimetre, the atoms being predominantly hydrogen. Using this observation the infall theory enables us to work out what the density of material should be at various distances from the Sun. The results of calculation are shown as follows:

Distance from the centre of the Sun (radius of the photosphere as unit)	2	20	200	2,000
Number of hydrogen atoms per cubic centimetre	1,000,000	30,000	1,000	30

The distance of 2,000 photospheric units corresponds to the radius of the tube of interstellar gas that the Sun is sweeping up according to the infall theory. Hence the value of 30 atoms per cubic centimetre gives an estimate for the density of the cloud of gas through which we are supposing the Sun to be now passing. If this value of the density could be confirmed by direct observation of the interstellar gas the theory would receive powerful support. Unfortunately it is not possible to decide by observation what density the interstellar gas possesses in the neighbourhood of the Sun. All we can do then, so far as the last column in the table is concerned, is to ask whether a density of 30 atoms per cubic centimetre is a reasonable value for the interstellar gas to possess. From what has already been said above it will be realised that the present calculated value is entirely appropriate: it will be recalled that in the minor clouds the density is about 10 atoms per cubic centimetre, while in the large dense clouds the density may be as high as 1,000 atoms per cubic centimetre (or perhaps even higher than this in exceptional regions). It follows that the infall theory requires the Sun to be immersed in a modest sort of cloud. No observations are known that contradict this requirement.

The possibility of obtaining a direct observational check on the theory accordingly depends on the entries in the second and third columns of the above table. But a slight difficulty arises at the outset. A neutral hydrogen atom is not susceptible to observation in the present case. It is only when an atom becomes ionised, when the electron and the proton become separated, that the atom makes any contribution to what can be observed. This is because it is the free electrons that are observed, not the whole atoms. Now the numbers of hydrogen atoms given in the above table include both ionised atoms and neutral atoms. It is therefore necessary to separate out those atoms that are ionised before a comparison with observation can be made. This is somewhat awkward to do. Hydrogen atoms become ionised by absorbing ultra-violet light from the Sun but unfortunately the amount of ultra-violet light emitted by the Sun is not known with sufficient accuracy to allow a close estimate to be made of the fraction of hydrogen atoms that must be ionised at the different distances from the Sun. An approximate calculation yields the following values, but these may be wrong by as much as a factor 2.

Distance from the centre of the Sun (radius of the photosphere as unit)	2	20	200
Number of *ionised* hydrogen atoms per cubic centimetre	500,000	10,000	300

It will be noticed that the reduction of the numbers given in the latter table below those of the previous table depends on distance from the Sun: there is a reduction by a factor 2 in the first column and by a factor 10/3 in the second and third columns. This is because more and more hydrogen atoms become ionised as the material approaches the Sun, a large fraction becoming ionised by the time the splash region is reached.

Recently Siedentopf and Behr have detected the presence of free electrons in interplanetary space and their results are in excellent agreement with the third column of the second table. Since the electrons presumably come from the ionisation of hydrogen atoms this gives strong confirmation of the infall theory.

To remove the unlikely possibility that this agreement is due to chance (that there might be a lot of gas in interplanetary space which was not connected in any way with the corona) it is necessary to consider the second column of the table. Here the problem of observational detection is at its most difficult. The density given in the first column can be checked by direct photographs of the corona taken during an eclipse of the Sun. The density given in the third column can be confirmed by observations carried out at night when the glare of the Sun is absent—the distance from the Sun is great enough for this to be possible. But neither of these methods can be used at the intermediate distance. The eclipse photographs cannot be used for reasons already given, while the distance from the Sun is much too small for nocturnal observations to be possible.

The problem of devising an effective method of observation

has been solved in a most ingenious fashion by Hewish, Machin, and Smith. The new method depends on radio detection instead of visual detection. Through the year the Sun appears to us to move against the background of stars (this arises of course from the motion of the Earth around the Sun). In the month of June the constellation of Taurus forms the background to the Sun. Now in Taurus there is one of the strange cosmic sources of radio-waves, about which we shall have much more to say in a later chapter. We receive radio-waves from this source all the year round but the waves that are received in June are of special interest because they pass through the corona before they reach us. Now radio-waves have their characteristics altered when they pass through material that contains free electrons and which possesses irregularities of distribution. Such alterations are detected when the radio-waves from the source in Taurus pass the Sun and they are detected as far out as the distance given in the second column of the table on page 122, thereby showing that the corona extends out to this distance. The corona does not stop at the splash region.

These observations do not immediately yield a value for the density of the ionised hydrogen atoms, however, because the effect on the radio-waves depends also on irregularities in the distribution of the material of the corona. To give reasonable agreement with the second column of the above table the irregularities would have to be about 500,000 kilometres in extent, a size comparable with the photospheric radius. Smaller irregularities would yield smaller densities and larger irregularities would give larger densities. But since it seems most unlikely that the irregularities can have sizes much smaller than 500,000 kilometres, the fair judgment is that the density of the far corona is probably in close accord with the requirements of the infall theory.

The new evidence makes it almost certain that the corona extends right out to the interstellar gas. Some astronomers have argued that this is not necessarily inconsistent with an internal theory of the origin of the corona. It could be that the material is flowing outwards from the Sun not inwards towards it. While this is not impossible it does raise issues of scientific method. A theory becomes open to suspicion if it turns out to require serious patching when new facts come to light. A few years ago it was thought that the corona 'ended' about 2 photospheric radii out from the centre of the Sun. This was argued as disposing of the infall theory in favour of some internal theory. Now that observations show the corona to extend out to the interstellar gas, as the infall theory required from the outset, it becomes highly suspicious to suppose that an internal theory might also provide such an extension. If this is so, it should have been stated to be so before observation revealed the existence of the far corona. To predict the result of a race after the race has been run is no prediction at all.

This does not exhaust the case for the infall theory. There are several other predictions that were made by the theory and which have subsequently been verified by observation.

Before the infalling material reaches the splash region it is to be expected that its kinetic temperature will remain comparatively low. It is only after the material has plunged into the splash region and only after the infalling particles have collided with the material of the Sun that we may expect high temperatures to be generated. This agrees with other observations by the Cambridge radioastronomers which indicate that the temperature in the splash region is considerably higher than it is farther out.

The temperature to be expected in the splash region can be calculated. It turns out that the kinetic temperature in the upper parts of the splash should be about 1,000,000° C., which is just of the order that is actually observed. Not only this but the theory requires the material of the splash to be in a boiling condition, and there to be differences of temperature even between points that are at the same height above the photosphere. In the higher parts of the splash a comparison of points at the same height above the photosphere should reveal regions with temperatures about twice as great as in other regions. In the lower parts, in the chromosphere, the variations of temperature should be greater still. All these expectations are also confirmed by observation.

These details when taken together build a strong case for the infall theory. It must be emphasised, however, that these considerations all refer to the general radial aspect of the solar atmosphere. It is certain that irregularities of the sort discussed in connection with Plates XII and XIII are produced by magnetic distortions of the atmosphere.

One way in which a disturbance can be caused is through a localised magnetic field interfering with the free boiling of the material in some part of the splash region. This prevents the energy of the infalling material from being transferred downwards into the Sun. Energy therefore accumulates in a localised region of the solar atmosphere. But this cannot go on indefinitely. Sooner or later an outlet for the energy must be found, and if a downward outlet into the Sun and a sideways outlet are prevented the relief must be obtained by sending the energy outwards in the direction from which it came. The way in which this probably happens contains several points of interest. The first effect of the accumulation of energy is to raise the temperature of the localised region in question. The maximum increase of temperature that can occur is about 10,000,000° C., compared with the normal temperature of about 1,000,000° C. in the higher parts of the splash. The average speed of motion of the particles increases as the temperature rises and by the time 10,000,000° C. is attained the particles are moving rapidly enough to move outwards away from the Sun. This provides the required outlet of energy. If the splash is prevented from boiling downwards it will sooner or later succeed in boiling outwards.

Now particles that evaporate outwards due to this sort of process will best be able to escape from the Sun if they move strictly radially outwards, because this makes it easier for them to fight their way through the stream of inward moving particles. The outward moving particles may therefore be expected to form a jet that is directed radially outwards. Such jets, or streamers, can often be seen in photographs of the corona. (We discussed in a previous section the emission of particles from the Sun by solar flares. This was a quite different process to that now contemplated. It is known that the Sun does indeed eject particles in two distinct processes, one associated with flares and the other with active spots in the corona. Our present arguments suggest how such active spots arise, by the interruption of the downward circulation of the material of the splash region.)

It may be wondered how, if a magnetic field interferes with the free boiling of the splash region, infalling material can ever penetrate into the magnetic field. The answer is that infalling hydrogen atoms are unaffected by a magnetic field so long as they remain neutral. We have already seen that a proportion of atoms probably reach the splash region before they become ionised. It is these atoms that presumably supply the energy responsible for exciting the corona jets and streamers. We may also notice that a magnetic field must interfere very seriously with the free boiling of the splash region wherever the lines of magnetic force happen to be orientated perpendicular to the outward radial direction.

The three theories of the solar atmosphere

Here then, as in Chapter 1, we have alternative theories. And as in Chapter 1 you may put your money where you wish. But this freedom of choice is unlikely to persist for very long. The rapid accumulation of new data must sooner or later make possible a clear-cut decision between the theories. A few more years and the mystery of the solar atmosphere will be solved.

Science does not build its theories by a single line attack. Whenever there is uncertainty, all manner of theories are put forward. Then observation is used to narrow down the field, rather as the list of candidates for a job is cut to a 'short list'. Often no one of the theories turns out to be wholly valid, and a composite theory is built out of the survivors from the narrowing process. In this book we are repeatedly meeting with alternatives. This does not mean that scientists are never able to make up their minds. It means that we are near the frontiers of knowledge.

CHAPTER EIGHT

The Sun and its Evolution

The pressure balance

Since time immemorial men have looked on the Sun in wonder and have pondered on what lies inside it. What does lie inside it? Well as we go inwards from the photosphere both the radiation temperature and the density rise steadily until at the centre of the Sun the temperature reaches the enormous value of 13 million degrees, the density being some 50 times that of water. Such a very high temperature is necessary in order that the central pressure be sufficient to withstand the enormous weight of the overlying layers—the pressure required amounts to about 1,000,000,000,000 lbs. per square inch, compared with a pressure of some 50 million lbs. per square inch near the centre of the Earth and with a mere 15 lbs. per square inch at the surface of the Earth. A man would need a tough hide to withstand the pressure inside the Sun.

Now what would happen if the inside of the Sun did not possess such an enormously high pressure? The Sun would collapse, not slowly like the changes to be described later in this chapter, but visibly to the naked eye in a few minutes. Just as a stone dropped over a cliff gains energy as it falls so the hypothetical collapse of the Sun would release energy. And the energy thus developed would be taken up in heating the material of the solar interior. The heating would proceed to such a degree that temperatures in excess of 10 million degrees would soon arise, the internal pressure rising correspondingly until it became sufficient to withstand the weight of the overlying layers, at which stage the collapse would be halted. So we see why there must be a high temperature inside the Sun; because if there were not, an adjustment would very quickly take place that would create a sufficiently high temperature for a state of balance to be reached. It can be shown that if by some magic all heat could suddenly be taken out of the Sun, within about an hour the Sun would take up a new state of balance at about half its present size.

The energy balance and the surface balance

If this experiment could actually be carried out it would be found that the state of balance reached by the Sun would possess a dynamical character, for the Sun would not take up just one definite size, it would oscillate inwards and outwards around the new state of balance. One oscillation of this sort would take a time of a few hours. So the Sun would present a remarkable and frightening aspect, alternately swelling and contracting sometimes glowing white-hot and sometimes blue-hot (blue-hot at smallest size and white-hot at largest size). In this situation it is doubtful if life could persist on the Earth: survival might just be possible in the N. and S. polar areas.

After a few centuries these oscillations would die away and the Sun would be left as a blue star somewhat brighter than at present. But this would not be all. The Sun would slowly expand back to its present size reaching it again after a time of a few million years. The reason for this re-expansion back to the present size depends on there being a second state of balance in the Sun, besides the pressure balance discussed above. This second balance is one in which the rate at which the Sun loses energy due to the emission of radiation into space, which is constantly going on at the photosphere, is compensated by processes depending on the nuclei of the atoms, processes that *produce* energy in the central regions of the Sun. These are just the processes that we have already discussed in Chapter 4. The reason for this second type of balance—an energy balance—is important. Once again the way to understand the reason for it is to see what would happen if the energy balance did not exist. If the radiation that constantly escapes from the photosphere were to give a loss of energy greater than the gain from nuclear processes occurring in the interior there would be a steady tendency for the internal pressure to be always falling below what is required to maintain the pressure

XI—THE ORION NEBULA

This great glowing cloud of gas can be seen by the naked eye as a hazy patch
in the 'sword' of Orion. New stars are forming continually inside clouds like
this one, which measures some 100,000,000,000,000 miles in its dimensions.

XII—THE SOLAR CORONA, AT THE ECLIPSE OF 1900, MAY 28

The spikes or 'plumes' at the north and south poles of the Sun can be clearly seen. These plumes are an indication that the Sun acts like a huge magnet.

XIII—THE SOLAR CORONA, AT THE ECLIPSE OF 1918, JUNE 8

Notice the arch-like structures in the corona. These are an indication of the existence of localized magnetic disturbances on the Sun.

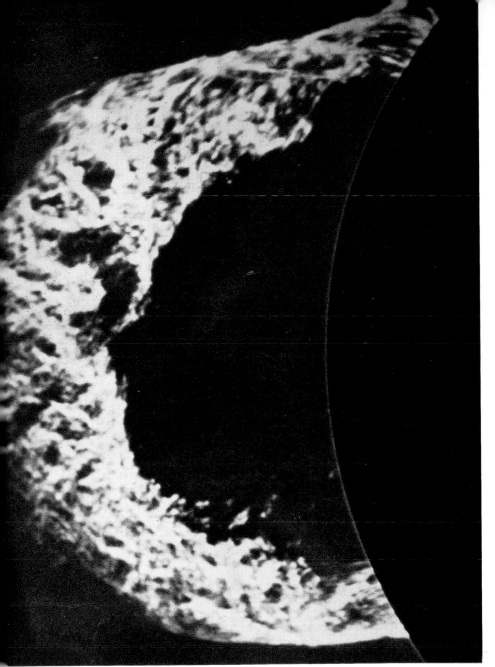

XIV—A COLOSSAL PROMINENCE IN THE SUN'S ATMOSPHERE
1946, JUNE 4

Contrary to what you might think, this is not a cloud of exceptionally hot gas, but a dense cloud of comparatively cool gas surrounded by very much hotter gas. The surrounding gas is too hot to be able to emit much visible light, and so appears dark in the picture.

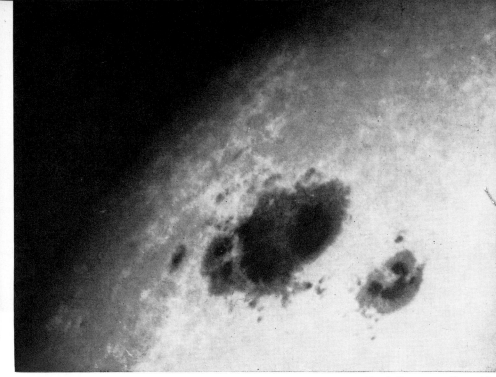

XV—Sunspots, 1926, January 20

Enormous magnetic fields are associated with sunspots. It is thought that the darkening of the spots is due to magnetic effects. These spots are very near the edge, the 'limb', of the Sun. Notice how the light falls away towards the edge. This is known as 'limb darkening'.

XVI—The Solar Corona at the Eclipse of 1926 January 14

Although the corona shows many intricate local details, it possesses an overall globular form that is well shown in this picture.

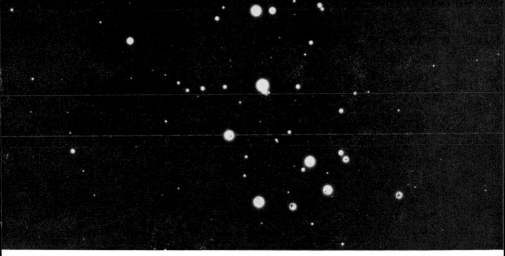

Dominion Astrophysical Observatory, Victoria B.C. J. A. Pearce

XVII—THE PLEIADES

A shower of stars with a common origin. This group situated some 2,000,000,000,000,000 miles away is easily seen with the naked eye.

XVIII—THE GLOBULAR CLUSTER, M 3

A far greater shower of about 100,000 stars also with a common origin.

Mt. Wilson and Palomar Observatories

XIX—The 200-inch Hale Telescope by Moonlight

The scale of this vast instrument can best be judged from the flights of steps that lead up to the large doorway, which measures perhaps 11 feet in height.

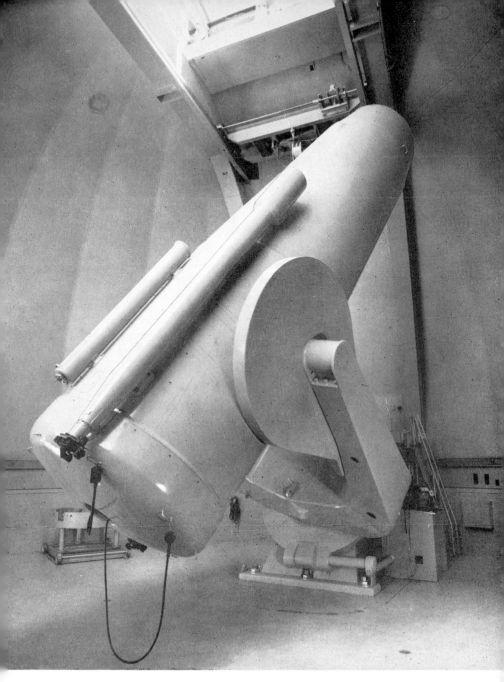

XX—The 48-inch Schmidt Telescope on Palomar Mt.

Forty-eight-inch Schmidt Telescope

XXI—THE GALAXY M 31 IN THE CONSTELLATION OF ANDROMEDA

This blazing galaxy contains about 100,000,000,000 stars, and is pretty well a twin of the Milky Way—the Milky Way would look like this if we could see it from outside. M 31 is a flat spiral galaxy seen obliquely. Notice the satellite galaxies M 32 and NGC 205 (the stars sprinkled over the picture are of course near-by local stars of the Milky Way). M 31 is distant some 450,000 parsecs. Since 1 parsec equals 19,200,000,000,000 miles, this means that the distance of M 31 in round numbers is 9,000,000,000,000,000,000 miles.

balance. In accordance with our discussion of the pressure balance this must cause the Sun to shrink. The shrinkage would however be a slow one taking millions of years, not the time of a few minutes that occurs in the hypothetical catastrophic case of an entire removal of the internal pressure that was considered previously. A shrinkage of the Sun arising in such a way would cause both an increase in the energy radiated from the photosphere and in the energy produced by the nuclear processes. But the latter would increase proportionately the faster, with the result that sooner or later the production of energy must become sufficient to balance the loss. A corresponding situation arises in the opposite case in which we imagine that the rate of production of energy is initially greater than the rate of loss. Then the tendency is for the internal pressure to rise above what is required to maintain the pressure balance. This must lead to a slow expansion of the Sun and the proportionate decrease in the production of energy is then greater than the decrease in the loss rate. So sooner or later the production of energy must again come into balance with the loss.

The second of these cases provides the reason why in our hypothetical case of a suddenly collapsed Sun there must be a final re-expansion back to the present size, even though for several million years the Sun would be smaller, bluer, and brighter than it is at present.

The upshot of all this discussion is that it is no accident that the Sun is in its present state. This is an outcome of two balancing requirements, one a pressure balance and the other an energy balance. If either were by some magically contrived interference put temporarily out of balance the Sun would quite invariably return to its present configuration.

The time of a few million years required for energy balancing to operate has led to the suggestion that the peculiar climate experienced by the Earth during the last million years may have been due to the Sun getting in some way out of adjustment. While it scarcely seems possible to entirely disprove this idea, the evidence would on the whole seem to be against it. The structure of the Sun is such a markedly self-stabilising one that it is difficult to see why the Sun should ever get out of adjustment, even to the comparatively minor degree that would be necessary to explain the fluctuations of terrestrial climate. The variations that we considered above were all hypothetical—that was why the phrase 'by some magic' seemed appropriate: the present-day meaning of the word 'magic' as something that one might consider to happen but which cannot is of course very different from the meaning that used to be attached to the word in ancient times, or even a few centuries ago.

The above discussion raises an important issue: why does radiation continue to escape from the photosphere out into space? The principle underlying the answer to this question is easily understood. Whenever a variation of temperature occurs inside material, energy must flow from the regions of higher temperature to the regions of lower temperature. So energy must of necessity flow outwards from the very hot central regions of the Sun, unless of course the whole Sun were everywhere as hot as it is at the centre. But in this case the photosphere would radiate at an enormous rate and would soon cool off thereby setting up a difference of temperature, so that even in this hypothetical case energy would of necessity soon start to flow.

It is as well for us that this latter case is indeed hypothetical. For if the surface of the Sun were at a radiation temperature of 10 million degrees or more the escaping flood of radiation would be so intense that the whole Earth would be entirely vaporised in a few minutes. But hypothetical as this case certainly is for the Sun, it does actually occur for some exceptional stars which have their outer parts suddenly stripped away by an enormous cosmic explosion. These are the supernovae, stars that will be allotted a special chapter later on.

The reason why the surface temperature of an ordinary star like the Sun takes up some definite value will be clear from the following argument: if the escape of radiation at the photosphere were greater than the flux of energy from the interior, the surface would simply cool down; conversely if the loss of energy outwards from the photosphere were less than the flux coming up from below, the surface would be obliged to heat up until a balance was again reached. In this way we see that a star must achieve a further type of balance in which the energy lost from its photosphere just equals the flow of energy out from the central regions. It is this further balance that decides what surface temperature a star shall have. We see then that the Sun is balanced in three ways, a pressure balance, an energy balance, and now thirdly a surface balance.

The pattern of energy flow

So far nothing has been said about the way energy flows in the Sun, except that it must occur whenever there is a variation of temperature. In an electric kettle heat is produced in the 'element'. This raises the temperature of the element above the temperature of the metal walls of the kettle and above any water it may contain. Common experience shows that after a time both the water and the outer walls of the kettle become hot. This happens by two quite different processes. Energy flows from the element to the metal walls by the process known as conduction. Heat is passed along by atoms being knocked by their neighbours, in rather the way that a bucket can be handed along a chain of men—the bucket can travel a long way without any man in the chain having to move very much. The energy passes from the element to the water in quite another way, by the process known as convection. It is as though the line of men, instead of handing buckets from one to another, were to break up and each man were to carry his own bucket. In this case the buckets and the men move the same distances. In a solid the atoms are in a chain gang, as it were; they are not free to move about and heat-flow occurs by conduction only, as in the metal walls of the kettle. In a liquid or a gas, heat may flow by both conduction and convection, although one or other will usually be the more efficient in any given case: water is heated in a kettle largely by convection, by a general bubbling around; but if mercury were heated in a kettle the main transfer would be by conduction even though mercury is a liquid. With a gas, convection is nearly always the more efficient, although there are some exceptions to this. In stars like the Sun the influence of conduction is well nigh negligible, however.

There is a third way that energy can flow, by radiation. When a man singes his trousers through standing too near an open fire the damage is done by radiation that travels directly across the space between the fire and the trousers. Conduction and convection take place by material contact and material motion: they cannot occur across a vacuum as radiation can. Radiation can transfer energy whether matter is present or not. Radiation is the main process of transfer deep inside the Sun where a great deal of material is present. It is also the means of transferring energy from the Sun to the Earth across regions where there is very little matter.

The radiation deep inside the Sun is not like the ordinary light and heat emitted outwards from the photosphere. It is not even for the most part ultra-violet light. Rather does it belong to the type of radiation that we call X-rays (this designation dates from the time when the nature of X-rays was unknown, the X denoting ignorance; the name has persisted for want of a better). Now X-rays and ultra-violet light are very efficient at knocking electrons out of the clouds that surround the atomic nuclei. This is the photo-electric process. So strong is this process that almost all the atoms inside the Sun have their electron clouds entirely removed: the electrons are left free to wander around, not being attached to any particular atom, except on rare occasions; from time to time an electron may become attached to a definite atom, but it soon gets knocked away again. It is because the atomic nuclei and the electrons are almost completely free to wander around that the material inside the Sun is a gas, even though in the central regions of the Sun the density much exceeds the density of water. (It will be recalled that in a solid the particles are not able to wander around, and even in a liquid the freedom to wander is only very partial.)

Although radiation is the most effective mode of transferring energy in the inner parts of the Sun, convection is the most effective mode in the outer parts, except that near the photosphere the transfer must again be by radiation. The differing zones of influence are depicted in Fig. 10. According to Fig. 10 the outer third or so of the Sun is convective. This does not mean that transfer by radiation ceases. It means that in order to pass on the flow of energy from the inner radiative zone, the outer zone must call on convection to aid in the transport, radiation alone being insufficient. The outer third of the Sun is a gas that is forced to boil in order to pass on the flow of

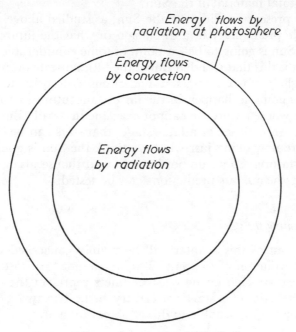

FIG. 10.   Zones of energy flow inside the Sun.

energy from inside. It is important to notice that the flow must change back to radiation at the photosphere to allow energy to escape outwards into space, for it is only by radiation that this can happen, only radiation can carry energy through the region outside the Sun where there is very little matter. It is precisely through this change-back that the third balance referred to above is able to operate—the photosphere must radiate energy out into space at just the rate that energy is transferred up from below.

The depth of the convection zone of Fig. 10 is a feature that has to be decided by calculation since the depth cannot be observed. Present calculations suggest that it must extend to a depth below the photosphere where the radiation temperature is about 3 million degrees and the density is about one third of that of water. Although the convection zone fills more than half the total volume it contains only one or two per cent of the total material of the Sun.

The present condition of the Sun, as studied above, forms a suitable preliminary to a discussion of what the future history of the Sun is going to be—a point of some considerable interest since it is this that will determine the ultimate fate of the Earth. It might seem a somewhat hazardous enterprise to predict what is going to happen in the far distant future to a material system whose nature we cannot examine in detail. But it turns out, as we shall see at a later stage, that stars can be observed that are now doing just what we think the Sun is going to do in the future. So we do not have to wait thousands of millions of years before our predictions can be tested.

Representing the stars

The rest of this chapter will be mainly concerned with the future evolution of the Sun. But we cannot turn to this topic yet. A discussion on how astronomers represent the outward characteristics of a star is necessary first. The two properties of a star most amenable to direct observation are:

(i) the amount of visible light emitted in a given interval of time—the *brightness* of the star as we shall call it;
(ii) the distribution of the light with respect to wavelength (i.e. with respect to colour).
From (ii) the temperature at the surface of the star can be estimated.

These two characteristics are represented in the way shown in Fig. 11. This is the famous Hertzsprung-Russell diagram, or the H-R diagram as we shall abbreviate it. There are a number of unusual things about the H-R diagram. It will be seen that the surface temperature is plotted so as to increase from right to left, instead of in the more conventional way from left to right. There is no advantage in this rather strange practice, which came about from the historical development of the subject. It could be changed but this has not been thought worthwhile since it is not a disadvantage either: it is just

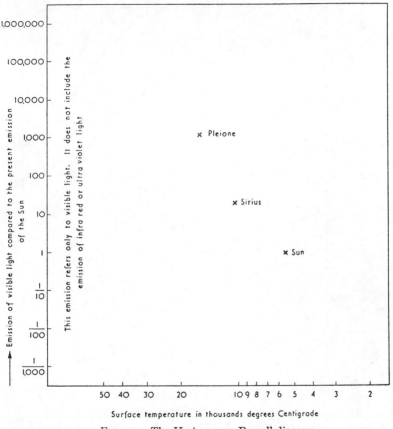

Surface temperature in thousands degrees Centigrade

FIG. 11. The Hertzsprung-Russell diagram.

as easy to go from right to left as from left to right. As in ordinary life a regard for conventions is on the whole a good thing but conformity can be carried to excess. It will be noticed that the way the brightness (comparative to the Sun) is marked also has a special character: it goes in jumps of ten.

Fig. 11 has the important advantage that once a star is

135

marked as a point in the diagram its brightness and its surface temperature can be read off at a glance. Three stars are marked in Fig. 11, the Sun, the well-known Sirius, and Pleione one of the brightest of the Pleiades (Plate XVII). It is at

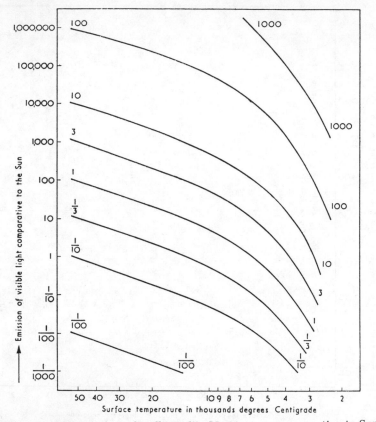

FIG. 12.   Contours of equal stellar radii. Markings are comparative to Sun

once apparent that Sirius is about 20 times brighter than the Sun, and that Pleione is more than 1,000 times as bright. The surface temperature of Sirius is close to 10,000° C. and Pleione close to 15,000° C.

The position of a star in the H-R diagram tells us something more besides its surface temperature and its brightness. It also tells us the size of the star, since the size can be determined by

136

calculation when both the surface temperature and the brightness are known. Contours of equal size have been drawn in Fig. 12, the unit of size being taken as the radius of the Sun (of the solar photosphere, that is). These contours enable us to estimate at a glance the size of a star placed at any point in the diagram. Sirius for instance is about half as large again as the Sun, and Pleione has a radius about 5 times greater than the Sun.

Now what determines the position that a star takes up in the H-R diagram? According to astronomical theory this depends on two things and on two things only. One is the mass of the star, how much material it contains, and the other is its composition, what chemical elements it is made up of. That is to say we must know how much stuff there is in a star and what sort of stuff. And if the composition is not everywhere the same throughout a star then of course we must know how it changes from place to place.

The simplest case to consider is that of stars with different amounts of material in them but the material being always of the same composition. This is not a useless idealisation because it represents very well the situation at the time stars are born out of the interstellar gas clouds. Stars that were born out of the interstellar gas clouds at the same time as the Sun seem to have a composition by weight approximately as follows:

Carbon, nitrogen, oxygen, neon, and other non-metals, apart from hydrogen and helium	1 per cent.
Metals	¼ per cent.
Helium	10 per cent.
Hydrogen	the rest.

Now what positions in our diagram do stars of differing masses, but all with this composition, occupy? Fig. 13 supplies the answer to this query. They fit on to the line shown. This line has a special name, it is called the main-sequence, and stars that lie on it or near it are called main-sequence stars. Fig. 13 shows that the Sun, Sirius and Pleione all fall near this curve. They are main-sequence stars.

Before leaving the main-sequence it is important to say in a little more detail how the mass of a main-sequence star affects its position on the curve. A star containing say one-fifth of the amount of material in the Sun would possess a brightness of about one-tenth of a per cent of the solar brightness. A star containing twice as much material as the Sun would have a brightness about ten times greater. A star containing ten times as much material as the Sun would have a brightness about a thousand times greater. The corresponding surface temperatures for these three cases would be about 3,000° C., 10,000° C., and 20,000° C. respectively. The relation of the position of a star on the main-sequence to its mass is indicated by the markings in Fig. 13.

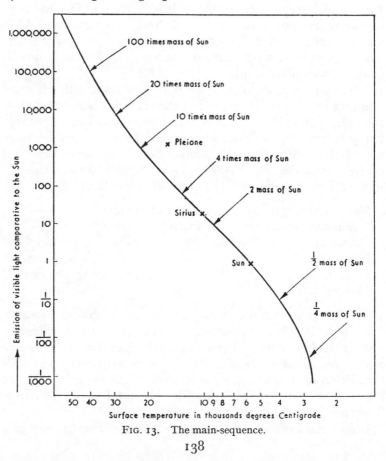

FIG. 13.   The main-sequence.

The evolution of the Sun

This discussion of the placing of a star on the main-sequence refers to the situation that follows the condensation of the star before nuclear processes have had sufficient time to produce a serious change in the composition of the material of the star. Inside stars with brightnesses not more than ten times that of the Sun the important nuclear processes are those already described in Chapter 4—a set of reactions that may be referred to as the proton-chain. A different set of reactions, known as the carbon-nitrogen cycle are of greater effect than the proton-chain inside more luminous stars, however.

The reactions of the carbon-nitrogen cycle, discovered by H. A. Bethe, are set out in detail in the following table:

Meaning of symbols

C^{12} (p, γ) N^{13} C^{12} (6 protons, 6 neutrons) plus a proton gives N^{13} (7 protons, 6 neutrons), a γ-ray being emitted.

N^{13} (β) C^{13} N^{13} undergoes a β-process, thereby changing to C^{13} (6 protons, 7 neutrons).

C^{13} (p, γ) N^{14} C^{13} plus a proton gives N^{14} (7 protons, 7 neutrons), a γ-ray being emitted.

N^{14} (p, γ) O^{15} N^{14} plus a proton gives O^{15} (8 protons, 7 neutrons), a γ-ray being emitted.

O^{15} (β) N^{15} O^{15} undergoes a β-process, thereby changing to N^{15} (7 protons, 8 neutrons.)

N^{15} (p, He^4) C^{12} N^{15} plus a proton gives C^{12}, He^4 (2 protons, 2 neutrons) being emitted.

The latest information on these processes is due to the work of W. A. Fowler.

The last of the reactions of the preceding table deserves comment. When a proton is added to N^{15}, instead of O^{16} (8 protons, 8 neutrons) being formed with the emission of a γ-ray something quite different happens: the nucleus changes back to the starting point C^{12} and helium is emitted. Evidently C^{12} (and nitrogen also) can go through this same cycle time after time. As in chemistry where a substance that promotes a reaction but without being changed itself is called a catalyst so we may think of carbon and nitrogen as nuclear catalysts. Energy is produced in the carbon-nitrogen cycle through the conversion of hydrogen to helium—which is the net effect of the set of reactions. The energy appears in several forms: in

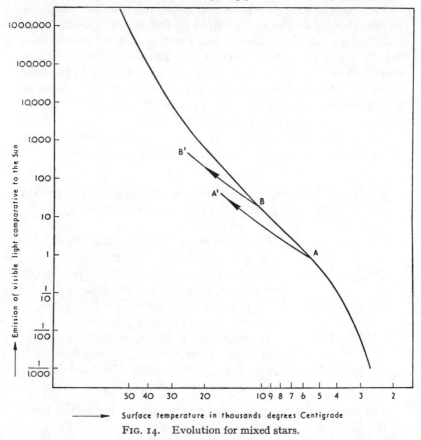

FIG. 14.   Evolution for mixed stars.

the γ-rays, in the electrons of positive character and the neutrinos emitted by the β-processes, and in the energy of motion of the He^4 particles emitted in the last reaction of the table. Of these contributions all but the energy of the neutrinos becomes absorbed into the material of the star. The neutrinos escape from the star and their energy is lost. As with the proton-chain the quantity of energy that can be produced by the carbon-nitrogen cycle is enormous when judged by ordinary standards—the conversion of but 100 tons of hydrogen into helium yields more energy than is used up in a year by the whole of humanity.

Now whether the carbon-nitrogen cycle or the proton-chain happens to be the main process of energy generation in a particular star the resulting change of composition is the same, hydrogen is built into helium—the building process is different in the two cases but the result is the same. The proportion of hydrogen decreases with time and the proportion of helium increases correspondingly. It used to be thought that the helium so produced gets mixed throughout the star by means of currents that circulate slowly within it. But in the last few years astronomers have come to doubt whether this is so—it now seems unlikely that any circulation occurs at all. This is the outcome of a recent investigation by L. Mestel. The only remaining uncertainty is whether or not magnetic fields inside a star may produce some partial degree of circulation.

The problem of determining the evolution of a star takes a very different form according to whether mixing of the helium occurs or not. When there is complete mixing the position occupied by the star on the H-R diagram changes slowly with time but not in such a way as to depart much from the line of the main-sequence. The changes are of the sort shown in Fig. 14. A star initially at A (near the Sun) would evolve along the line A to A'. A star initially at B (near Sirius) would evolve along the line B to B'. The lines of evolution are not quite along the main-sequence, they move off slightly to the left.

In the more likely case that the helium stays put where it is produced the future evolution of the Sun will be along a line of the form shown in Fig. 15. This is a dramatic evolution. The Sun is at present just beginning to work its way towards the kink of the curve at M. Once round this kink the swoop of the curve up to O implies a very large increase in brightness, sufficient eventually to vaporise the Earth. The lowering of the surface temperature during this phase arises because of a tremendous expansion of the Sun. At point O the Sun will be some 200 or 300 times its present size. This expansion will enable the Sun to engulf Mercury, Venus, and possibly also the Earth. After the turn round at O a general shrinkage sets in. Accompanying the shrinkage there is a falling off in brightness and a rise of surface temperature. By the time P is reached the Sun will have become a blue star with a size similar to its present size but with a much greater brightness. The nature of the evolution beyond P forms a topic to be discussed in a future chapter.

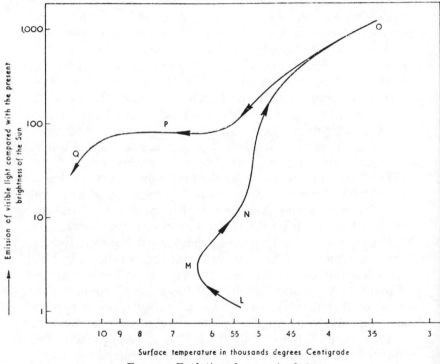

FIG. 15. Evolution of an unmixed star.

Extinction of life on the Earth will not have to await this spectacular sequence of events. Already by the time the kink at M is reached the Sun will be about 3 times as bright as it is now. This would be sufficient to raise the average temperature on the Earth to near the boiling point of water, with a disastrous consequence to all forms of life.

Now the evolution will not take place at a uniform rate. The position of the Sun will not move at a steady rate along the curve of Fig. 15. The time required to reach the kink at M will be something like a hundred times longer than the time required for the evolution from O to P. What happens is that at first the evolution is extremely slow but once the kink at M is passed the evolution goes more and more rapidly. Not only are the later changes very spectacular but their onset comes about with comparative rapidity. This explains why the Sun is spending so long in reaching M, why it has spent about 4,000 million years and has still not reached the kink. Another 5,000 million years will, however, be sufficient to tip the scale. The Sun will then enter on a career of violence, in marked contrast to the placid existence that it has so far enjoyed. The game will be up with the Sun in 5,000 million years time, and with others besides.

The evolution of the stars of the globular clusters

Stars with masses not too different from the Sun also go through lines of evolution very similar to the curve of Fig. 15. Those with more material in them than the Sun go through their evolution more quickly than the Sun does. Those with less material require more time than the Sun. These differences raise an intriguing problem. Suppose a whole group of stars all condensed at effectively the same time and suppose their compositions were initially identical. Then at the time of condensation their positions in the H-R diagram would lie on the line of the main-sequence, the position of a particular star simply depending on how much matter it happened to contain. Stars with large quantities of material would lie high on the main-sequence, those with comparatively small quantities would lie low on the main-sequence. The problem is then to decide how the distribution in the H-R diagram of the whole group of stars will change as time goes on. What will the distribution be after 100 million years, after 1,000 million years, after 5,000 million years? One of the central lines of investigation in astronomy today is concerned with the answering of this problem. It leads us naturally into a discussion of stars other than the Sun.

Let us put a precise query: what will the distribution of a group of stars in the H-R diagram be after a time of 5,000 million years, the stars being taken as initially of uniform composition, and of the same age? The answer is that we expect the stars to fall on a track of the general form A to D in Fig. 16.

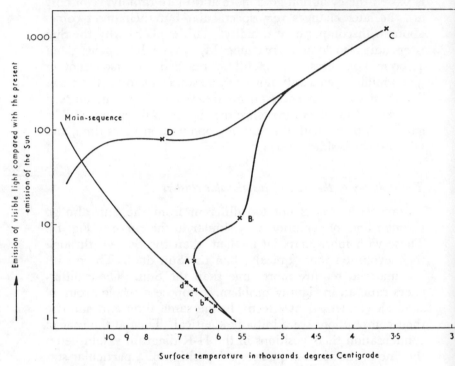

Surface temperature in thousands degrees Centigrade

FIG. 16. Evolutionary sequence of a group of stars of identical ages.

The points marked in this figure are important. The points A, B, C, D, have a correspondence to the points a, b, c, d, on the main-sequence, in that stars at A after 5,000 million years were initially at a, stars at B were initially at b, stars at C were initially at c, stars at D were initially at d. It will thus be seen that all the stars found after 5,000 million years in the part of the track from A to D are derived from the small segment of the main-sequence between a and d. What then has happened to all the stars that initially were on other parts of the main-

sequence? Stars initially lower down the main-sequence than
a are still there; in 5,000 million years they have not had sufficient time to evolve significantly. This is just the case with the
Sun. The Sun is still down near *a*. It has not yet had sufficient
time to go through much evolution, but it belongs to the next·
batch of stars that are booked for rapid evolution.

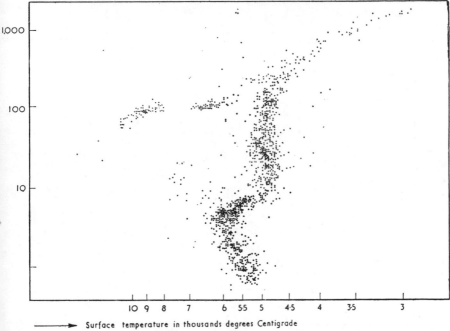

Surface temperature in thousands degrees Centigrade

FIG. 17. The stars of the globular cluster M 3 (Sandage).

Now how do we know that the Sun is thus poised on the
brink? Because other stars of a little greater mass than the
Sun, and perhaps also of a little greater age have already
taken the plunge. The double-star system known as ζ Herculis
has a component that contains only about ten per cent more
material than the Sun. Yet this star has already evolved to
about the position B of Fig. 16. This is a particularly well
documented case, and there are many other slightly less well
determined examples that could be added to it.

Turning away from the Sun, what then about the stars that

145

initially lay higher up the main-sequence than the point *d*? Where would they lie after a time of 5,000 million years? In no part of the diagram indicated in Fig. 16. They have evolved along their respective lines of evolution. The fate of these stars, what happens to them after they pass the stage of their evolution corresponding to the point D of Fig. 16 will be discussed in the next chapter. We shall then consider how stars die.

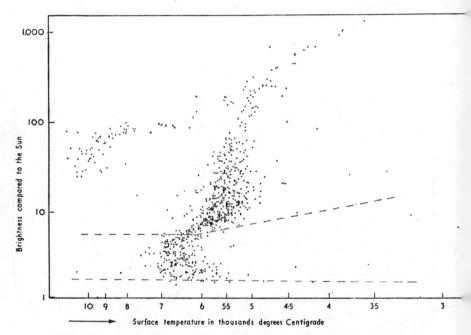

FIG. 18.   The stars of the globular cluster M 92 (Arp, Baum and Sandage).

How do we know all this? In part by theory, but even more certainly by observation. In Fig. 17 the actual plot in the H-R diagram of the stars of a particular group is shown. This is a case with an interpretation identical to that already given for Fig. 16. The observations are due to A. R. Sandage and were made on a special group of stars, the stars of the globular cluster, shown in Plate XVIII (catalogue designation M 3). Similar plots for other globular clusters have been obtained by H. C. Arp, and by Arp, Baum, and Sandage. Fig. 18 is the corresponding diagram for the cluster with catalogue designation M 92. As its name implies a globular cluster is an almost spherical group of stars. The very high concentration of stars in such clusters—there may be as many as 100,000—makes it clear that they are not a chance aggregation but a group with a common origin, as our interpretation requires.

CHAPTER NINE

The Evolution of Stars of a Medium Content

The observational work summarised in Figs. 17 and 18 represents a decisive turning point in astronomy. Besides showing clearly what the fate of our Sun is going to be the observations shed light on a whole range of basic problems. The potentialities of this work were fully appreciated many years ago by Walter Baade, and stressed by him at the time of the inauguration of the 200-inch Hale telescope. Let us consider another important application of the results of Figs. 17 and 18.

The age of the Milky Way

Figs. 17 and 18 enable the ages of these globular clusters to be estimated. And since there is reason to believe that the globular clusters originated at the same time as the whole Milky Way system (see Chapter 17), it is clear that such an estimate has the added importance of telling us the age of the great system of stars in which we live.

To see how this is done we go back to Fig. 16. This was drawn so that the time of evolution from the main-sequence was 5,000 million years. Now do the stars of Figs. 17 and 18 fall on the curve of Fig. 16, in which case these two globular clusters must be about 5,000 million years old? Or do the stars fall below the curve of Fig. 16, in which case the globular clusters must be older than 5,000 million years? Or do the stars fall above the curve of Fig. 16, in which case the globular clusters must be younger than 5,000 million years?

A clear-cut decision between these possibilities depends on Fig. 16 being a correct representation of the situation after

5,000 million years. How do we know that this is so? By a theoretical calculation: the present method of estimating star-ages depends crucially on our being able to calculate the evolution of the stars with great accuracy. Although present calculations still fall seriously short of the desirable degree of precision, the indications are that the stars shown in Figs. 17 and 18 do fall near and perhaps slightly below the theoretical curve drawn for an age of 5,000 million years. Opinions still differ as to how close the agreement is. My own impression is that the curve calculated for an age of 5,000 million years lies quite close to the evolutionary sequences of the globular cluster stars. Perhaps the best age estimate that can be given at the present time is from 5 to 6 thousand million years. It will be recalled that the age of the Earth is about 4,000 million years. Evidently the Earth is not very much younger than the whole Milky Way itself. Our residence in the Universe has a very respectable antiquity. We are all of a very respectable pedigree.

This discussion brings out the importance of a theoretical understanding of the processes of stellar evolution. It was stated in the previous chapter that the evolution of the Sun and of stars like the Sun—stars of medium capacity, is along a track of the form shown in Fig. 15, and this was made plausible by an appeal to the observations shown in Figs. 17 and 18. But it may be wondered why the conversion of hydrogen into helium, the helium staying put where it is produced, should lead to such a remarkable evolution. The main aim of the present chapter is to deal with this query thereby serving to complete the discussion of the previous chapter and also making way for further developments.

The evolution from L to M (Fig. 15)

In the early stages of the evolution the most rapid production of helium is at the centre of the star. This is because the temperature and density of the material are highest there; and the higher the temperature and density the faster the nuclear reactions take place. Complications eventually arise, however, because after a time all the hydrogen in the central regions becomes converted into helium. The star develops a core of nearly pure helium as shown in Fig. 19. When this happens energy ceases to be generated in the core. Yet energy must continue to be produced in the star in order to maintain the energy balance. How is this achieved? The answer to this question was given many years ago by Gamow and Critchfield. The energy must be produced in a skin that surrounds the helium core, as indicated in Fig. 19. To effect a sufficient degree of energy production the inside of the star shrinks, thereby increasing the temperature in the skin until the necessary degree of energy production is achieved.

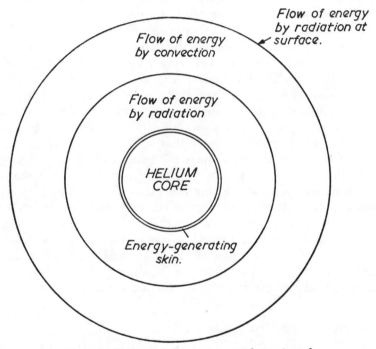

FIG. 19.   Star with helium core—not drawn to scale.

Now although the inside of the star shrinks during the early stages of evolution this does not mean that the total radius of the star gets less. Whether it does or not has to be decided by calculation: it turns out that the total radius of the star does not shrink; between L and M of Fig. 15 it remains nearly the same; and after M towards N it actually increases very considerably.

Next we must consider how the outward flow of energy is maintained as the star evolves. The pattern of flow outside the core is much the same as it initially was. First there is a region in which energy flows by radiation alone. Then the main flow is taken over by convection—the star boils, and this continues outwards until the extreme photospheric layers are reached where a change-back to flow by radiation occurs in order that there shall be a free escape of energy outwards into space.

A tricky question remains to be cleared up however. What happens to the energy flow in the helium core? Either the energy flow must effectively cease altogether or the core must go on shrinking in order to supply by gravitation the energy that constantly flows out of it. Our problem is to decide which of these alternatives must be chosen.

According to recent calculations it turns out that after shrinking for a time the energy flow ceases. The reason for this is connected with the pressure balance.

It will be recalled that the necessity for maintaining a pressure balance inside a star is overriding. In the case of the Sun we saw that any serious departure from balance would immediately, in a few minutes, lead to devastating effects. Indeed we used the necessity for maintaining a pressure balance to explain why the material of the Sun's interior is very hot. It is now necessary to say that our former argument had validity in this respect only because the internal density of the Sun is not very great. This is a strange point but an important one. In stars with internal densities less than about 1,000 times water, all our previous arguments can be applied. But when the density rises above this—when a pint jug would contain more than half a ton of material, a new type of pressure known as degeneracy pressure begins to develop as an outcome of the sheer squashing together of material. The more the material is squashed the higher this new form of pressure becomes. Squashing is the determining factor for degeneracy pressure, not a high temperature as is the case with the ordinary pressure inside the Sun.

This has relevance to our helium cores. Provided a crucial condition is satisfied it can be demonstrated by exact calculation that sooner or later shrinkage must come to a stop, because after a certain stage further shrinkage would cause the pressure in the inner regions to become too high: too much squashing of the internal material would raise the degeneracy pressure above what was needed to withstand the weight of the overlying layers. The condition that has to be satisfied is one of the most curious in all astronomy, so curious that such a great astronomer as Eddington could never bring himself to accept it. The mass of the helium of the core must not exceed 1.44 times the Sun. In the title of this chapter we referred to stars of medium content. This was intended to mean stars with masses large enough for them to have undergone a significant degree of evolution—masses upwards of 1.1 times the Sun say, but not with masses large enough for this present condition ever to be infringed. Throughout this chapter we shall be concerned with stars that have masses ranging from about 1.1 to 1.4 times the Sun.

Although it is not our present purpose to consider stars of large mass—this is deferred to Chapter 12—it may be wondered what would happen if the core should infringe the 1.44 condition. Then (as was first shown by E. Stoner and extended by S. Chandrasekhar) no degree of shrinkage could ever develop sufficient degeneracy pressure to balance the weight of the overlying layers.

In case there should seem to be pedantry in this point, let it be said that the whole manner of the death of a star is determined by the 1.44 criterion—by Chandrasekhar's limit as it is usually called. Whether a star ends its days in a comparatively peaceful way, as the stars considered in this chapter do, or whether a star bursts out as one of the most violent explosions in the Universe, depends on Chandrasekhar's limit.

The upshot of all this argument is that the shrinkage that occurs at first in the helium core of a star of medium content cannot continue indefinitely, because sooner or later degeneracy pressure becomes great enough to prevent any further shrinkage from occurring. At this stage the energy flow in the core must cease, since no source of energy then remains—both the gravitational energy released by shrinkage and the energy generated by the conversion of hydrogen to helium have stopped. This requires the temperature to become everywhere the same throughout the core since otherwise energy would be bound to flow because energy always flows from material at a higher temperature to material at a lower temperature. Accordingly we reach the conclusion that the star must take up a structure with a degenerate constant temperature (isothermal) core.

Outside the core comes the energy-generating skin, then a region with a radiative flow of energy, then the boiling convective region, and ultimately the radiative zone at the photosphere. It is likely that this structure becomes established by the time the point M of Fig. 15 is reached. The temperature in the core of the star at this stage lies in the range from 15 to 20 million degrees, according to the precise mass of the star.

The type of structure just described was first proposed by Gamow and Keller in 1945. At that time it did not receive a general approval among astronomers, but opinion has steadily hardened in its favour. Alternative suggestions for the change of structure that accompanies evolution from L to M of Fig. 15 now appear implausible.

Evolution from M to O (Fig. 15)

Evolution from M to N of Fig. 15 proceeds in a fairly straightforward fashion. Hydrogen is changed to helium in the skin that surrounds the helium core. As a consequence more and more helium gets added to the core. The process is rather like skinning an onion in reverse. Instead of taking off successive skins, successive skins are added. Accompanying the growth of the core the outer convection zone must become deeper and deeper. Indeed by the time the point O of Fig. 15 is reached the convection zone extends inwards almost to the energy-generating skin.

The section of the evolutionary track of Fig. 15 from N to O is characterised by a general rise of temperature in the core and in the energy-generating skin, a rise that is caused by the onion process. By the time the point O is reached the temperature at the centre becomes high enough—about 100 million degrees—for an interesting new situation to arise in the core. This is in part due to a novel sort of energy-producing reaction. It may be wondered how any energy-generation can occur in the core since all the initial hydrogen has become converted to helium. The answer is that the new process makes use of the helium as a fuel, a possibility first noted by E. Salpeter. At the higher temperatures now occurring in the core, helium becomes converted into carbon, oxygen, and neon by nuclear reactions (the details of which we shall consider in a moment) and this liberates energy.

The curious feature of the new situation is not limited to the onset of helium-burning, however. An explosive condition develops in the core, causing it to expand very suddenly in a time of a few minutes! The expansion goes on until the degeneracy pressure disappears and the star assumes a more or less normal structure once again. This 'popping' of the core is not sufficiently violent to blow the star to pieces as the explosions to be considered in Chapter 12 do. But the popping of the core has an important effect on the evolution. This is apparently the cause of the 'turn round' at O; it starts the stars on the stage of their evolution from O to P. Stars on their way from O to P are thus characterised by deriving their energy from two sources, from the burning of helium in the core and from the burning of hydrogen in a shell that surrounds the core.

The helium-burning reactions and the popping of the core

It is as well to look at some of these statements in a little more detail before we continue with the discussion of the evolutionary track of Fig. 15 beyond the point O. The reactions that yield energy from helium are given in the following table:

Reaction	*Meaning of Symbols*
He^4 ($2He^4$, γ) C^{12}	A nucleus of ordinary helium He^4 (2 protons, 2 neutrons) together with two other helium nuclei give C^{12} (6 protons, 6 neutrons), a γ-ray being emitted.

Reaction	Meaning of Symbols
C^{12} (He^4, γ) O^{16}	C^{12} plus He^4 gives O^{16}, a γ-ray being emitted.
O^{16} (He^4, γ) Ne^{20}	O^{16} plus He^4 gives the isotope Ne^{20} (10 protons, 10 neutrons) of neon, a γ-ray being emitted.

When helium-burning starts up near the point O of Fig. 15 it is likely that the material in the central parts of the core is degenerate. This leads to explosive conditions for a reason that will now be explained.

Referring back to the Sun it will be recalled that there is a good reason why an energy balance must exist inside the Sun. If not enough energy were being generated to balance the outward flow to the surface, the Sun would slowly shrink and the internal temperature would slowly rise. The rise of temperature would then increase the rate of energy-production until an energy balance was reached. Conversely if the Sun were initially generating more energy than is flowing out to the surface, a slow expansion would take place, the internal temperature falling meanwhile. The fall of temperature would decrease the rate of energy-production until a balance was again reached.

This self-governing property depends very critically on the material inside the Sun behaving like an ordinary gas, on it not being 'degenerate', for L. Mestel has recently shown that self-governing does not take place in degenerate material. Indeed the very opposite of self-governing occurs, since the slightest initial unbalance becomes more and more accentuated in degenerate material as time goes on. If initially the energy-production is less than the outward flow, the material does not raise its temperature; instead it cools off thereby decreasing the energy-production. The unbalance is accordingly increased. Conversely if the energy-production initially exceeds the outflow the material instead of reducing its temperature actually heats up. The heating up increases the energy-production and the unbalance is again accentuated.

The heating of the helium core of our evolving star by the reverse-onion process eventually sets the helium-burning reactions of the above table working to a degree that causes the energy-production to exceed the outflow that also starts up in the core. The material being degenerate, the condition of instability described in the previous paragraph therefore arises. What happens? The material heats up more and more, the helium-burning reactions becoming more rapid meanwhile. But there is a limit to the amount of heating up, because eventually the ordinary high temperature form of pressure takes over control from the degeneracy pressure. When this happens the core is able to cool itself by expansion and thereby to bring the helium-burning reactions under control.

Calculation shows that the fate of the star is a rather touch and go affair. So much energy is released by the helium-burning reactions before they are thus brought into moderation that the star is very nearly blown to pieces. The situation is in many respects like a terrestrial atomic bomb—by the time material becomes hot enough to expand, explosion conditions have been generated. But because the core lies inside the rest of the star its explosion, as a sort of monstrous helium bomb, is controlled by the tamping effect of the outer parts of the star which succeed in holding the core in. The core is thereby restrained to a 'popping', the popping whose effect is to reverse the evolution of the star from the point O of Fig. 15 towards P.

The R R Lyrae Stars

A comparison of Fig. 15 with Fig. 17 shows that the point P is situated in a curious gap in Fig. 17. This gap is not intended to indicate an absence of stars—many stars of the cluster M 3 lie inside the gap, but that this region is characterised by a singular property. In the previous chapter we discussed what would happen to the Sun if by some magic the internal high temperature could suddenly be removed. We saw that the Sun would collapse swiftly down to about half its present size and would then oscillate inwards and outwards about a new position of pressure balance, the oscillations going through a full cycle in a time of a few hours. The stars in the gap of Fig. 17

are oscillating inwards and outwards in this fashion, the time for a full cycle depending on the position of the star within the gap: the time varies from almost eight hours at the left end to about a day at the right end.

It is to be emphasised that no suggestion is being made that the cause of the oscillations are the same as our hypothetical sudden withdrawal of the heat inside the Sun. The cause of the oscillations of these stars is at present entirely unknown. It seems to be connected quite critically with the structure of the star. Thus a star situated just outside the gap does not oscillate but one just inside does. The changeover from non-oscillation to oscillation is an extremely sharp and significant transition.

Oscillating stars occur also in other globular clusters, for instance in the cluster M 92, the stars of which are plotted in Fig. 18. But the proportion of oscillating stars is widely different in different clusters. For example, although M 3 and M 92 are clusters with roughly the same total stellar populations, M 3 contains about 150 of these oscillating stars whereas M 92 contains only 6. Other globular clusters tend apparently to be more like M 92 than M 3; M 3 would seem to contain a quite unusual proportion. A comparison of Figs. 17 and 18 shows immediately what the difference consists of. While M 3 has a considerable group of stars in the region of the point P of Fig. 15, the corresponding group in M 92 occurs in the region of the point Q. Why this difference should occur is another problem whose solution is not yet understood.

The oscillating stars at present under discussion are often referred to as 'cluster variables', a name derived from their presence in the globular clusters. But since this kind of star is by no means entirely confined to the globular clusters the name is not really a suitable one. The designation 'R R Lyrae stars' is often preferred to that of 'cluster variables' for this reason. The latter name is derived from the particular star R R Lyrae which is a typical example. The name 'R R Lyrae stars' will be used in all later discussions.

The R R Lyrae stars not only oscillate in size but they vary in brightness. This makes them easy to recognise observationally, a point of importance in the next chapter. Fig. 20

157

shows the relation that exists between the time of oscillation and the percentage change in brightness. This figure demonstrates quite clearly what astronomers have suspected for some years, that the R R Lyrae stars must be divided into two kinds, those with oscillation periods longer than 10 hours (marked

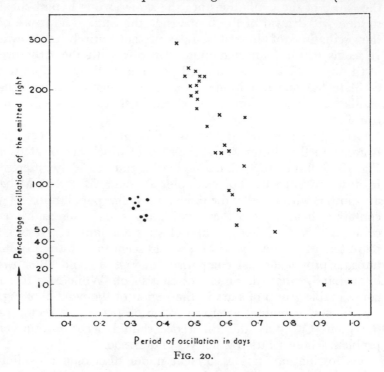

FIG. 20.

X in Fig. 20) and those with periods less than 10 hours (marked ● in Fig. 20). It is thought that these two groups represent different modes of oscillation, but once again the cause of the difference is not understood—a somewhat dolorous note.

The last stages of evolution

The evolutionary track of Fig. 15 has been redrawn in Fig. 21. It will be seen that the track now extends beyond the point Q. The part of the track from Q to T represents the last stages of evolution that take place once nuclear reactions cease to produce energy within the star. Eventually all the hydrogen of the star becomes exhausted (we shall have more to say later about the details of how this happens) and no more

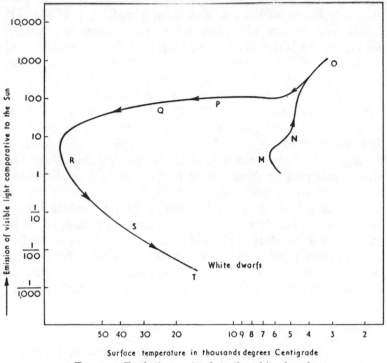

FIG. 21.   Evolutionary track to the white dwarfs

energy is then produced by the conversion of hydrogen into helium. Helium-burning in accordance with the reactions of the table on page 154 must also cease eventually because of an exhaustion of the helium. And in a like manner any other nuclear fuel that may arise in the star must eventually become exhausted. (For the possibility of other reactions see Chapter 12.)

When this happens the star cools off along the track Q to T of Fig. 21. As the temperature of the interior material falls, degeneracy pressure takes over control throughout the star (with the exception of the immediate photospheric layers). Degeneracy pressure is able to do this because we are now considering stars that have masses below Chandrasekhar's limit.

Calculation shows that the time for cooling becomes progressively longer as the star goes from S to R to T in Fig. 21. Ultimately the rate of evolution becomes so slow that within the age of the Milky Way no star has had time enough to cool much beyond T. Hence we expect to find most dying stars lodged in the part of the diagram from R to T. This agrees very well with observation. Stars are found in considerable numbers in the region R to T. They are known as the white-dwarf stars, a name derived from their shrunken size and from their surfaces which are white-hot. A typical white dwarf is no larger than the planet Jupiter, although its mass may be 1,000 times greater than that of Jupiter. Evidently the white-dwarf stars are very squashed indeed.

On account of their low intrinsic brightness, white dwarfs cannot be detected by observation unless they happen to be quite close to us. But in spite of this handicap two hundred or more of them have so far been discovered, notably by Luyten. White dwarfs seem to be rather common: there are a dozen or so of them within our immediate stellar neighbourhood.

The novae

It is unlikely that stars die without a spectacular protest. We can see how this comes about by considering how the last dregs of a star's hydrogen become exhausted. It is apparent that the energy-generating skin of Fig. 19 cannot work its way entirely to the surface, since the temperature required for energy-generation exceeds 10 million degrees and the star cannot have a surface as hot as this, otherwise the flood of radiation emitted into space would be impossibly large. Yet stars apparently do consume their hydrogen right to the surface. This has been shown by Bidelman and by Greenstein who have observed such stars in the region P to Q of Fig. 21.

One way for the outer hydrogen to be consumed would be for it to be carried downward into an interior energy-generating

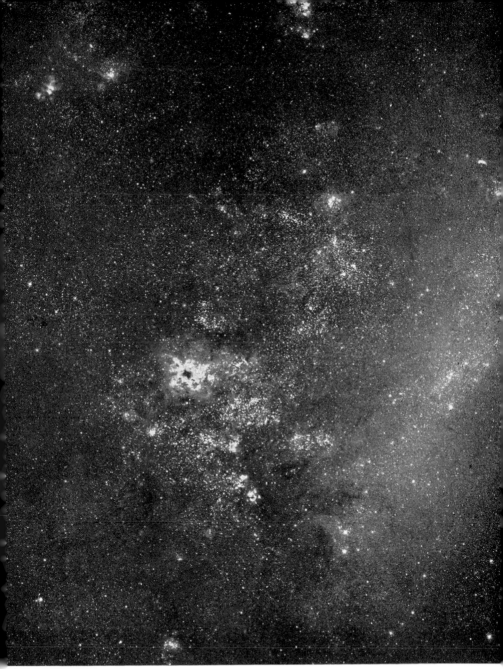

XXII—THE LARGE MAGELLANIC CLOUD

This is the brighter of the two famous clouds of Magellan. It lies outside the Galaxy at a distance of some 50,000 parsecs (1 parsec equals 19,200,000,000,000 miles). This galaxy is chockablock with blue giants, supergiants, and glowing clouds of gas. The very bright patch of nebulosity is known as the Tarantula Nebula. It has been estimated that if the Tarantula Nebula were as near to us as the Orion Nebula (Plate XI) it would appear as bright as the full Moon.

XXIII—THE SMALL MAGELLANIC CLOUD

Much to the surprise of astronomers vast tracks of hydrogen gas have recently been discovered in this Cloud. But there is little dust and few giants here. Why the two Magellanic Clouds should be so different in their stellar populations is an unsolved problem.

Mt. Wilson and Palomar Observatories

XXIV—THE GALAXY M 81 IN URSA MAJOR

This galaxy at a distance of about two and a quarter million parsecs is one of
the most beautiful of all spirals. M 81 lies outside the Local Group and shares
in the expansion of the Universe.

A photograph like this makes it possible to believe that our Galaxy contains
100,000,000,000 stars. Every speck in this picture is a star. The Sun is no
more remarkable than any one of this myriad of specks.

Forty-eight-inch Schmidt Telescope

E MILKY WAY

The nearer stars, appearing brighter than the rest, have rings around them.
This is an optical phenomenon. The stars should always be thought of as
points of light.

Mt. Wilson and Palomar Observatories

XXVI—THE GALAXY NGC 4594, THE 'SOMBRERO HAT'

This galaxy possesses hundreds of associated globular clusters. They can be distinguished by a softness of outline from the hard circular star images. The latter are of course just local stars of the Milky Way. The globular clusters each contain perhaps 100,000 separate stars, while NGC 4594 itself probably contains upwards of 100,000,000,000 stars. Its distance must be approaching 10 million parsecs. The dark band of the 'Sombrero' is due to the obscuring effect of huge dust clouds.

XXVII—THE GLOBULAR GALAXY M 87, A MONSTER MEMBER
OF THE VIRGO CLOUD

This galaxy has three outstanding peculiarities: it possesses about a thousand associated globular clusters; it contains near its centre a blue jet of gas (not visible in this picture); and it is an intensely powerful transmitter of radio-waves.

Mt. Wilson and Palomar Observatories

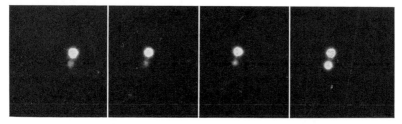

Sproul Observatory

XXVIII—FLARE ON THE STAR KRUGER 60B

Four exposures of the double system of Kruger 60 A and B (the C component is not shown here), the interval between the exposures being about two and a quarter minutes. Notice the spectacular change in the brightness of Kruger 60 B. Flares like this occur also on the Sun.

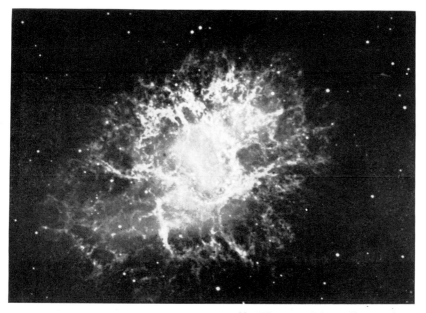

Mt. Wilson and Palomar Observatories

XXIX—THE CRAB NEBULA

The remnants of a cosmic explosion, equivalent in violence to the simultaneous explosion of about 1,000,000,000,000,000,000,000,000 hydrogen bombs. This cloud now has a diameter of some thirty million million miles.

Mt. Wilson and Palomar Observatories

XXX—A Portion of the Looped Nebula in Cygnus

Notice the delicate tracery in this glowing gas, which measures about a hundred million million miles in length.

XXXI—The 'Elephant's Trunk'

The dark sinuous 'trunk' consists of a cool opaque cloud. It is probably being squeezed by a hotter surrounding translucent gas.

Mt. Wilson and Palomar Observatories

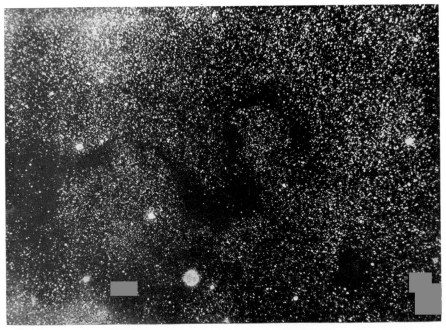

region by circulating currents. This would mean that the helium produced in the energy-generating region instead of being entirely added to the core was in part exchanged with hydrogen from the surface. While this process may well occur in some degree there is strong reason to believe that it is not the whole story, that the last of a star's hydrogen may be got rid of in quite a different way.

We have spoken of the material becoming degenerate throughout the star except for the immediate photospheric layers. If the outer skin of hydrogen should ever become degenerate—or an appreciable portion of it become degenerate— an explosive condition must arise in a way similar to that already discussed in connection with the 'popping' of the core. This has been pointed out by Mestel, who considers that violent outbursts may occur in this way. There is an important practical difference between the present case and that of the popping of the core. The explosion now occurs on the outside of the star where it should be much easier to observe.

The results of a precise calculation can be expressed in two ways. If the energy released were entirely converted into motion then—in the absence of the restraining gravitational field of the star—the exploding material would blow outwards from the star with an average speed of about 1,000 kilometres per second. If on the other hand the energy were all converted into heat, and if the amount of hydrogen concerned in the explosion were say 10 per cent of the mass of the Sun, the star could keep shining for several weeks at a rate that exceeded the Sun 100,000 times. This suggests a relation with the exploding stars known as novae. A typical nova is a star that is observed to increase suddenly in brightness from about 30 times the Sun, corresponding perhaps to the point Q of Fig. 21, to about 100,000 times the Sun. A typical nova maintains this brightness for a week or two and then declines steeply. Not only this, but material is fired off the star with a speed of about 2,000 kilometres per second. That this velocity is higher than the average speed suggested by our calculations is probably important. It suggests that most of the exploding hydrogen is retained by the strong gravitational field of the star: that the heated hydrogen expands but for the most part does not possess enough speed to leave the star. This again agrees with the indications of observation which suggest that the amount of material actually expelled by a nova is very small, amounting to no more than about a hundredth of a per cent of the whole mass of the star. After a time the main mass of the heated hydrogen must cool off and sink back to its former state. The process must be then repeated a second time, and a third time, and so on. About 1,000 such outbursts would probably be required to rid the star of the last of its hydrogen. This enables an interesting calculation to be made. In the whole of the Milky Way there are perhaps 100 million stars now evolving along a track similar to Fig. 21. Reckoning that each such star will experience 1,000 outbursts this gives a total of 100,000 million outbursts for the whole group of evolving stars. Since the time of evolution of these stars is about 5,000 million years this would imply that novae occur at a rate of about 20 per year. Estimates have been made of the number of novae actually occurring in the whole Milky Way each year. The result is about 20 or 30—an excellent agreement.

CHAPTER TEN

The Measurement of Astronomical Distances

Astronomical distances have the air of a conjuring trick. The vastness of cosmic dimensions fills us with astonishment. Yet like a conjuring trick it all looks very obvious when we see how it is done. The methods of measurement are indeed of a very mundane character.

Perhaps the most important is in essence just the method that an automobile driver uses at night to judge the distance of an approaching car. If the car's headlights seem faint we judge it to be far away; if they appear very bright we regard the car as being rather close. A correct judgment in such cases depends on our having a pretty good idea of how bright the headlights would look from some standard distance, say at a range of 50 yards. It is clear from practical experience that we go wrong in estimating distance if an approaching car happens to be carrying headlights that are intrinsically particularly bright. In this case we suppose the car to be nearer than it really is. Conversely if the oncoming car is equipped with headlights that are intrinsically rather dim we tend to misjudge the distance thinking the car to be farther away than it really is.

Now if we tried to use the stars indiscriminately as 'headlights' for astronomical distance determinations we should run immediately into a serious difficulty, because the intrinsic brightnesses of the stars are highly variable. A tenfold difference between a very bright automobile headlight and a dim one would represent a fairly extreme case. But the stars differ in their intrinsic brightnesses much more than this. Hence if we are to use the 'headlight' method of judging distances we must be particularly careful to use only stars with known true brightnesses. Since the intrinsic brightness of the Sun is known with great accuracy we could for instance decide to use stars that are very similar to the Sun. But such a procedure would have two disadvantages. First because the Sun

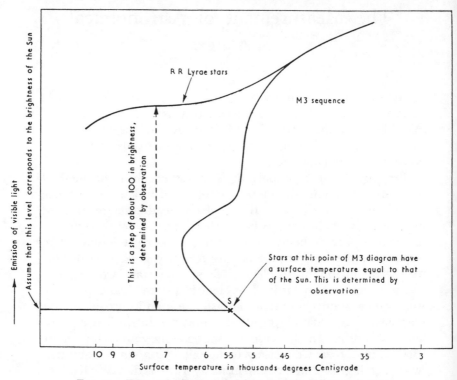

FIG. 22. Fixing the intrinsic brightness of the R R Lyrae stars.

is not a very bright star, similar stars cannot readily be detected if they are far away from us. Second, a rather tedious search, in which many stars were examined, would be necessary in order to pick out those special stars that happened to be like the Sun.

Both these disadvantages are overcome by using the R R Lyrae stars as 'standard headlights'. The R R Lyrae stars are about 100 times brighter than the Sun intrinsically and therefore they can be detected at much greater distances than could be done for stars like the Sun. Moreover their characteristic type of oscillation allows them to be picked up very readily.

The R R Lyrae Stars as distance indicators

The application of the R R Lyrae stars as distance indicators requires an observation to be combined with an item of knowledge. Taking the observation first, the more or less casual motorist's judgment of the apparent brightness of an oncoming headlight must be replaced by a strict measurement. This can be done by photographing our R R Lyrae star in an exposure of known duration, the apparent brightness being estimated from the intensity with which the star marks the plate. The calculation of the distance of the star also requires a knowledge of the intrinsic brightness of an R R Lyrae star. This was stated above to be about 100 times the Sun. How is this known?

The answer is given pictorially in Fig. 22. The sequence of the stars of the cluster M 3 is shown there together with the territory occupied by the R R Lyrae stars. Now stars near the point S in this figure emit light with a very closely similar distribution of colour to the light emitted by the Sun. Moreover the stars near the point S are almost certainly on the main-sequence as the Sun is. It accordingly seems a reasonable inference that these stars are also similar to the Sun in their intrinsic brightness. Accepting this, the scale of brightness becomes fixed for the whole diagram. It was indeed in just this way that the scale of Fig. 17 was determined. The last step is to read off the factor 100 by which the brightness of an R R Lyrae star exceeds the stars at S. This step depends on the fact that all the stars of M 3 (Plate XVIII) are effectively the same distance from us, so that the observed ratio of the apparent brightnesses of two stars is just the same as the ratio of their intrinsic brightnesses.

It is convenient at this stage to say a few words about the Milky Way. The stars of the Galaxy—as the Milky Way is often called—form a flattened lens-like structure probably with a pronounced central bulge or nucleus as indicated in Fig. 23. The Sun and the planets lie well out from the centre as is also indicated in Fig. 23. How far out? An answer to this question has been given by Walter Baade. By measuring the distances of a large number of R R Lyrae stars in the nucleus Baade was able to estimate the frequency with which these

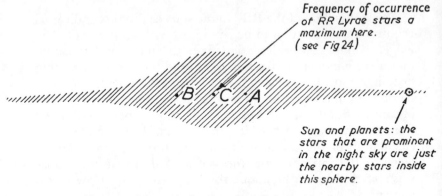

FIG. 23.   Schematic drawing of our Galaxy seen edge-on.

special stars occur in space. He found a distribution of the sort as shown in Fig. 24. The interpretation of the curve of Fig. 24 is that the R R Lyrae stars have a maximum frequency of occurrence at the centre, corresponding to the point C in Fig. 23. Away from the centre the frequency falls off: the point A is away from the centre on the near side and B is away from the centre on its far side. This is made clear by the corresponding marking of the points in the two figures. The distance of the Sun from the centre of the Galaxy then follows simply by reading off the distance of the peak of the curve of Fig. 24. Baade's result was a little in excess of 8,000 parsecs—in more conventional units about 150,000,000,000,000,000 miles, a goodly step.

The parsec is the unit of distance used by astronomers. Its meaning is easily understood. Consider the diameter EF of the circle shown in Fig. 25. Take two lines drawn from your eye, one to the point E and the other to F. Evidently there is an angle between these two lines. The diameter EF is said to subtend this angle at the eye. Now move the circle farther and farther away keeping it square on to the eye. Then the angle subtended by the diameter EF gets less and less. Indeed by moving the circle away to an appropriate distance we can make the angle come as small as we please. For example there would be a definite distance at which the angle subtended by EF was 2 seconds of arc. (It will be recalled that in a right angle **L**

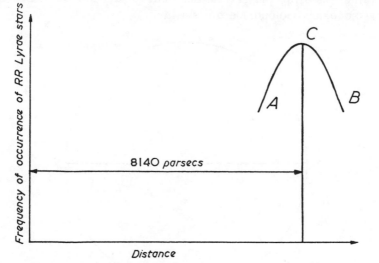

FIG. 24. Determining the distance of the centre of our Galaxy.

there are 90 'degrees'; in 1 degree there are 60 'minutes'; in 1 minute there are 60 'seconds', not of course of time but of angular measure—this is indicated by the words 'of arc'.) Now imagine that the diagram of Fig. 25 represents the orbit of the Earth around the Sun, and that the line EF is a diameter of the Earth's orbit. The distance at which the line EF subtends an angle of 2 seconds is called a parsec. Light, travelling 186,000 miles for every second of time, takes a little more than 3 years to cover a distance of 1 parsec. For comparison light takes only 8 minutes to travel from the Sun to the Earth and about 5 hours to reach Pluto the most distant of the planets. Clearly then a distance of 1 parsec is very vast indeed compared to the dimensions of the planetary system.

The reason why astronomers like to use the parsec as a unit of distance—to talk of distances as being so many parsecs, is partly because the parsec is about equal to the average distance between the stars and partly because all distances within our Galaxy come out at very reasonable numbers. It is much more convenient to say that the Sun is at a distance of about 8,000 parsecs from the centre of the Galaxy (Baade's actual value was 8,140 parsecs) rather than to say that the centre is 150,000,000,000,000,000 miles away.

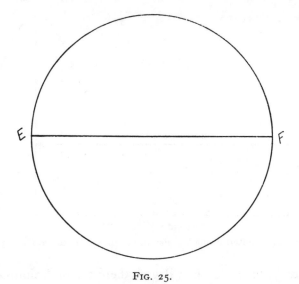

FIG. 25.

Distances outside the Milky Way

Besides being used for measurements within our Galaxy the R R Lyrae stars can be used to determine distances outside our Galaxy. It must now be stressed that our Galaxy is an isolated system of stars. If we were to go out on a journey into space in any direction after travelling sufficiently far we would come clear of the Milky Way altogether. This would happen at a distance of perhaps 30,000 parsecs—a statement that seems at first sight to be inconsistent with the picture of the Galaxy sketched in Fig. 23. In this figure the Sun is drawn lying in the outskirts of the Galaxy, so that we might expect to come clear of the stars of the Galaxy very quickly unless it just happened that we were to set out in a direction towards the centre, and even in this case we might still expect to come clear of the Galaxy in a distance of not much more than 15,000 parsecs.

But what is not shown in Fig. 23 is the great diffuse halo of stars that surrounds our Galaxy. Fig. 23 is correct so far as the main distribution of the stars is concerned, but a very extensive halo of stars must be thought of as surrounding Fig. 23. This is indicated in Fig. 26. The distance across this halo may be as great as 60,000 parsecs.

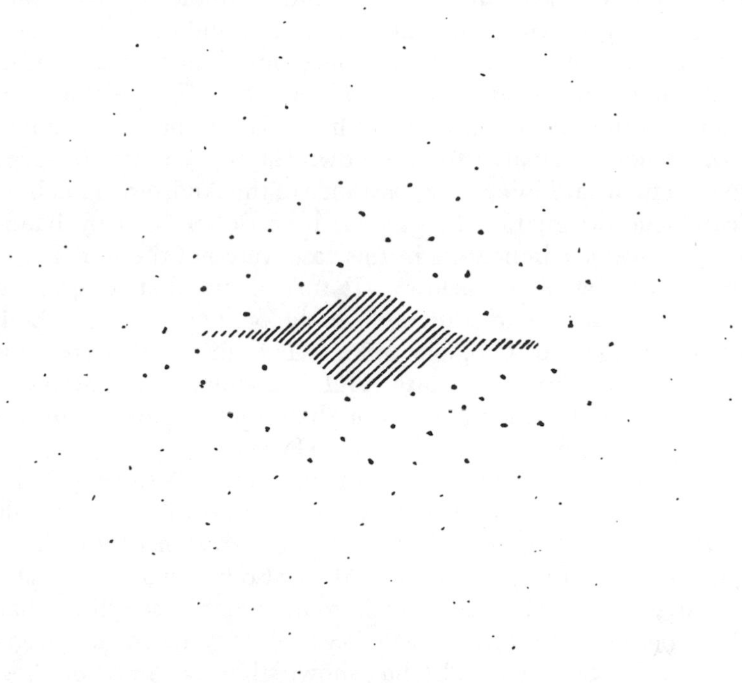

FIG. 26. The halo around our Galaxy.

At a distance of about 30,000 parsecs from its centre the Galaxy also seems to possess a number of satellite star systems. These are groups of stars larger than globular clusters but small compared to the Galaxy itself (they probably contain about 10 million stars, as compared with roughly 100,000 in a globular cluster, and with roughly 100,000 million in the Galaxy itself). They are appropriately named satellites because they probably move around the Galaxy rather as satellites of the solar system move around their parent planets, or as the planets themselves move around the Sun—except that moving around the Galaxy takes not a few months or years as is the case within the solar system but about 2,000 million years. Such satellite star systems have been detected by the survey of the heavens that is now being carried out at Palomar Mt.

Eventually our traveller would come clear of the Galaxy. He would then pass out into space, but he would not find space entirely empty. Here and there he would find other great star systems. Some would be very like our Galaxy itself. One such similar system is shown in Plate XXI. This is the great galaxy in the constellation of Andromeda, at one time thought to be somewhat smaller than our own Galaxy, but now believed to be somewhat larger. The distance of the Andromeda nebula (catalogue designation M 31) has been determined by Baade but the distance indicators in this case were not the R R Lyrae stars (as we shall see below). It turned out that M 31 is at the almost fantastic distance of nearly 450,000 parsecs—about 10,000,000,000,000,000,000,000 miles. The distance across the part of M 31 shown in Plate XXI is about 25,000 parsecs as compared with not much more than 15,000 parsecs for the corresponding distance in our own Galaxy.

In addition to what is shown on Plate XXI, M 31 also possesses a halo too faint to be easily photographed. The halo in the case of M 31 may extend out to a distance as great as 50,000 parsecs from the centre. M 31 also has two satellite star systems. These are very much more notable satellites than those possessed by our own Galaxy. A very recent investigation by M. Schwarzschild has shown that the mass of these satellites may be some 5 per cent or so of the whole mass of M 31. In the case of our Galaxy the mass of the satellites is probably not greater than a tenth of a per cent of the total.

The great system of M 31 is not by any means the nearest of the external star systems but it is the nearest of the really large systems. All nearer ones are comparatively faint unspectacular groups but their importance to astronomers is nevertheless very great. The nearest visible in the northern hemisphere of the Earth is a recently discovered system in a direction that lies in the constellation of Draco. It is now under active investigation by the observers at Palomar Mt. Still nearer external star systems are visible to observers in the southern hemisphere of the Earth. The nearest are indeed notable objects even to the unaided eye. These are the Magellanic clouds—the clouds of Magellan, appropriately named after that intrepid explorer, shown in Plates XXII and XXIII. Their distances, determined by Thackeray and Wesselinck using the R R Lyrae distance indicators, are about 50,000 parsecs. This is close enough to make one wonder whether or not they should be classed as satellites of our Galaxy. Present opinion is that probably they should not but the question is still an open one. What seems likely is that these two star systems form a connected pair. It has been shown by the Australians F. J. Kerr and J. V. Hyndman that the two clouds are moving in orbits around each other, rather like the two stars of a double star system. This result has been established by a new method of radio-astronomy to be described in a later chapter.

The Magellanic clouds have a very special importance in astronomy. As well as containing all the normal sorts of stars they also contain most of the freaks that are found in the Galaxy. But whereas the study of freak cases is made difficult in the Galaxy because their distances are often entirely unknown, the distance of all the stars in the Magellanic clouds are immediately known from the use of the R R Lyrae stars (the clouds are of small size compared to their distance so that all parts of them may be considered to be the same distance away from us, to a high degree of accuracy). This is an important feature to which several references will be made later on. At the present time this work is only just getting under way at the Radcliff Observatory, Pretoria and at the Commonwealth Observatory, Mt. Stromlo. It is safe to say that many advances in astronomy will be forthcoming in the next decades from a close study of the Magellanic clouds.

Distance measurements by the surveying method

It was mentioned at the beginning of this chapter that several methods of measuring distances are used by astronomers. So far we have been concerned with only one of them. Now it is opportune to say something of a second. The first astronomical distances were measured by a method identical in principle with that used by a surveyor. This is illustrated in Fig. 27. A and B are to be thought of as known points and AB as a known line. C is the point whose distance is sought. The method consists simply in sighting C from A and from B. The first observation settles the slope of the line AC compared with AB, as in

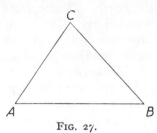

FIG. 27.

(a) of Fig. 28, while the second observation settles the slope of line BC, as in (b) of Fig. 28. Then C lies where the two directions intersect each other, the one from A and the one from B. The surveyor uses this method when C is some inaccessible spot, say the top of a mountain. The astronomer also uses the method with C as an inaccessible spot, a distant astronomical body.

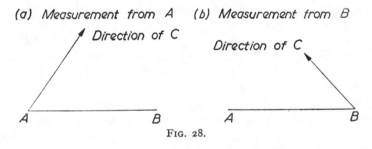

FIG. 28.

The essence of the surveying method is that the points A and B must be accessible and the distance from A to B must be known. One way to ensure that this condition is satisfied would be to take A and B as points on the surface of the Earth, say the positions of two observatories, the two observatories carrying out simultaneous measurement of the directions of C. This is in fact the way that distances inside the planetary system are measured. The distances of the planets from the Sun given in Chapter 5, were determined in essentially this fashion.

The surveying method suffers from a serious handicap however. It depends on our being able to distinguish between the directions of C as seen from A and B. When these two directions become nearly indistinguishable, as they do when C is very far away—see Fig. 29—the method tends to break down. This is particularly serious in astronomy because the distances we wish to measure are always very large compared to the distance from A to B, so that the triangle ABC is always very elongated, very much more so than in Fig. 29. Two

FIG. 29.

things have to be done. One is to measure directions very accurately so that the difference between the directions of C as seen from A and B can be distinguished even if it is very small. Indeed so accurate are astronomical measurements that differences of direction that are as small as one-thirtieth of a second of arc can be measured. But with even the most careful precautions accurate measurement is difficult when the difference of angle becomes less than this.

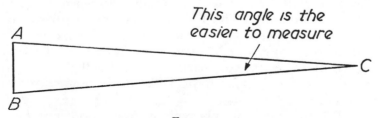

FIG. 30.

It is also of great importance to make the distance from A to B as large as possible. This is evident because the larger AB the greater the difference between the directions of C becomes, as can be seen by comparing the triangle of Fig. 29 with that of Fig. 30. Now what is the largest distance we can achieve for AB, bearing in mind that A and B must be points that we can actually go to—in order to make the angle measurements of course. Two points on opposite sides of the Earth, as in the measurement of planetary distances? This would be entirely insufficient to measure the distance of even the nearest star. Yet is this not the greatest possible distance consistent with the accessibility requirement? The answer is, no! We can achieve a much greater distance if we take A and B to be points at opposite ends of a diameter of the Earth's orbit around the Sun. This gives an increase of more than 20,000 times in the length of AB; while the Earth's motion around the Sun makes the points A and B accessible once every year. By making 6 monthly measurements of the direction of C, first from A then from B, then back to A, and so on, the distances of the nearest stars can be accurately measured. But although distances are very reliable out to 10 parsecs, distances of 100 parsecs are less reliably measured, and distances appreciably beyond 100 parsecs cannot be measured at all by the surveying method. The surveying method accordingly provides a very accurate guide to the distances of stars that lie in the immediate neighbourhood of the Sun but is quite useless at larger distances. At the larger distances we must use the 'headlight' method.

Brighter headlights

Even the R R Lyrae stars fail as indicators when we go to really great distances. The R R Lyrae stars can perhaps be used to a distance of 200,000 parsecs but not much farther, not as far as the great galaxy M 31 in Andromeda which lies at a distance of some 450,000 parsecs. The headlight method requires extension if it is to yield distance measurements as great as this.

The R R Lyrae stars must be replaced by some other brighter type of star. Any brighter star that possesses an easily recognised peculiarity and whose intrinsic brightness is known can be used. We shall consider several kinds of star that satisfy these requirements in later discussions. Two of the most effective types have intrinsic brightnesses more than 1,000 times greater than the R R Lyrae stars (more than 100,000 times brighter than the Sun). Such stars can be used to measure distances perhaps up to about 10 million parsecs.

Before we discuss the significance of such distances it may be asked how we can know that a particular star is, say 1,000 times brighter intrinsically than the R R Lyrae stars. The best way to make such a determination is to find a system of stars all at effectively the same distance away from us in which both the star in question and R R Lyrae stars can readily be observed. A straightforward comparison then tells us how much brighter our special type of star is. The Magellanic clouds are ideal systems for use in this sort of work. They are not only sufficiently near to us for the R R Lyrae stars to be readily distinguished but they contain almost every known type of star. Actually owing to the fact that the Magellanic clouds are only visible from the southern hemisphere of the Earth very little of this work has so far been done on them. Perversely astronomers have insisted on doing things in a much harder way from the northern hemisphere. It can hardly be doubted however that the Magellanic clouds will be used more and more in the future for this purpose. They provide us with an ideal way of calibrating our various types of stellar headlights.

Let us return now to the statement that the brightest stellar headlight yet discovered (actually the novae, and a certain type of irregular oscillating star—these will be discussed in later chapters) make distance determinations up to 10 million parsecs possible. The great nebula M 31 (Plate XXI) at a distance of about 450,000 parsecs lies well within the range of possible measurement. Indeed the measurement of the distance of M 31 does not demand the use of the brightest possible type of headlight, although it does demand a brighter type than the R R Lyrae stars.

Beyond M 31 are about 1,000 other galaxies whose distances might be measured with the aid of the brightest stars for which the headlight method is applicable. So far only a few have had their distances measured in this way. The beautiful galaxy M 81 shown in Plate XXIV is one of these. According to the recent work of A. R. Sandage, M 81 is at a distance of about 2,500,000 parsecs.

It should eventually be possible to measure the distance of such galaxies as the one shown in Plate XXVI (catalogue designation N.G.C. 4594), which is probably at a distance approaching 10 million parsecs. This galaxy shows a most pronounced central bulge. Also the clouds containing dust are shown as a dark band: this is similar to the 'fog' within our own Galaxy. The large number of objects which can be seen lying outside the galaxy but grouped symmetrically around the nucleus is a third point of interest. These are not foreground stars of our own Galaxy but a group of globular clusters belonging to N.G.C. 4594. The distance of N.G.C. 4594 is so great that even the vast array of stars in a globular cluster (compare with Plate XVIII for a globular cluster in our own Galaxy) shows only as a faint blur. Another galaxy with a very large number of globular clusters is shown in Plate XXVII (catalogue description M 87).

The last two Plates XXVI and XXVII suggest that instead of using an individual star as headlight it might be possible to take a group of stars together. One hopeful possibility is to use a whole globular cluster, the brightest of which are about 10,000 times more luminous than an individual R R Lyrae star. This possibility is under active investigation at the present time. Difficulties lie in making an effective calibration of the intrinsic brightnesses of the whole range of globular clusters (it is obvious from a glance at Plates XXVI and XXVII that globular clusters do not all have the same intrinsic brightness, as for instance the R R Lyrae stars all seem to have). It is hoped that the work now being carried out at the Mt. Wilson and Palomar Observatories and by N. U. Mayall at the Lick Observatory will eventually lead to whole globular clusters becoming useful as distance indicators.

Even globular clusters however would not be capable of measuring the full distances in which astronomers are interested. These 'ultimate' distances go out into space to 1,000 million parsecs—for comparison the distance of the Earth from the Sun is but one two-hundred-thousandth part of one parsec. This is so enormous that only a source of light that exceeded the Sun ten thousand millionfold in brightness could be used as a standard headlight. We shall take up the question as to how such a source can be obtained in a later chapter.

CHAPTER ELEVEN

Dwarfs and Giants

The stars in general

The comparative simplicity of the evolutionary sequence shown in Fig. 17 is due to the fact that the stars plotted there belong to the same cluster and therefore presumably had a common origin and now have a common age. When we consider the totality of all stars of the Milky Way the picture becomes far more complex; for in place of the one degree of variation that exists in a globular cluster—variation of mass from star to star—we now have three degrees of variation at least: variation of mass, variation of age, and variation of initial composition. To these some astronomers might add a variation of magnetic field but it is not yet known whether this is a matter of any real importance.

In Chapter 8 the initial composition possessed by stars that formed in the Milky Way contemporaneously with the Sun was listed. Have stars ever formed with compositions importantly different from this? Yes, the first stars to condense in the Galaxy had a considerably smaller metal content. It may come as a surprise that this difference should turn out to have important consequences since even the metal content of a young star is probably less than a per cent by weight, while that of an old star is much smaller still. Yet metal atoms can have a deceptive importance on the surface balance of a star. It will be recalled that in the photospheric layers the energy must always be made to flow by radiation. In stars with photospheric temperatures less than about 5,000° C.—stars that lie to the right of the Sun in the H-R diagram—the metal atoms can have a decisive importance in controlling the photospheric energy flow even if their abundance is very small.

Because of the three possibilities of variation the full totality of stars of the Milky Way scatter very widely over the H-R diagram. According to the part of the diagram in which they lie the stars are given rather picturesque names: blue giants,

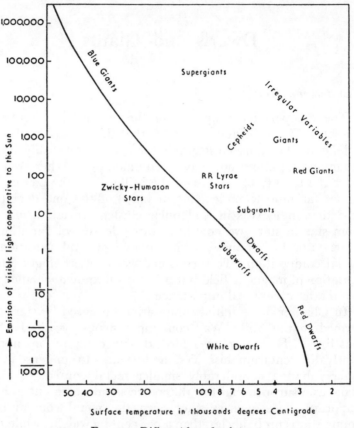

FIG. 31.   Different brands of star.

dwarfs, red dwarfs, sub-dwarfs, white dwarfs, giants, sub-giants, red giants, and supergiants. There are also characteristic parts of the diagram in which lie oscillating stars—R R Lyrae stars, Cepheids, and the irregular variables. This is illustrated in Fig. 31.

At the time of their condensation the stars lie on or near the main-sequence, their positions being dependent on their masses. Those of large mass lie high on the main-sequence in the territory of the blue giants. The stars of small mass at the bottom of the main-sequence are the red-dwarfs and those like the Sun are just plain dwarfs. The task of the astronomer is to explain how the stars evolve away from the main-sequence and thereby to understand how the various regions of the diagram come to be populated.

During its evolution a star moves from one region to another. The globular cluster stars for instance evolve along a track of the form of Fig. 15. They start as dwarfs on the main-sequence, then they move into the region of the sub-giants and thence to the giants. After the turn-round at the point O of Fig. 15 the stars move down and to the left into the R R Lyrae region. Still moving to the left and downwards they cross the main-sequence and then enter the territory of the Zwicky-Humason blue stars. In the last phases of their evolution the stars then move downwards until at last they reach the realm of the white dwarfs.

We may suppose that a star initially well up the main-sequence, higher than the dwarfs, follows an evolutionary track with the general form of Fig. 15 but lifted in the diagram according to the starting point. Such stars could therefore evolve into higher regions into the territory of the super-giants. There is accordingly no difficulty in understanding in a general way how the upper parts of the diagram come to be occupied but subtleties will arise when we come later to discuss details.

Stars initially lower down the main-sequence than the Sun would if they were given sufficient time evolve into the region of the diagram to the right of the sub-giants and below the red-giants. But the Galaxy is not yet old enough for this to have happened, so that we expect these parts of the diagram to be still unoccupied—an expectation that is in accordance with observation.

We may add a remark on evolution times. The time required for a significant evolution of stars near the bottom of the main-sequence, the red-dwarfs, may be as long as 1,000,000,000,000 years, as compared to about 10,000 million years for the Sun, about 1,000 million for a star like Sirius and no more than 10 million years for stars that are very high on the main-sequence.

The stars of the solar neighbourhood

The Sun and the planets are moving at a speed of about half a million miles an hour around a huge orbit that circles the Galaxy. This motion takes us past other stars and sometimes through gas clouds of the Milky Way. One would suppose that the protagonists of the more romantic aspects of space travel would wax enthusiastic about our journeying thus among the stars since no rocket they will ever construct will take them so swiftly or so comfortably through the Galaxy.

The stars among which we are moving at the present time are plotted in Fig. 32. It is at once apparent that these nearby stars cover only a very limited part of the diagram. The main-sequence is represented to a brightness about 50 times greater than the Sun, but most of the stars lie on the main-sequence below the Sun. In addition to the main-sequence stars there are two white dwarfs (catalogue designations Wolf 1346 and AC + 70° 8247), two sub-dwarfs (Groombridge 1830 and 66° 717), several sub-giants and a number of red giants, of which Arcturus and Aldebaran are the most noteworthy examples.

The absence of very bright stars, blue giants and super-giants, is simply due to the extreme rarity of such highly luminous stars—we do not happen to be near any of them at the present time. The stars plotted in Fig. 32 are just common stars. We see that the Sun, negligible compared with the giants, is nevertheless brighter than the average star.

There is no special characteristic about the distribution of the nearest stars over the sky. But this was not understood by the astrologers of the ancient world, who sought to relate the stars to human experience. Attempts were made to associate groups of stars with animals and people: the stars in one patch of the sky became Draco the dragon, another became Leo the lion, Pisces the fishes, Ursa Major the great bear, Orion the hunter, Andromeda after the heroine of ancient legend, Virgo the virgin, and other such fanciful names. These imaginary associations became known as the constellations. They are still retained as appellations in modern astronomy in spite of their complete lack of physical significance, partly for their attractive descriptions and partly because it is often convenient

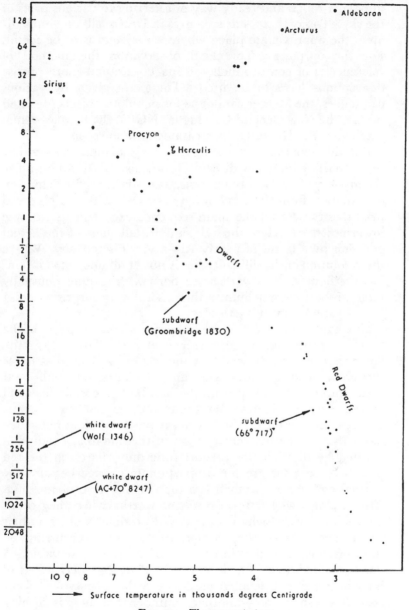

FIG. 32. The nearest stars.

181

to have a rough and ready way of referring to various parts of the sky. To say that a star system is in Draco tells one immediately the approximate place where the system is to be found. For the purposes of practical observation this method of reference is of course much too inaccurate and more precise descriptions have to be used. These are given by various catalogues, the Messier catalogue for nebulous objects (denoted by M), the New General Catalogue (NGC), the Shapley-Ames catalogue, the Henry-Draper catalogue, and so on.

But although the nearby stars may be just common stars they nevertheless abound in difficult problems. Take for instance the mystery of the faint red dwarfs. Calculations of the emission of radiation from the stars agree very well with the observed brightnesses over all the main-sequence except in its extreme lowermost part. Here the calculations fall short of the actual emission by a factor of nearly 10—a vast discrepancy. Where the resolution of the difficulty lies is not at all understood. Unless the faintest red-dwarfs were born with a quite unusually large proportion of helium in them, some very surprising point has apparently been overlooked.

In Chapter 7 when we were discussing the atmosphere of the Sun we mentioned the occurrence of solar flares. It is the flares that apparently send out the jets of particles that cause the great geomagnetic storms and the aurora borealis and which produce outbursts from the Sun both of cosmic rays and of radio-waves. Flares also occur on the red dwarf stars. Whereas a flare on the Sun, even a big flare, does not make more than a one per cent change in the amount of radiation emitted by the Sun (for a short time only) flares on the red dwarfs cause a far greater proportionate change because the normal emission is so much less than in the case of the Sun. This explains why flares are so noteworthy when they occur on a faint star and why it has proved possible to observe their occurrence. Flares of a comparable intensity occurring on stars brighter than the Sun would be quite unobservable. A flare on a red dwarf star is shown in Plate XXVIII. It is of interest to see that detailed processes in the solar system occur also on a cosmic scale—another reminder that there is nothing particularly privileged in our position.

The sub-dwarfs are a further mystery. What makes them differ from the normal dwarf stars of the main-sequence? Of the three possible causes of variation of position in the H-R diagram (mass, age, composition) variation of mass gives a shift of position not into sub-dwarf regions but along the main-sequence. Variation of age seems no more hopeful: the evolution arising from increasing age takes the stars along an upward evolutionary track, not downwards into the sub-dwarf region. This leaves the possibility of composition differences. Now it is true that a composition difference does exist between the sub-dwarfs and the normal main-sequence dwarfs: elements other than hydrogen (and possibly helium) are much less abundant in the sub-dwarfs. It is also true that such a shortage would take a star into sub-dwarf territory but not nearly as far as the observations seem to require!*

After these rebuffs it is as well to come to a problem whose solution is satisfactorily understood. Fig. 32 shows clear evidence of an evolutionary track that branches off the main-sequence at nearly the same place as the evolutionary track of the stars of the globular clusters (compare with Fig. 17). The evolving stars of Fig. 32 must be of much the same mass as the globular cluster stars—say 1.1 or 1.2 times the Sun, and of much the same age—say 5,000 million years.

But there are differences of detail. The evolutionary sequences of the globular clusters pass through the sub-giants to the ordinary giants, whereas the sequence of Fig. 32 runs from the sub-giants to the red-giants—it moves more to the right in the diagram. Why is this? Because of a difference of composition: as in the sub-dwarfs the proportion of metals in the stars of the globular clusters is considerably less than the proportion present in the evolving stars of Fig. 32. Now the surface balance requires the flow of energy to be carried by radiation in the photospheric layers, and this is controlled in stars of low photospheric temperature by the metal atoms. So the operation of the surface balancing condition is changed by alterations in the abundance of the metal atoms, the changes turning out

* Just before this book goes to Press, I have received some recent calculations which show that composition differences have more effect than used to be thought. The text is therefore too pessimistic. It now seems quite likely that the sub-dwarfs arise from differences of composition.

to explain very accurately the difference between evolution to the giants (Fig. 17) and evolution to the red giants (Fig. 32).

Yet the evolutionary sequence of Fig. 32 contains another puzzle. There is no sign of the sequence turning back to the left into the domain of the Zwicky-Humason stars. Is this a genuine difference or is the absence of a swing-back in Fig. 32 due to the smallness of the number of stars—perhaps we see the swing-back in the case of the globular clusters because their populations are so much larger? For myself I believe the difference to be genuine but if so the cause of the difference is mysterious. Perhaps the core instead of popping at the top of the sequence, as in the globular cluster stars, explodes with sufficient violence to shatter these stars completely.

Let us take a final problem, one that can be readily understood. The main-sequence persists in Fig. 32 well above the point at which the evolutionary track branches off. Now the evolution times for the stars that are highest on the main-sequence are substantially less than the times for the stars that are actually evolving—about 500 million years as compared with 5,000 million years. Why then if stars that require 5,000 million years are now actually evolving have stars on the main-sequence that require only 500 million years not evolved long ago? The answer is straightforward. Because the stars of the solar neighbourhood are not of a uniform age. One group of stars has ages of some 4,000 or 5,000 million years—the Sun is one of these; another group has ages less than 500 million years. The two groups have been plotted together in Fig. 32. This is the cause of the apparent peculiarity.

The Cepheids

We begin a more systematic study of the general distribution of stars in the H-R diagram by making a tentative hypothesis: that given sufficient time every star evolves along an evolutionary track of the form shown in Fig. 33, irrespective of the position on the main-sequence of the starting point A. We know from the globular clusters (Figs. 17 and 18) that our hypothesis is certainly satisfied when A lies among the dwarfs near the Sun. Our concern is now to extend the evolutionary development to cases where A lies above the dwarfs. Whether or not the present hypothesis then yields results that agree with observation is a matter that will be discussed in detail at a later stage. We shall find that the hypothesis is apparently satisfied in some cases but not in others.

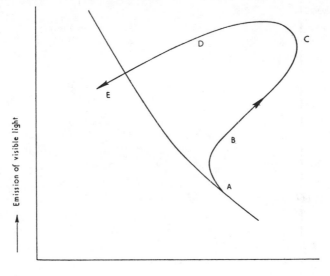

FIG. 33.   The evolutionary hypothesis.

The scales of brightness and of surface temperature have not been marked in Fig. 33 for the reason that the starting point A is intended to be any point on the main-sequence. The general features are that from A to B the star grows both brighter and redder implying a considerable increase of size, the star swells as it grows brighter. This continues until a turning point near C is reached. At C the star is about 1,000 times brighter than it was at A. Thereafter the star shrinks and becomes less bright as it passes through D and E. In analogy to the R R Lyrae stars we might also expect that some characteristic oscillatory state might be set up near the point D.

Oscillating stars are indeed found in the zone of the H-R diagram indicated in Fig. 34. For comparison the R R Lyrae stars have also been marked in this diagram. The oscillating stars occupying the zone from P to T are the famous Cepheid

185

variables. The Cepheid zone is not to be regarded as part of an evolutionary track. Rather does it seem that the stars oscillate when their evolutionary tracks intersect the zone, as indicated by the dotted lines of Fig. 34. The particular part of

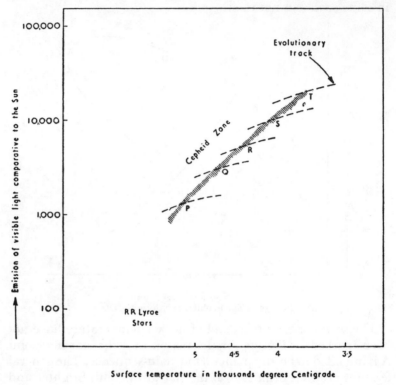

FIG. 34. The Cepheid zone.

the zone crossed by the evolutionary track of a given star depends where on the main-sequence the star was initially placed. Since stars that lie initially quite near the Sun on the main-sequence are known to follow evolutionary tracks that carry them through the R R Lyrae region it seems likely that stars with evolutionary tracks that pass through the Cepheid zone at the lowermost point P (this point being not much above the R R Lyrae region) also cannot have had initial positions much further up the main-sequence than the Sun.

186

Stars initially about 50 times brighter than the Sun might be expected to cross the Cepheid zone in the neighbourhood of Q and R, while stars initially two or three hundred times brighter than the Sun should cross the Cepheid zone near

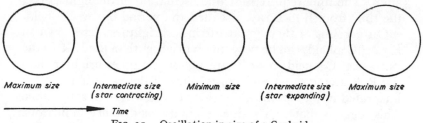

Maximum size   Intermediate size   Minimum size   Intermediate size   Maximum size
(star contracting)   (star expanding)

→ Time

FIG. 35. Oscillation in size of a Cepheid.

S and T. It would therefore seem as if the whole Cepheid zone can be accounted for in terms of stars that initially lie in the range of the main-sequence from about 10 times the Sun up to perhaps 400 times the Sun. The stars of the solar neighbourhood shown in Fig. 32 that occupy the higher part of the main-sequence are just the sort of stars that we should expect to evolve eventually through the Cepheid zone.

The oscillation of a Cepheid seems to consist of a radially inwards and outwards pulsation. Various stages of the pulsation are indicated in Fig. 35. And a Cepheid oscillates not only

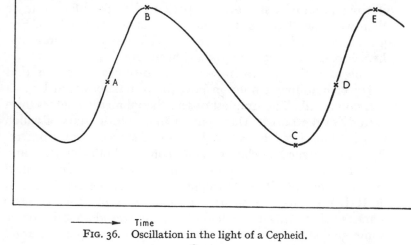

→ Time

FIG. 36. Oscillation in the light of a Cepheid.

in size but also in its brightness, the characteristic type of variation being that shown in Fig. 36. Successive times of maximum brightness at B and E of Fig. 36 do not coincide exactly with the times of minimum size but occur somewhat after. The time required for one oscillation of the light curve, the time from B to E say, is called the period of the Cepheid.

On account of their great intrinsic brightness (as shown in Fig. 34 Cepheids can be very much brighter than the R R Lyrae stars—e.g. Cepheids near T are about 300 times brighter than the R R Lyrae stars) and on account of the variation of light illustrated in Fig. 36 the Cepheids are easily recognisable stars. This suggests that we consider their use as distance indicators.

The problem is not the same as in the case of the R R Lyrae stars, for the Cepheids do not form an even approximately uniform group. Cepheids at T of Fig. 34 are about 100 times brighter than Cepheids at P. There can be no suggestion therefore that the Cepheids as a group may be used as a single 'standard headlight'. What makes the Cepheids of great use as distance indicators, however, is an important property of their periods of oscillation. This varies systematically from P to T (Fig. 34), being about $2\frac{1}{2}$ days at P, 5 days at Q, 10 days at R, 20 days at S, 35 days at T. Evidently if the period of oscillation of a Cepheid is determined by observation we know straight away where in the zone from P to T it must lie— if observation of a star gives a period of 10 days for example then we know that the star must lie near R. Hence from Fig. 34 we can read off the intrinsic brightness of the star and hence we can use it as a 'standard headlight'.

The Cepheids are so important as distance indicators that it is worth adding a note on how the results shown in Fig. 34 were obtained. The simplest observational method comes from a study of the Larger Magellanic Cloud, all the stars of which can be considered to be at the same distance away from us. Now the Larger Magellanic Cloud contains both Cepheids and R R Lyrae stars. The distance can accordingly be determined by observing the R R Lyrae stars. (It will be recalled that R R Lyrae stars can be used to a distance of about 200,000 parsecs. The Magellanic clouds are nearer than this, being some 50,000 parsecs away.) With the distance of the Larger

Magellanic Cloud thus determined, the intrinsic brightnesses of the Cepheids in it can then be read off (when we know how far a car is away the apparent brightness of its headlights tells us at once how bright they really are). In this way it can be shown that the Cepheids occupy the zone marked in Fig. 34. Then finally an observational determination of the periods of oscillation of the Cepheids that lie in the different parts of the zone tells us how the period varies as we go from P to T.

Because Cepheids near T are about 300 times brighter than the R R Lyrae stars their use as distance indicators enables measurements to be made at distances that are far too large for the R R Lyrae stars. Cepheids near T of Fig. 34 can be used to measure distances out to about 4 million parsecs. It was mentioned in Chapter 10 that Sandage has recently shown the galaxy M 81 (Plate XXIV) to be at a distance of some 2,500,000 parsecs. The use of a Cepheid as a standard headlight was one of the several methods employed by Sandage in this determination.

Why stars should start to oscillate when their evolutionary tracks enter a particular zone in the H-R diagram is not known, any more than the cause of the oscillation of the R R Lyrae stars is understood. What can however be shown by astronomical theory is why, granted oscillations to occur, the Cepheids have the periods that we observe, why for instance the Cepheids near P of Fig. 34 oscillate in a period of about $2\frac{1}{2}$ days, why in a period of 10 days at R, why in 20 days at S, and so on. In short the dependence of period on position within the Cepheid zone is understood (this being just the property that allows the Cepheids to be used as distance indicators). The theoretical work in this field was first laid down by Eddington. A recent review of the theory by Schwarzschild and Epstein has shown excellent agreement between the calculated periods and the observed periods.

The irregular variables

The irregular variables are the only brand of star appearing in Fig. 31 that has not so far been mentioned. To understand how these stars come to be thus placed in the H-R diagram it is necessary to introduce the idea that two oscillatory states apparently occur on the evolutionary track of Fig. 33. One is the state near D that we have already considered. The other occurs near the uppermost point of the track, near the point C.

The two states are easy to distinguish from each other. In the Cepheids the periodicity of the oscillations is maintained with extreme constancy and the shape of the light curve (Fig. 36) is also maintained without variation from one cycle to another as near as can be determined. The irregular variables on the other hand show changes both in their periods and in the shape of their light curves from one oscillation to the next.

Examples of irregularly oscillating stars are found in the globular clusters near the tip of the evolutionary sequence (near the point O of Fig. 15). Many irregular variables also occur among the scattered stars of the Milky Way, although none of them is to be found among the nearest stars. When these 'long period variables' as they are often called are plotted on Fig. 32 they fall on an extension of the evolutionary sequence beyond the star Aldebaran. A famous example is the star Mira (The Wonderful).

Certain irregular variables are among the brightest of all stars—over 100,000 times brighter than the Sun. These very bright oscillators have readily recognisable peculiarities that make them useful as distance indicators. One such star was used by Sandage in his determination of the distance of the great galaxy M 81—as with the Cepheid method this irregular oscillator gave about 2,500,000 parsecs for the distance.

The mystery of the missing supergiants

We shall now examine how far the evolutionary hypothesis made above leads to results that agree with observation. It will be recalled that the whole range of Cepheids from P to T in Fig. 34 is apparently derivable from the range of the main-sequence from about 10 times the brightness of the Sun up to perhaps 400 times the brightness of the Sun—stars not more than about 6 or 7 times the mass of the Sun. Now what about stars that are initially much brighter than this? How about the Cepheids corresponding to the evolutionary tracks of stars that initially were more than 400 times brighter than the Sun? The answer is that no such Cepheids are found. The point T of Fig. 34 represents the observational upper limit to the Cepheid zone.

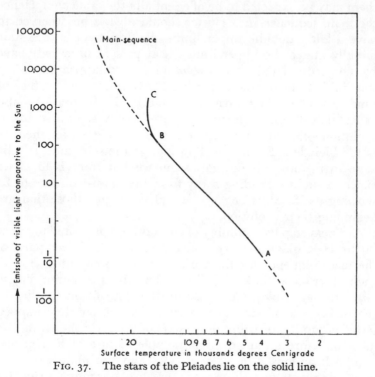

FIG. 37.   The stars of the Pleiades lie on the solid line.

The conclusion suggested by these considerations is that stars initially higher up the main-sequence than about 400 times the solar brightness do not satisfy our evolutionary hypothesis—they apparently evolve in some entirely different way. This conclusion is so important that it is desirable to seek other evidence that may support it. Confirmation comes from an entirely different line of argument, an argument based on observations of the groups of stars known as open clusters. The open clusters differ importantly from the globular clusters in that they are much less populated and their constituent stars are not necessarily of very great age, as the stars of the globular clusters are—indeed very bright young stars are often found in the open clusters. The Pleiades (Plate XVII) form an open cluster.

Now clusters possess the important feature that all stars in them may be expected to be of essentially the same age. Hence the main-sequence in a cluster should always be observed to have a fairly definite upper limit—the argument is that stars initially above the upper limit (as at present observed) have by now completed their evolution and disappeared, while stars initially below the upper limit have not yet had sufficient time to evolve; their turn will come in the future. We also expect that stars near the upper limit will show signs of incipient evolution—the sort of situation sketched in Fig. 37 for the case of the Pleiades. From A to B of Fig. 37 the stars must still be close to the line of the main-sequence but from B to C we expect a slight spreading away from the main-sequence to be showing itself. Stars between B and C are just those that are beginning their evolution.

As a next step let a number of clusters be represented together in the H-R diagram. We notice first that the lower parts of the main-sequence for the various clusters must fit on top of each other since these are all stars for which evolution has so far been negligible—they must all therefore fit on the line of the main-sequence irrespective of which cluster they happen to belong to. A distribution of stars of the form shown in Fig. 38 is therefore obtained. The notable feature of Fig. 38 lies in the deviations a, b, c, d, e . . . from the main-sequence. They represent just those stars that are beginning to evolve away from the main-sequence in the various clusters: the stars of the deviation e belong to one cluster, those of d to another cluster, and so on from the deviations c, b, a. An interpretation of Fig. 38 can be given in terms of different ages for the various clusters. The cluster with the deviation a is the youngest, b is the next youngest, then c, then d, and e is the oldest. As time passes cluster a will come to look like b, then like c, then like d, and so on.

These remarks refer only to the stars of the clusters that lie on or near the main-sequence. Now how about stars away to the right of the main-sequence—what about the stars that have

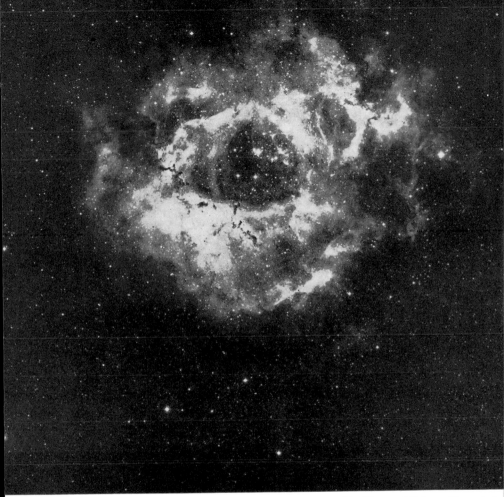

XXXII—THE ROSETTE NEBULA

Notice the small dark globules that can be seen when they are projected against the bright background of the nebulosity. Star showers are probably born out of such globules. The dimensions of nebulae like this are to be measured in hundreds of millions of millions of miles.

Mt. Wilson and Palomar Observatories

XXXIII—NGC 6611, a Hot Cloud of Gas Expanding
into Cooler Gas

The hot gas is heated by stars and is bursting outwards like a bomb. Notice
the curious irregularities of shape.

Mt. Wilson and Palomar Observatories

XXXIV—THE TRIFID NEBULA

This cloud is a weak transmitter of radio-waves.

XXXV—THE RADIO TRANSMITTER IN CASSIOPEIA

One of the most powerful radio transmitters in the Milky Way. This is a negative print—that is to say the sky is shown white and the stars shown dark. The radio transmitter is not located in the stars. The radio emission comes from a twisted mass of gaseous filaments. Some of the filaments, distant about 30,000,000,000,000,000 miles, can be seen in the left-centre of the picture.

XXXVI—IC 1613, AN EXAMPLE OF A STRUCTURELESS, LOOSE GALAXY

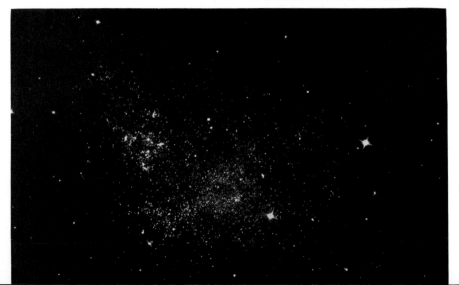

Mt. Wilson and Palomar Observatories

XXXVII—M 33, Galaxy in Triangulum

Our Galaxy and M 31 (Plate XXI) are the most important members of the Local Group. M 33, an Sc spiral, is the next most important member. The distance across this galaxy is about 40,000,000,000,000,000 miles.

Mt. Wilson and Palomar Observatories

XXXVIII—GALAXIES OF THE VIRGO CLOUD

A negative print. Astronomers like to use negative prints because more can be seen on them. The distance across this cluster of galaxies is about 20,000,000,000,000,000,000 miles.

Mt. Wilson and Palomar Observatories

XXXIX—The Central Regions of the Coma Cluster

Notice the difference between distant galaxies and local stars. The local stars of the Milky Way have hard circular outlines. The galaxies are fuzzy in outline and are not usually of circular shape.

Mt. Wilson and Palomar Observatory

XL—THE CLUSTER OF GALAXIES IN CORONA BOREALIS

Notice again the difference between local stars and distant galaxies. Very
bright stars show a cross in addition to a circle. This is an optical effect.

undergone extensive evolution? It is here that a strange situation arises. Stars far away from the main-sequence are found in some clusters but not in others. Their occurrence or absence seems to be controlled by a definite criterion. If the stars near

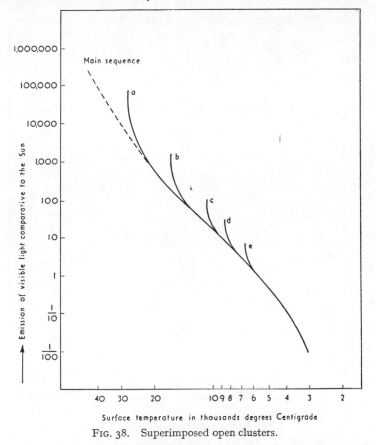

FIG. 38. Superimposed open clusters.

the upper limit of the main-sequence are not more than about 400 times the brightness of the Sun, evolution far to the right of the main-sequence is found. For instance this is the case in the cluster represented in Fig. 39, the cluster Praesepe. If on the other hand the stars near the upper limit of the main-sequence are more than about 400 times the brightness of the Sun no evidence of the looped evolution of Fig. 33 is found

—e.g. in the Pleiades. The clusters *c*, *d*, and *e* of Fig. 38 would show evolution, but not *a* and possibly not *b*. This curious situation was pointed many years ago by Trumpler. The likely inference is I think that stars evolving far to the

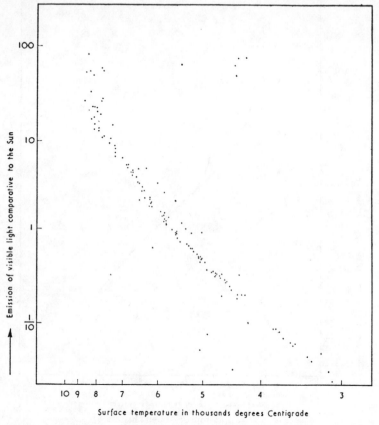

Surface temperature in thousands degrees Centigrade

FIG. 39. The stars of the open cluster Praesepe.

right of the main-sequence are not found in the very bright clusters for the reason that they do not occur there.

When we take this evidence from the open clusters with our previous discussion of the Cepheids the conclusion becomes well nigh overwhelming that stars initially more than about 400 times as bright as the Sun do not evolve far away to the right of the main-sequence in the same way that fainter stars do. The situation seems to be that all stars if they are given sufficient time begin to evolve by turning away to the right from the main-sequence. If their initial brightness is less than about 400 times the Sun they continue to move away from the main-sequence by embarking on an evolutionary track of the form indicated in Fig. 33. If on the other hand their initial brightness is more than about 400 times that of the Sun something quite different happens to them. The question is what? This question, a vital one in the understanding of the evolution of the stars, has been much emphasised by Otto Struve. We shall consider a possible answer to it in the following chapter. We must defer our suggested solution of the mystery of the missing supergiants until then.

The mystery of the demon stars

To end the present chapter we shall consider one final puzzle. This concerns a particular type of double-star system, the Algol binaries—named after their prototype Algol. The special characteristic of the Algol binaries is that at certain times in

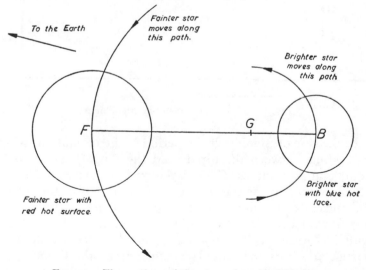

FIG. 40.   The motions of the stars of an Algol binary.

the motion of the two stars around each other the fainter component eclipses the brighter one, thereby cutting off much of the light of the system. The situation is shown in Fig. 40. It will be seen that in these systems the fainter star is the larger of the two.

As the stars move around in their orbits a stage is also reached where the brighter star partially eclipses the fainter one. This also causes a decrease in the amount of light that we receive, but not nearly so markedly as when the brighter component is eclipsed. The light we receive thus oscillates in the manner shown in Fig. 41, the big dips in the curve correspond to the occasions on which the brighter component is eclipsed, and the small dips when the faint component is eclipsed.

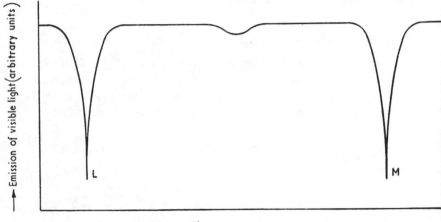

FIG. 41. The light curve of an Algol binary.

In the case of Algol itself the period of the oscillation (which is the time between the dip L and the dip M) is 2 days 20 hours and 49 minutes. This variation is so marked that it is readily visible to the naked eye. To the minds of the men of the ancient civilisations any change occurring in the heavens was fraught with great consequences to human affairs. Algol with its readily visible regular oscillations seemed to be a particularly fearsome star. Hence its name—the Demon Star.

Because the fainter star is the larger, the Algol double stars have an important bearing on our evolutionary picture. Such a situation would not be possible if the two components were both main-sequence stars, for in this case the fainter component would of necessity have to be of smaller size. The fainter star can only be the larger if it has evolved to the right of the main-sequence, thereby increasing its size appropriately. But observation shows that the brighter star still lies on or near the main-sequence. How is this possible? How is it possible to explain an evolutionary development of the faint star such as is indicated in Fig. 42 without the bright star also evolving?

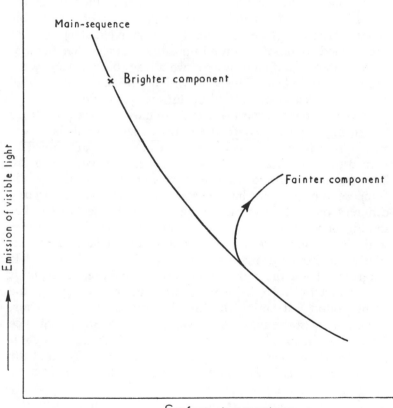

FIG. 42.   Improbable evolution of an Algol binary.

Our general evolutionary picture can be reconciled with the pattern of evolution shown in Fig. 42 only if the bright star is much younger than the fainter one. This is a possibility to be considered. Reference to Fig. 32 shows that it would be possible to pick out two stars from the solar neighbourhood, one a young main-sequence star about 100 times brighter than the Sun and the other an older sub-giant. The combination of two such stars into a double system would yield an Algol-type binary. But is it plausible to suppose that a double system could originate through a random combination of stars from entirely different age groups, particularly double systems in which the two stars are very close together as they are in the Algol binaries? All the indications of the theory of how double systems originate (to be discussed in a later chapter) are that such a mode of origin is quite impossible. The evidence is that the two stars of a double system are always born at closely the same time and place. This view which I think is shared by all astronomers leaves us with an evolutionary paradox.

Either we must discard our evolutionary picture (and there are so many points where it fits the observational data that such a step is scarcely to be thought of) or we are forced to regard the Algol systems as the seat of some singular process. The tracing of this process is a matter for detective work. Suppose to begin with that the stars of a binary system occupy different places on the main-sequence. Suppose further that the higher star is not more than about 400 times the brightness of the Sun, so that we can apply our general ideas of an evolution away from the main-sequence to the right in the H-R diagram. Then the star higher up the main-sequence must be the first to evolve. We have the situation of Fig. 43, the points B and F denoting the initial positions of the two stars.

Now as the star initially at F evolves from the main-sequence it increases in size. And for a binary in which the two component stars are very close together this has the effect that the star B soon finds itself inside the evolving star: rather as we imagine that the inner planets Mercury, Venus, and possibly the Earth may come to lie one day inside an enormously distended Sun. But whereas a distended Sun would readily gobble up such a tiny body as the Earth, the star evolving from F does not gobble up the star B. The situation is reversed: the material of the distended star is gobbled up by B. This produces an interesting situation, as we shall now see.

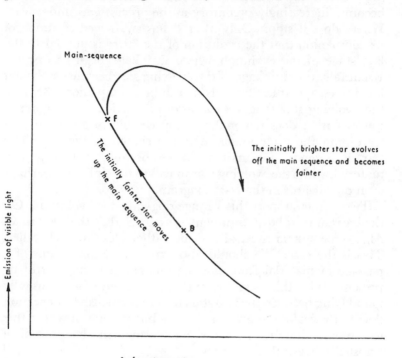

FIG. 43. Evolution of an Algol binary by interchange of material.

It will be recalled that evolution away from the main-sequence is produced by the helium core coming to contain an increasing proportion of the material of a star. We have thought so far of this happening through hydrogen being converted into helium in the deep interior and through the helium core growing steadily in consequence. There is a second way in which the proportionate importance of the core can be increased however—by taking hydrogen away from the outside of a star; and this is just what gobbling up by B does. So gobbling up by B, instead of sending the evolving companion back towards the main-sequence actually fosters the evolution, tending rather to promote the swelling than to hinder it. And as the evolving star swells, the star B takes up more and more material. Thus B, initially the more sedate of the two stars, becomes increasingly predatory as the process gets under way. Where does it stop? Only after B has swallowed so much of its companion that the evolution of the latter is pushed to the late stage of the evolution where shrinkage begins to occur. Eventually the shrinkage of the evolving star becomes sufficient for it to escape at last from its marauding companion. Because the evolving star thus loses a large proportion of its material the evolution does not make it appreciably brighter, so that we obtain the evolutionary diagram shown in Fig. 43. The star B ascends the main-sequence because it has gained material, while the evolving star moves to the right and perhaps even downwards in the H-R diagram.

Two points support this strange dog-eats-dog evolution. On the basis of the above argument we expect that the stars in an Algol-type system must always be rather close to each other. This is the case. We should also expect that some signs of a passage of material from one star to another should still be present. It is I think significant that a reservoir of gas is usually found lying between the two stars in these systems. Observation does not reveal the source of this gas but it is not unreasonable to suppose that it represents a late stage in the process of transfer between the two stars.

Another curious issue may be raised: what will happen when the now brighter component begins its own evolution away from the main-sequence? It may be expected to swell and to engulf the companion that it robbed so unfeelingly in the past. What will then happen almost defies the power of analysis. There is the possibility that the predatory star will be forced to make amends for its former behaviour by returning material to the (at present) fainter star. In the interests of cosmic justice it is to be hoped that this happens but whether it does or not is unsure.

It is also interesting to consider how evolution proceeds in the case where the component stars are not close together as in the Algol systems but are widely distant from each other. Because of the wide separation there is then no question of the initially fainter star coming to steal material from the evolving star. Instead we have a development illustrated in Fig. 44. Here we have the possibility of a double-system that contains the main-sequence star F, together with a star that may lie high in the diagram near C. Such systems may be very spectacular.

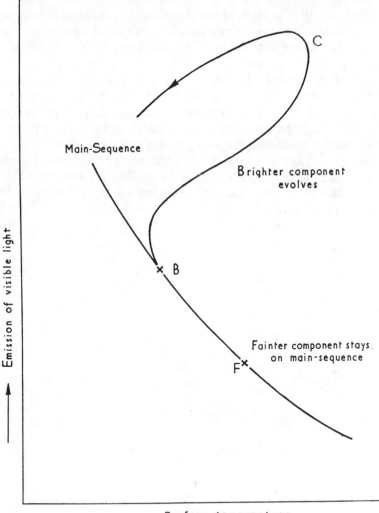

Main-Sequence

Brighter component
evolves

× B

Fainter component stays.
on main-sequence

F×

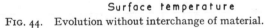

Surface temperature

FIG. 44.   Evolution without interchange of material.

201

Suppose F is 100 times brighter than the Sun and B is initially 300 times brighter than the Sun. When evolution has taken the star initially at B to C we have the combination of F with a very large red star about 300,000 times brighter than the Sun. Such systems are known. A famous case is the system of VV Cephei.

Just one final remark about Algol itself. Algol has four component stars, not two. But two of the four have no relevance at all to the above discussion. The two important stars are the ones we have considered—it is these that serve as the prototype of the Algol binaries. They are close to each other, moving completely around one another in 2 days, 20 hours, 49 minutes. The other components lie afar off, the third moves around the important inner two stars in a time of 1.873 years and the fourth lies so far away that it takes rather more than 188 years to move around the other three. Imagine the planets Mercury, Jupiter, and Pluto to be puffed up into veritable stars: the solar system would then have a mild similarity to the amazing system of Algol.

CHAPTER TWELVE

Exploding Stars

Chandrasekhar's limit

The ultimate course of evolution described in Chapter 9 is impossible for a star with mass greater than Chandrasekhar's limit. It will be recalled that in the last stages of this evolution the pressure balance was maintained by degeneracy effects, by pressure developed through the sheer squashing together of material. When degeneracy thus took over control the star was able to cool off. It was the cooling off that took the evolutionary track downwards in the H-R diagram into the territory of the white dwarfs.

But the singular condition will also be recalled that the masses of the stars had to be less than 1.44 times the Sun—less than Chandrasekhar's limit, otherwise degeneracy could not maintain the pressure balance. Our present concern is to discuss the case where the mass lies above Chandrasekhar's limit. The trail of investigation then leads to thoroughly remarkable conclusions.

We start by noticing that if the pressure balance cannot be maintained by degeneracy then the only alternative means for maintaining it is by ordinary high temperature pressure, of the sort operative in the Sun. So if the pressure balance is to be maintained the star can never cool off. And because cooling off cannot occur the star is unable to reduce the outflow of energy from the hot interior—energy must always flow from a higher temperature to a lower temperature, the precise mode of flow being irrelevant to the present argument. It would seem then that when the mass exceeds Chandrasekhar's limit the star cannot succeed in ever reducing to any really important degree the energy that flows out from its central regions to the surface, and which is thence radiated away into space.

Now where does this energy come from? How does the star manage to balance its energy budget? Nuclear reactions can supply energy for a limited time only, for the reason that every nuclear fuel, whether hydrogen, helium, or some other, has only a limited lifetime—sooner or later it becomes exhausted. Hence we cannot appeal to nuclear energy to maintain the energy balance indefinitely. The one source of energy that we can always call on, however, is the gravitational energy that is released by a shrinkage of the star. Does the star, after exhausting its nuclear energy, then maintain itself by an indefinite shrinkage? Does it go on contracting endlessly? Does it contract down to a size less than the Earth and then to sizes smaller still—perhaps only a few miles in diameter, or even less?

These queries are so remarkable that we may ask whether the argument leading to them is really inevitable. Is there any loophole? The answer is that the above argument is inevitable unless we dispense with the condition that the pressure balance be maintained. The penalty for dispensing with this condition is catastrophic however; for if the pressure balance is not maintained, the star must either collapse catastrophically or blow up catastrophically.

It follows that the fate of stars with masses greater than Chandrasekhar's limit is certainly most curious, whichever alternative they elect to follow. One possibility is that they shrink indefinitely, the other that a fantastic catastrophe occurs. Which? Our conclusion, reached below after much detailed discussion, will be in favour of a catastrophe—or rather of two catastrophes, first a catastrophic collapse, then a catastrophic explosion. The explosion turns out to solve the star's problem, for it removes so much material that the mass is brought below Chandrasekhar's limit. When this happens degeneracy can take over control of the pressure balance, the star can cool off, and evolution can proceed tranquilly to the white-dwarf state, just as in the case of the stars that were studied in Chapter 9.

Nuclear fuels

For a considerable way along the evolutionary track of a star, say of mass 3 times the Sun, things proceed in much the way we have described already in Chapter 9. We expect hydrogen-burning to take the star along the part A to B to C of its track (see Fig. 33). During these stages hydrogen-burning causes the core to grow. Eventually near C the release of

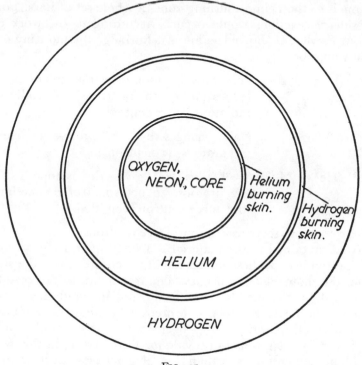

FIG. 45.

gravitational energy through the addition of helium to the core becomes sufficient to heat up the core to the stage at which helium-burning reactions start up—this occurs at a temperature somewhat higher than 100 million degrees. We then have a double-source star, a star in which energy is produced by nuclear reactions in two quite distinct ways, by helium-burning near the centre and by hydrogen-burning farther out. As a result of the helium-burning an oxygen-neon inner core tends to form at the centre of the star, and we then have the sort of internal structure shown in Fig. 45.

It will be seen from Fig. 45 that the helium-burning skin is separated by a helium zone from the outer hydrogen zone. This suggests that hydrogen is never mixed with the products of helium-burning, a view that is probably largely correct. But if even a small quantity of hydrogen were to penetrate through to the helium-burning zone, a whole set of important subsidiary reactions would occur. According to the work of W. A. Fowler, G. Burbidge, and M. Burbidge the most important would be

Ne^{20} (p, γ) Na^{21} Ne^{20} plus a proton gives the isotope Na^{21} (11 protons, 10 neutrons) of sodium, radiation being emitted.

Na^{21} (β) Ne^{21} Na^{21} changes by a β process to Ne^{21} (10 protons, 11 neutrons).

Ne^{21} (He^{4},n) Mg^{24} Ne^{21} plus He^{4} gives the isotope Mg^{24} (12 protons, 12 neutrons) of magnesium and a free neutron is emitted.

These reactions serve as a source of free neutrons.

Now contained in the material is a small quantity of metals of the iron group, these metals having been present in the star from the moment of its origin. The free neutrons are readily absorbed by the metals, the effect being to build them into heavier and heavier elements. Moreover the absorption of even a quite small quantity of hydrogen by the Ne^{20} would supply sufficient free neutrons to provide for the building in this way of all the elements heavier than zinc, of which arsenic, strontium silver, tin, barium, gold, platinum, lead, and uranium are examples. It is a curious reflection that but for the occurrence of these reactions inside stars there might have been no gold or uranium in the Earth; and this would have meant no atomic energy, no nuclear weapons, and a changed economy for S. Africa.

So far the evolution differs importantly from the case of a star with a mass less than Chandrasekhar's limit only in that much more hydrogen is left in the outer envelope at the moment that helium-burning starts up.

A further important difference arises, however, as more and

more helium is burnt. As the oxygen-neon core increases in mass towards Chandrasekhar's limit an important shrinkage takes place (since the pressure balance in the core can no longer be maintained by degeneracy).

We therefore visualise the star as adopting the structure of Fig. 45 and its innermost regions as shrinking slowly in a time of a few million years. As the star shrinks its internal temperature rises steadily, from 300 million degrees upwards. Now although the oxygen and neon are quite inert at 300 million degrees they do not remain inert if the temperature is raised sufficiently. With rising temperature new nuclear reactions must start up sooner or later. An analysis of the matter shows that the first important process to occur happens to the Ne^{20}, probably at a temperature of about 600 million degrees.

The neon is destroyed and magnesium is produced in its stead. This neon-burning supplies the star with a further temporary phase in which the energy balance is maintained in the inner regions by the nuclear reactions. The chemistry of the star is now even more complicated than before. We can distinguish the four zones of Fig. 46, the innermost region now consisting mainly of the elements oxygen and magnesium, with the neon being burned; the next region with oxygen and neon; then a helium zone, and lastly an outer hydrogen skin. It is possible that some degree of mixing takes place between the different zones, but present-day theory is too undeveloped to decide this with any definiteness.

When the inner parts of the star run out of neon the process is repeated once again: the inner parts shrink and the internal temperature rises still further until some new nuclear reaction is set up. The next phase is one of oxygen-burning. The reactions that occur in this phase are so intricate that instead of describing them in detail we shall simply mention their results. The main effect is to build silicon, the essential constituent of the rocks of the Earth. But many other elements are also built up by the complex reactions that accompany the oxygen-burning. The most abundant of these other elements are sulphur, aluminium, calcium, and argon, but other elements are also produced at this stage—phosphorus, chlorine, and potassium. The largest nuclei so built up contain about 40 particles; for example Ca⁴⁰ the isotope of calcium with 20 protons and 20 neutrons. The temperature at which all this occurs is in the neighbourhood of 1,500,000,000 degrees.

By this stage the chemical structure of the star is still further

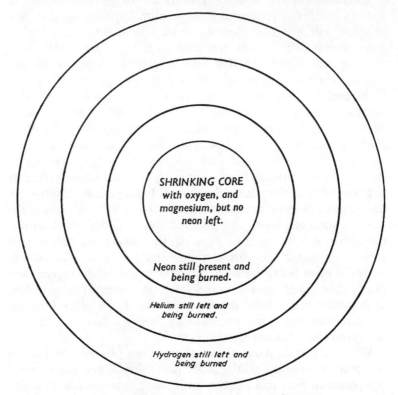

SHRINKING CORE
with oxygen, and magnesium, but no neon left.

Neon still present and being burned.

Helium still left and being burned.

Hydrogen still left and being burned

Fig. 46.   Schematic drawing of a four-zoned star.

increased in complexity to six main zones—an innermost region with magnesium, aluminium, silicon, phosphorus, sulphur, chlorine, argon, potassium and calcium and with oxygen being burnt; a second zone with oxygen, sodium, magnesium, and with neon being burnt; a third with oxygen, neon and with carbon being burnt; a fourth zone with oxygen, carbon and neon, and with helium being burnt; a fifth zone of helium alone; and lastly an outermost skin of hydrogen. Once again some mixing may occur between the zones.

When eventually the oxygen-burning phase ends in the inner regions due to exhaustion of oxygen, the shrinkage is once again resumed. With the rising temperature a new effect becomes increasingly more important. At temperatures in excess of 1,000 million degrees the radiation inside a star is of the extremely short wavelength variety known as γ-rays. The intensity is also very great as may be judged from the fact that the pressure exerted by the radiation amounts to some 100,000,000,000,000,000 lbs. per square inch (compare with the pressure of the Earth's atmosphere which is only 15 lbs. per square inch). Now under these conditions radiation begins to strip particles out of the atomic nuclei. This process becomes extremely powerful when the temperature rises to about 2,000 million degrees (this knocking-out of particles from the nuclei should not be confused with the knocking-out of electrons from an atom—the latter is a comparatively trivial process, no atom has any electrons permanently attached to it in these stars).

This knocking-out of particles from the nuclei at 2,000 million degrees means that no nucleus is then stable. Particles get knocked out of them all, even out of such a tightly bound nucleus as that of silicon. This is not equivalent to saying that the nuclei are entirely broken down into individual neutrons and protons, however, for a particle that gets knocked out of one nucleus recombines with another; for instance a proton that gets detached from a nucleus does not remain detached for very long: it quickly gets recombined with some other nucleus.

Perhaps it will appear surprising that it should be possible to calculate what happens in such a complicated situation with any degree of definiteness but this can in fact be done, once the temperature becomes high enough (above about 2,000 million degrees) for the knocking-out and the recombination processes to become very frequent. This allows a method of averaging to be used and the resulting simplification makes the calculations straightforward.

The outcome of the calculations is also rather surprising. Instead of the nuclei being broken down the reverse situation applies, heavier nuclei are built up. The calculations show that in the temperature range from 2 to 5 thousand million degrees the previously existing nuclei—magnesium, aluminium, silicon, phosphorus, sulphur, chlorine, argon, and calcium mainly—are almost entirely changed to a quite different set of nuclei—nuclei of titanium, vanadium, chromium, manganese, iron, cobalt, nickel, copper, and zinc. Of these latter iron is much the most abundant, followed by nickel, chromium, manganese and cobalt, exactly in the order of abundance found in nature.

The change of composition from the 'silicon group' of elements to the 'iron group' supplies energy, so once again the inner parts of the star have a source to draw on. Not until this source becomes exhausted (i.e. not until the silicon group is entirely converted into the iron group) does the shrinkage of the innermost parts of the star continue and not until then does the temperature of these regions rise above about 2,000 million degrees. When the conversion to the iron group is eventually completed and shrinkage of the central regions starts again the chemical structure of the star has become most complex: we can now distinguish seven general zones as indicated in Fig. 47. In the inner region we have the iron-group of elements. In region 2 where the temperature of the material has not yet reached 2,000 million degrees we still have the silicon group of elements; in region 3 the temperature is lower and oxygen-burning is still incomplete; in region 4 neon-burning is still incomplete; in region 5 carbon-burning is still incomplete; in region 6 helium is still present; and the seventh zone is the outermost hydrogen skin. It is seen therefore that the star contains all the elements from helium, carbon, oxygen, neon, etc., up to iron, cobalt, nickel, copper, and zinc but with various groups resident in different parts of the star which now is indeed like an onion with skins of quite different materials.

Nuclear refrigeration

At this point of the evolution the stage is set for catastrophe. The nuclear reactions occurring in the iron core of the star introduce a new and increasingly drastic source of energy loss from the star. The relevant reactions are the β processes that change protons into neutrons. Now in β processes neutrinos are emitted and the energy carried by them is lost from the star. This source of loss becomes acute for temperatures above 2,000 million degrees, when it exceeds the loss from the outflow

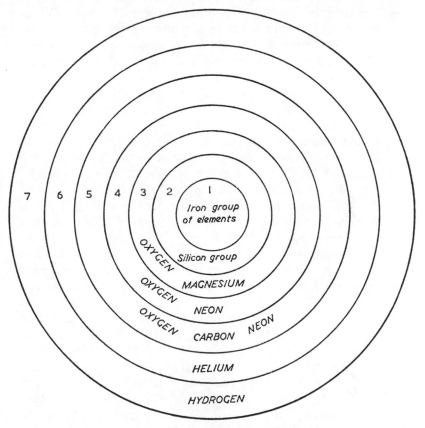

FIG. 47. Schematic drawing of a seven-zoned star.

of radiation. The star is thereby obliged to shrink faster in order to supply the energy required to make good what is being lost through the neutrinos. Gravitation still supplies enough energy, however, both to make good this loss and to maintain the pressure balance. So the catastrophe is held off for the time being. But in maintaining the pressure balance the temperature has to rise higher and higher, and this only increases the rate of loss through the emission of neutrinos. The star is now in desperate straits. It is forced to shrink faster and faster in order to supply the rapidly increasing drain on its energy. When the internal temperature has risen to 3,000 million degrees shrinkage becomes appreciable in a year, as compared with the former time of millions of years. When the internal temperature has risen to 4,000 million degrees, shrinkage is appreciable in only a month—and the shrinkage is even more rapid than this for still higher temperatures.

Yet the neutrino loss is not the cause of the final disaster. The hard-pressed star now has to face an even more inexorable process. It is this that applies the *coup de grâce*. It has been explained above that the knocking-out of particles from the nuclei and their recombination with other nuclei produces a situation in which the general abundances of the nuclei can be calculated with a considerable degree of accuracy. It was on the basis of these calculations that the 'iron group' of elements was said to be built up from the 'silicon group'. This was for a temperature of 2,000 million degrees. Now as the temperature rises the 'iron group' of elements continues to be maintained until the temperature reaches about 5,000 million degrees. At this temperature an extremely sharp change sets in. Instead of the material of the innermost part of the star continuing to belong to the iron group a dramatic change of composition occurs. The material changes back into helium. This is an unexpected situation. We have followed the material of the inside of the star as it changed, first from hydrogen to helium, then from helium into carbon, oxygen, and neon, then from carbon, neon, and oxygen (in that order) into elements ranging from sodium to calcium—the silicon group, then from the silicon group into the iron group. Now we have a reversion to helium at a temperature of about 5,000 million degrees. Astonishing as this may be there can be no doubt at all about its correctness. The calculations depend on very well known and reliable principles and the calculations leave no element of uncertainty—the material must change almost entirely into helium if the temperature rises to a value in the neighbourhood of 5,000 million degrees.

The collapse

The inner regions of the star are now faced by a crisis. After drawing steadily on the energy yielded by the conversion of helium into heavier elements in successive stages the star is suddenly called on to pay all the energy back, for to convert the 'iron group' back into helium requires just as much energy as the star received while the building processes were going on. After living for millions of years on borrowed energy the star is suddenly called on to pay back its borrowings, and without delay too. Naturally the star calls on its assets, namely on its gravitational field to foot the bill—the inner part of the star shrinks. But the demand for energy is now so acute that the energy released by the shrinkage is not sufficient any more both to foot the energy bill and to raise the temperature sufficiently to maintain the pressure balance. What happens can be calculated, the paying back of energy must proceed at such a rate that the pressure balance cannot be maintained. We saw in Chapter 8 that if the pressure balance were to fail inside the Sun then a catastrophic collapse would occur in about half an hour. The situation is even more extreme in the case of our star. The long shrinkage of the star over its extensive evolution has greatly increased the density of the material in the inner regions—a match-box full of material taken from the star's centre must contain between 100 and 1,000 tons, and at this sort of density the collapse is much swifter than in the case of the Sun. The collapse takes place in about a second. No human bankrupt has ever collapsed so dramatically.

The explosion

But the star manages to make a remarkable recovery from disaster. Lack of energy in the innermost parts of the star leads to an excess of energy in the outer parts. The collapse of the inner parts removes the pressure that has hitherto held up the outer parts, just as the collapse of the inside of the Earth would remove the support of the outer crust which would then be pulled catastrophically inwards by the Earth's gravitational

213

field. So in the star there is a catastrophic infall of the outer parts as well as of the inner parts. The infall of the outer parts is limited, however, by a further remarkable situation that arises. Infall releases a supply of gravitational energy and this causes the temperature of the outer material to rise. A rise of temperature hastens the nuclear reactions that are still taking place in the outer material and since the reactions in the outer parts of the star are still of an energy-producing kind, the effect if sufficiently drastic must be to produce an excess of energy on the outside of the star.

Calculation shows that a rise of temperature to 3,000 million degrees in the oxygen-burning zone, for instance, leads to an extremely rapid release of energy. The whole of the energy derivable from oxygen-burning is released in a time of about a second, this being comparable with the time of collapse of the star. The implication is that an explosion occurs in the outer regions of the star. The situation is in many ways similar to the explosion of a nova but the present explosion is on a vastly greater scale.

When the amount of material in the outer part of the star is specified the amount of energy released can be worked out. For an amount equal to the mass of the Sun the energy released by the nuclear reactions in only a second of time is as much as the nuclear reactions inside the Sun yield in about 1,000 million years. This gives a graphic idea of the tremendously explosive effects of the nuclear reactions that promote the oxygen-burning, neon-burning, etc., when the temperature is suddenly raised by the gravitational energy released in the sudden collapse of the star. It is the sudden rise of temperature promoted by the collapse of the inside of the star that triggers the explosive effects.

The amount of energy released is sufficient to endow the exploding outer parts of the star with velocities of 2,000 to 3,000 kilometres per second, and is sufficient to enable the star to radiate at 200 million times the rate of the Sun for a time of about a fortnight. Exploding stars with exactly these properties are observed to occur. They are called supernovae to distinguish them from the much milder outbursts of ordinary novae. For comparison an ordinary nova ejects a mass of material that is only about one ten-thousandth part of the mass of the Sun, whereas a supernova ejects an amount of material that is comparable with the total mass of the Sun itself. Not only this but a supernova explosion is some 10,000 times brighter than an ordinary nova explosion. Although there are these big differences between novae and supernovae the two types of outburst have one important point in common, the velocity of ejection of material. This is probably because both types of explosion arise from an uncontrolled release of energy by nuclear reactions that yield to each unit quantity of material much the same amount of energy in the two cases. The supernova differs so much from the nova not because each unit quantity of material releases much more energy but because much more material is concerned in the supernova case. This can be seen from the difference in the amount of material ejected and in the differences in the amount of light emitted in the explosion which are both some 10,000 times greater in the supernova.

Plate XXIX shows material that was ejected from a super-nova. This supernova occurred in A.D. 1054. Its occurrence is without mention in the European records of the period but it was very carefully documented by Chinese astronomers from whose writings Baade has been able to reconstruct the general characteristics of the explosion and to show that these characteristics are extremely similar to those of supernovae that have been observed in our own day (of which more will be mentioned below). The gases of the Crab Nebula, as the gaseous mass of Plate XXIX is called, are found to be still streaming outwards with a velocity of about 1,000 kilometres per second, a rather slow rate for a supernova explosion. Since it is now 900 years since the outburst was first observed and the gases have been moving outwards for this length of time at the speed of 1,000 kilometres per second, it is clear that they must have expanded quite a way by now. A simple calculation shows that the gaseous cloud of Plate XXIX must be about 2 parsecs across.

This raises an interesting point. Sometimes in particular cases astronomical distances can be measured in a way that differs from the two main methods discussed in Chapter 10.

Here we have such a case. Knowing the general velocity of expansion and knowing the age of the Crab Nebula—about 900 years, we have seen that a simple calculation gives the size of the nebula. But if we know the true size of any object its distance can readily be estimated from its apparent size—this is pretty well the way that the human eye judges distance. It can be seen from Fig. 48 how this method works. Let P be an observer and O some object. Then the apparent size of O is given by the angle made by the object at P. This angle not only depends on the size of the object but on its distance from P. Evidently a measurement of the angle subtended by an object, say by the Crab Nebula, will tell us the distance if the real size of the object is known but not otherwise. It is impossible for the eye to judge distance on a uniform snowfield

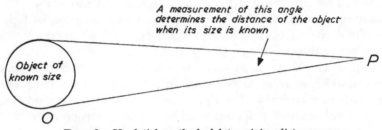

FIG. 48. Yardstick method of determining distance.

for instance because there are no objects of known size that can be used as a reference. Mountaineers are very conscious of just this point. The whole problem of judging the scale of a mountain depends on knowing the true size of various irregularities—of boulders, rock pinnacles, snow slopes, etc. Then the distance can be judged from the apparent size of the irregularities, just as the distance of the Crab Nebula is judged. The distance of the Crab Nebula turns out to be about 1,000 parsecs, a distance roughly 4,000,000,000,000,000 greater than the scale of Mt. Everest, the Earth's highest mountain.

This method of judging distances may be added to our two previous methods. We may call it the method of the standard yard-stick. Just as the method of the standard head-light depends on the observation of a source of light of known intrinsic brightness, so the method of the standard yard-stick depends on the observation of an extended object of known size. The method of the standard yard-stick has not so far been much used in astronomy but there are indications that for the purpose of determining very great distances, distances of galaxies at many millions of parsecs, the standard yard-stick method may ultimately turn out to be of very great value indeed.

The next question concerning the general problem of super-novae and its relation to the Crab Nebula is whether any remnants of the star that exploded in A.D. 1054 can now be found. Such a remnant is to be expected since it seems unlikely that the outburst, violent as it was, can have been sufficient to destroy the entire star. Of the several stars found in the neighbourhood of the centre of the Crab Nebula it is significant that one is of a highly peculiar type, so that it seems natural to associate this star with the supernova of A.D. 1054.

The expectation that a stellar remnant is left behind after the explosion prompts the remark that any remnant must proceed eventually to the white-dwarf state. The explosion serves to rid the star of sufficient material to bring its mass below Chandrasekhar's limit. Evolution can then proceed exactly as in the final phases of the stars that were discussed in Chapter 10. There are several very notable cases of white dwarfs that are probably remnants from supernovae. The star Sirius is a member of double-system, its companion being a white dwarf with mass little below that of the Sun. The star Procyon also has a white dwarf companion. Although Sirius and Procyon are now the dominant components of their respective systems at one time they must have been the inferior members. But their spectacular companions, being initially the more massive and higher on the main-sequences, have completed their evolution. Sirius and Procyon are now accompanied by dying stars with nothing left of their former splendour—and so all prodigal stars end.

The fate of the missing supergiants

Our evolutionary picture now possesses an important new development that enables us to modify the hypothesis made in the preceding chapter. Fig. 49 is a reproduction of Fig. 33. We make the better hypothesis: that a star proceeds along the evolutionary loop of Fig. 49 only so long as the mass of hydrogen that is consumed does not appreciably exceed Chandrasekhar's limit. When the consumed hydrogen exceeds this amount the star becomes shattered by a supernova explosion in accordance with the processes discussed above.

It is important to realise that two quite different criteria are concerned here. The extent of the evolution along the loop of Fig. 49 is determined by the fraction of the mass of the star that comes to reside in the core. The relevant fractions are those marked in Fig. 49: it will be seen, for instance, that the star evolves to the highest point of the loop when about 40 per cent of its mass lies in the core. The explosion point, on the other hand, is determined by the total mass in the core, quite regardless of what fraction of the star this happens to be. Evidently a star of mass 1.5 times the Sun will not explode until almost the whole mass comes to reside in the core. Hence such a star does not explode until it reaches a late stage of the evolutionary loop. But a star of mass 15 times the Sun will explode on our hypothesis when only about 10 per cent of its hydrogen has been consumed. Such a star would therefore be disintegrated at almost the beginning of the evolutionary track. For a star to evolve appreciably to the right of the main-sequence its mass should not exceed about 6 times the Sun.

This would seem to clear up the mystery of the missing supergiants. It will be recalled from the previous chapter that there is strong evidence to show that when the starting point A of Fig. 49 is sufficiently high on the main-sequence the star does not evolve along a looped evolutionary track. We see now how this can come about—because the evolutionary development is interrupted by disintegration. We see why the H-R diagram of young open clusters may be of the form shown in Fig. 37, without any stars far to the right of the main-sequence. The most massive stars of the cluster after evolving a little way from the main-sequence burst and strip off their remaining hydrogen, so that the stellar remnant takes up a new position in the diagram—a position en route for the white dwarfs.

It is also to be expected that stars may explode when they are partly along their evolutionary tracks. The situation in such a cluster as Praesepe might be taken as evidence of this. From Fig. 39 it is seen that the beginning of the evolution from the main-sequence occurs in this cluster but none of the later

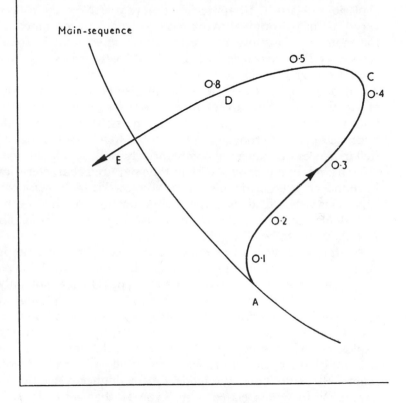

Fig. 49. The evolutionary hypothesis.

stages of evolution are found. We might offer as an explanation that the evolution proceeds to the point occupied by the last stars and that explosion occurs there.

The two types of supernova

Our ideas can be put to an interesting test. If it is correct that stars explode when the mass of the core exceeds Chandrasekhar's limit, supernovae may be expected to occur in cases where the total mass only slightly exceeds the limit—these are cases where explosion occurs in the late stages of the evolutionary track. Now such cases will differ from the explosions occurring in appreciably more massive stars in that very little of the original hydrogen will be left unconsumed at the moment of explosion. We therefore expect that in some cases very little hydrogen will be found in the gases expelled from a supernova. These cases are not likely to be so rare as might be thought at first sight, because stars with a mass say of 1.5 times the Sun are of much more frequent occurrence than stars with say 15 times the solar mass; so that although hydrogen-poor supernovae can occur only in a narrow range of stellar masses the range is a comparatively well populated one.

Two kinds of supernovae with just the required characteristics have indeed been distinguished by Minkowski: hydrogen-poor supernovae described as Type I supernovae, and hydrogen-abundant supernovae described as of Type II. The Crab Nebula seems to be of Type I.

Another difference to be expected between the two types is that the energy released in Type I should be less than in Type II, since the energy released in the Type II case not only contains contributions from an oxygen-burning explosion, a neon-burning explosion, and a carbon-burning explosion, as the Type I supernovae do, but also a hydrogen-burning explosion—which the Type I supernovae do not. It is uncertain whether this theoretical prediction is correct or not. There seems to be some tendency for higher velocities of expansion to be associated with Type II than with Type I, which would be in accordance with the prediction. But the visual brightness of a Type II supernova is actually less than of a Type I supernova. This may not be real contradiction, however, for the observed brightnesses refer only to light that falls in the visual range of wavelengths. There is a strong indication of a large ultra-violet emission in the case of Type II but not of Type I. It is therefore conceivable that the total radiation emitted by a Type II supernova is indeed greater than the emission from a Type I supernova.

The origin of the elements

We have seen that along the evolutionary track of a star various chemical elements are produced by nuclear reactions in the interior—more precisely all the elements and their isotopes ranging from carbon to zinc. Not only this but it can be shown that these various elements are produced in much the same abundances relative to each other as they are found in the Earth and in stars like the Sun. This suggests that the elements are built inside stars.

A difficulty that might previously have been raised to this idea now disappears. Formerly it might have been argued that to produce materials deep inside a particular type of star was scarcely a solution to the origin of the chemical elements, since the materials so produced would simply stay put inside their parent stars. But we see now that the very stars in which the elements originate are just the ones that come to scatter their materials into space through the supernova process. We can see this scattering process going on in such a case as that of the Crab Nebula (Plate XXIX). What eventually will happen to the material of the Crab Nebula? As it spreads out farther and farther it will become more tenuous. Some of the material will eventually impinge on the normal clouds of gas that lie between the stars (Plate XI). The material from the supernova will then become entangled with the normal interstellar gas. Thereafter it will be available for condensation into new stars. Some of the material from the Crab may fail to impinge on any interstellar gas, however. On account of its high speed we may expect such material to escape entirely from our Galaxy and to pass out into the realms of space between the galaxies.

The suggestion that by this process the Universe builds all materials other than hydrogen can be given some immediate quantitative support. The fact that the weight of hydrogen in the Sun is something like 100 times greater than the weight of the elements from carbon to zinc suggests that about one per cent of the interstellar gas (the Sun having formed from interstellar gas) must have been derived from supernovae. Has there been a sufficient number of supernovae to explain such a total amount of non-hydrogenic material?

The total quantity of the interstellar gas is not known with any great certainty. Perhaps a fair estimate would be about 20,000 million times the mass of the Sun—if all the interstellar gas were made into bodies like the Sun there would be something like 20,000 million of them. The elements from carbon to zinc comprise about one per cent of the total, giving a mass of about 200 million times the Sun in these elements. We must now compare this estimate with the material thrown off by all the supernovae that have occurred since our Galaxy was formed some 5,000 million years ago. The main contribution is probably derived from supernovae of Type II. Now we have seen that supernovae of Type II come from stars with masses greater than about twice the Sun. We can estimate the number of such stars. About 1 in 300 of the stars found in the solar neighbourhood have a mass greater than twice the Sun. Reckoning the total available population of stars as 30,000 million this would give 100 million for the number of Type II supernovae. And if on the average each supernova distributed two solar masses of elements ranging from carbon to zinc, we obtain the required quantity of material. The agreement is as good as can be expected in view of the uncertainties of the calculation.

Our discussion of the origin of the chemical elements is incomplete in that we have referred explicity only to elements whose nuclei contain a sum total of protons and neutrons that range from 12 to about 66. Of the elements with numbers less than 12, hydrogen is the primeval element and helium is amply provided for, since helium must be ejected from supernovae along with the group from carbon to zinc. The remaining elements with less than 12 nuclear particles are lithium, beryllium, and boron. The situation is still not entirely satisfactory for these three elements, although it is possible to understand in some measure how they are produced.

The elements with more than 66 protons and neutrons, gallium to uranium, are present on the Earth and in the stars only in very small abundances. Thus the combined abundances of the 62 elements from gallium to uranium amount to only about one-hundredth of one per cent of the combined abundances of the 25 elements from carbon to zinc. Consequently the formation of these 'upper' elements must be a somewhat marginal process. One possible explanation of their origin lies in the processes that were mentioned on page 206.

Let us now return to the materials added by the supernovae to the interstellar gas. A point was left over from our discussion of this process that now requires comment. It is easy to see how elements other than hydrogen come to be present in stars that are condensing at the present time—these are just the elements distributed by past exploding stars. But how about stars that were formed very early in the history of the Galaxy, before very many supernovae had added their quota of elements to the interstellar gas? Where did such stars get their elements from? A partial answer is that the oldest stars contain only very low concentrations of elements other than hydrogen and helium: the sub-dwarfs and the stars of the globular clusters possess concentrations that are only about one-twentieth of the concentration in the Sun. This observation lends powerful support to the idea that the proportion of 'heavy' elements in the interstellar gas has increased steadily during the lifetime of our Galaxy and that the younger a star is, the greater its content of 'heavy' elements should be. The observation of the deficiency in the present respect of the old stars indeed goes far towards establishing the general correctness of the evolutionary picture described above. But should not the very first stars have contained nothing but hydrogen, without even a trace of other elements? This is a deep question that we shall defer to a later chapter. We end the present discussion by noticing that while such stars are significantly deficient in heavy elements there seem to be no stars in which heavy elements are entirely absent. Whether or not this is in disagreement with our general evolutionary picture we must leave over for a subsequent settlement.

The material of the Earth

We have now come a long way from the discussion of the opening chapters. Starting with the Earth, then with planets, then with the Sun, then with stars like the Sun, then with stars not so like the Sun, we moved to exploding stars, then to the origin of the chemical elements, and so at last we come back full circle to the Earth, to the origin of the material of the Earth. The rocks of the mantle, the iron of the Earth's core, the objects that we handle in everyday life all were at one time inside a supernova. The carbon, nitrogen, and oxygen inside ourselves were once deep inside a star, inside a particularly spectacular sort of star that scattered its material by explosion into interstellar space where it became available for the process that led to the origin of the Sun and planets.

We spoke at an early stage of the dualistic nature of matter— of atoms and of the different structures that can be built out of atoms. We saw that a structure is something more than the units out of which it is built. An iron atom in a supernova is entirely the same as an iron atom in the cutlery that you use to feed yourself but the structures into which the iron is built are utterly different in the two cases. The ramifications of which matter is capable are truly astonishing. It is fashionable nowadays to use the appellation 'materialist' in a derogatory sense, largely I suppose because it has become a catchword in a war of political ideologies. This apart, the notion that matter is something inert and uninteresting is surely the veriest nonsense. If there is anything more wonderful than matter in the sheer versatility of its behaviour, I have yet to hear tell of it.

Mt. Wilson and Palomar Observatories

XLI—The Cluster of Galaxies in Hydra

These galaxies are so distant that even though they may each contain
100,000,000,000 stars they nevertheless appear fainter than single stars within
our own Galaxy. The latter appear as the hard circular images. The galaxies
appear as faint fuzzy dots near the centre of the picture.

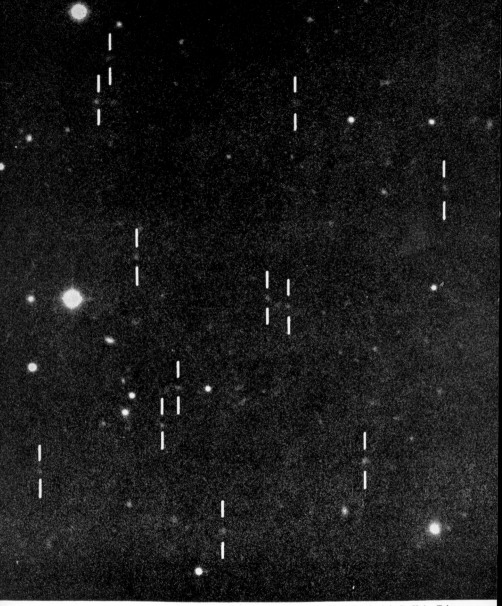

XLII—THE LIMIT TO WHICH MAN CAN REACH OUT INTO SPACE

The bracketing marks show the positions of galaxies near the limit of detecta-
bility. Such galaxies may be 1,000 million parsecs away—in miles this distance
is 20,000,000,000,000,000,000,000, a long step indeed.

XLIII—The 200-inch Hale Telescope

Notice the flight of steps and the door at bottom-centre. These fix the huge
scale of the instrument.

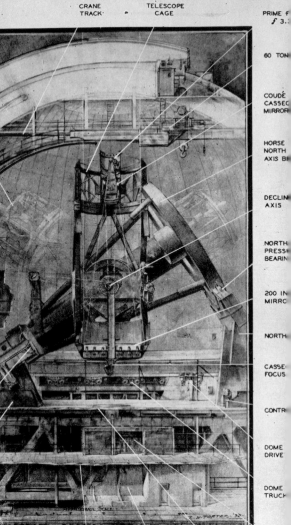

PHANTOM DRAWING SHOWING HOW THE
OBSERVER GETS ON AND OFF THE TUBE

CRANE TRACK

TELESCOPE CAGE

PRIME F
f 3.

PRIME FOCUS PLATFORM

DOME. 137 FEET DIAMETER

DOME SHUTTER 30 FT OPENING

RIGHT ASCENSION DRIVE

PASSENGER ELEVATOR

DOME BALCONIES

COUDÉ FOCUS f 30

CONSTANT TEMPERATURE ROOM

OBSERVATORY WALL

AIR CONDITIONING DUCTS

SOUTH POLAR AXIS BEARING

60 TON

COUDÉ CASSE MIRROR

HORSE NORTH AXIS BE

DECLIN AXIS

NORTH PRESS BEARIN

200 IN MIRRO

NORTH

CASSE FOCUS

CONTR

DOME DRIVE

DOME TRUCK

ELECT CONTF PANEL

SOUTH PIER   GROUND FLOOR   BASE FRAME SUPPORTS   MEZZANINE FLOOR   OFFICES   OBSERVATION FLOOR 5598 FT ABOVE SEA LEV

THE TWO HVNDRED INCH TELESCOPE

XLIV—Diagram of the 200-inch Hale Telescope

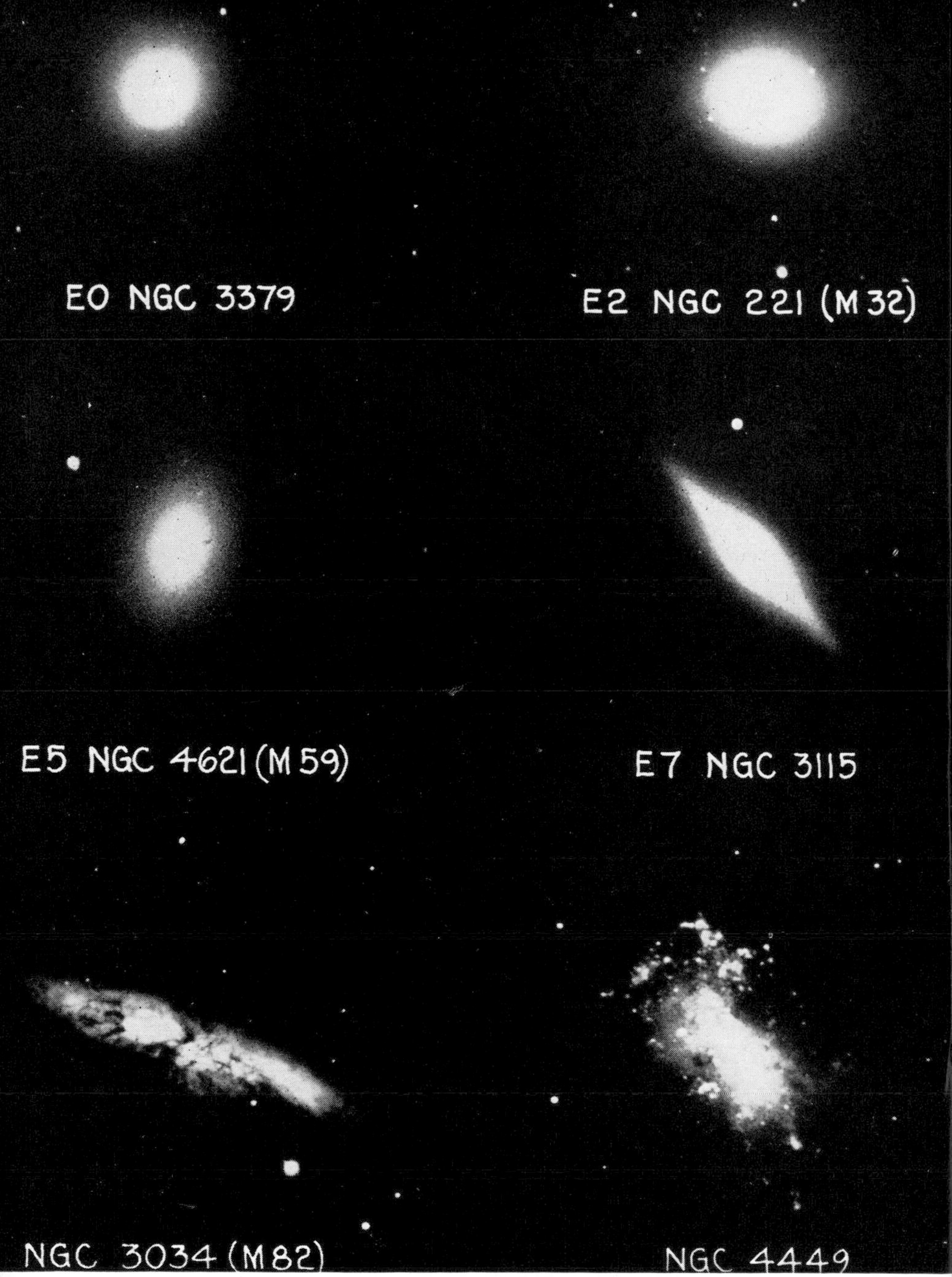

EO NGC 3379

E2 NGC 221 (M 32)

E5 NGC 4621 (M 59)

E7 NGC 3115

NGC 3034 (M 82)

NGC 4449

Mt. Wilson and Palomar Observatories

XLV—ELLIPTICAL AND IRREGULAR GALAXIES

Mt. Wilson and Palomar Observatories

XLVI—The Galaxy NGC 2841

Notice the numerous tight wrappings of the spiral arms of this galaxy.

Mt. Wilson and Palomar Observatories

XLVII—The 'Whirl-pool' Galaxy M 51

A good example of spiral structure. Notice how one of the arms extends as a bridge to the outlying system.

Sa NGC 4594

SBa NGC 2859

Sb NGC 2841

SBb NGC 5850

Sc NGC 5457 (M101)

SBc NGC 7479

Mt. Wilson and Palomar Observatories

XLVIII—THE CLASSIFICATION OF SPIRAL GALAXIES

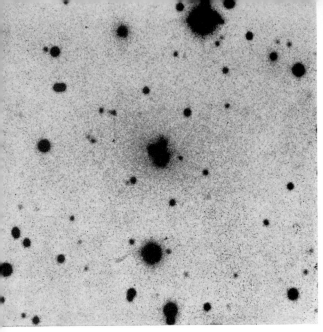

XLIX—THE COLLIDING GALAXIES IN CYGNUS

The fuzzy object in the centre of the photograph represents two distant galaxies in collision with each other, probably two large spiral galaxies. This is the most powerful known transmitter of radio-waves, surely one of the most powerful of the Universe.

Mt. Wilson and Palomar Observatories

L—THE RESOLUTION OF THE ELLIPTICAL GALAXY NGC 147 INTO INDIVIDUAL TYPE II STARS

NGC 147 is one of the small members of the Local Group.

Mt. Wilson and Palomar Observatories

CHAPTER THIRTEEN

The Spiral Arms of Our Own Galaxy

There has scarcely been any necessity so far to explain the inner plan of this book—the outer plan is just the obvious one that every book on astronomy must more or less follow: to start with the Earth and our particular immediate locality in space and then to open up vistas on an increasingly large scale until the problems of the whole Universe come ultimately into focus. The inner plan consists of three parts, three separate movements. In the first part, the part that ended with the previous chapter, we were concerned with discussing planets one at a time and stars one at a time. While it is true that occasionally we referred to groups of stars, to open clusters, globular clusters, and sometimes to whole galaxies, these references were aside from the main discussion. In the second part, the movement that will occupy this and the four succeeding chapters, we shall be concerned with the internal structures of galaxies. Instead of being concerned with stars one at a time we shall now be concerned with galaxies one at a time. Only when we come to the third and final part will we engage with the greatest of all problems, the structure that is built out of the galaxies themselves, the Universe itself. And as in dealing with the stars one at a time we started with the nearest and most familiar star—the Sun, so we shall now start with the nearest and most familiar galaxy—the one in which we live, our own.

Our Galaxy and its twin

Partly because we lie inside it and partly because of the dust that lies along the plane of the Milky Way which acts as a sort of fog, it is not very easy to get a clear idea of what our Galaxy would look like if we could see it as a whole from outside. But painstaking and difficult researches have in recent years shown that our Galaxy, if we could see it from outside, would have a very similar general appearance to that of our sister galaxy in the constellation of Andromeda, the galaxy M 31 shown in Plate XXI. Our Galaxy is somewhat the smaller of the two. The distance of the outer parts of M 31 (the outer parts in Plate XXI, that is) from the centre is about 12,000 parsecs as compared with a corresponding distance of some 8 or 9 thousand parsecs in the case of the Galaxy. We already saw in Chapter 10 that the solar system lies well out from the centre of the Galaxy, at a distance slightly greater than 8,000 parsecs.

Both M 31 and the Galaxy are rotating like great wheels. The solar system partakes in the rotation. We on the Earth are moving along with the Sun and the other planets at a speed of some 225 kilometres per second along a more or less circular orbit around the centre of the Galaxy. It takes us rather more than 200 million years to complete a single circuit of this orbit. Since their formation the Sun and planets have completed about 20 trips round the Galaxy.

I find the craze for speed difficult to understand. To drive a car at 100 m.p.h. seems very unimpressive compared with our everyday speed of some half million m.p.h. around the Galaxy. It may be said that our trip through the Galaxy gives us no impression of speed, whereas driving a car at 100 m.p.h. does. But the impression of speed that we get from driving a car comes from the shaking and lurching of the car. It would be just as effective to be jiggled about in an otherwise stationary box.

Spectral lines and velocities

Our discussion in Chapter 10 described ways and means of determining distances and sizes. But from time to time speeds have also been mentioned, for instance the speed of our motion around the Galaxy. How are motions measured? Before we go further it may be as well to clear up this point. To do so we must go back to the electron clouds that surround the nuclei of ordinary un-ionised atoms. These clouds possess a structure—

or rather they can possess one or other of a number of structures, known as the 'states' of the atom. For the most part the cloud of electrons is to be found in one particular state, namely the state of lowest energy. But every now and then the atom collides with another particle and then the electron cloud may get jolted into one of the other states, into a state of higher energy. When this happens the cloud reverts to its initial state by a spontaneous rearrangement of itself and in so doing light is emitted. This is one of the main processes whereby matter is able to emit light.

The light emitted in any particular change of state has a characteristic wavelength, a characteristic pitch as we might say in analogy to a note of sound. The pitch of light is just what we mean by colour. Atoms that undergo the same change of state emit light of the same colour. This we describe by saying that the atoms emit a spectral line.

Now when emitting atoms are moving towards us or away from us the colour of the light that we receive is altered by the motion. If the moving atoms are coming towards us the pitch of the light is raised, just as the note of an automobile horn is raised when a car is coming towards us. Conversely the pitch of the light is lowered when the atoms travel away from us. Not only this but the degree to which the pitch is raised or lowered depends on the speed of motion towards or away from us, the larger the speed the greater the shift.

This explains the powerful method used by astronomers for determining cosmic velocities: a measurement of the spectral lines that are received from the material in the atmosphere of a star or in a cloud of gas enables one to decide whether any change of pitch has taken place, and if so to what degree. The speed of motion required to cause the measured shift can then immediately be inferred.

It is particularly to be noticed that only motions towards us or away from us can be so determined. This is because sideways motions do not cause any changes of pitch and consequently cannot be estimated in this way.

The spiral arms of the Galaxy

The arms that can be seen winding their way from the nucleus of M 31 to the outermost parts are a most notable feature. They take the form shown schematically in Fig. 50. A very important and recent development in astronomy has been the demonstration that our Galaxy also possesses spiral arms. Three quite different methods have been used with entirely concordant results.

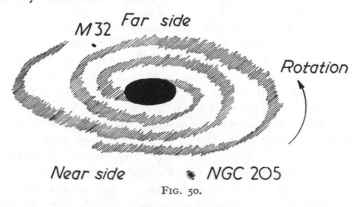

FIG. 50.

The first one, used by Morgan, Whitford, and Code depends on the stars of the ordinary main-sequence. So long as we know for certain that a star lies on the main-sequence its brightness can be judged from an observational estimation of its surface temperature. We simply use the main-sequence as a means of reading off the brightness once the surface temperature has been determined, as is indicated in Fig. 51. Once the brightness is thus known the star can be used as a standard headlight. This method of determining distances has been known for many years. It is the method by which the distances of open clusters are determined, for instance. Evidently it can be used to the greatest effect if stars high on the main-sequence are employed, since these are so bright that they can be observed when very far off.

But simple as this may seem, it has proved very awkward to apply the method in practice. There are two difficulties. One arises from the dust contained in the clouds of gas that lie between the stars. Light from a star far off in the Milky Way has to pass through such clouds before it reaches us and in doing so some of it is absorbed. Even if light of different colours were absorbed equally, application of the headlight method

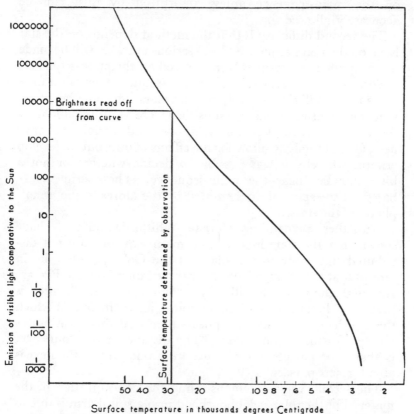

FIG. 51.   Use of main-sequence to determine intrinsic brightness of a star.

would still lead to serious errors unless allowance for the absorption by the dust were made. But light of different colours is not equally absorbed and this adds a further complication; blue light is absorbed more strongly than red light, which introduces errors in estimating the surface temperatures of stars. This is particularly serious when we aim to use stars high on the main-sequence as standard headlights. The steepness of the upper part of the main-sequence means that even a small misjudgment of the surface temperature leads to a large error in the brightness that we read off from the curve. Evidently the method is quite unusable for stars high on the main-sequence unless absorption by dust can be accurately allowed for.

The second difficulty is that the method depends on the star lying on the main-sequence. Very serious mistakes will be made if it is applied to stars that have evolved off the main-sequence.

For these reasons the use of the main-sequence for calibrating standard headlights, notably among stars high on the main-sequence, had not yielded results that were at all reliable until the recent work of Morgan, Whitford, and Code, who have been able not only to allow for the effects of dust but to develop criteria whereby it was possible to decide whether or not a blue star lies near the main-sequence. These criteria are based on the spectral lines emitted by the atoms in the atmospheres of the stars.

With these precautions Morgan, Whitford, and Code have shown that the stars high on the main-sequence are not distributed uniformly in the plane of the Galaxy. They lie in groups that are arranged along the three lanes shown in Fig. 52. Although the survey is still very incomplete the implication is that these lanes are portions of spiral arms, in one of which the Sun happens to lie. It appears then that there is a multiplicity of arms in the Galaxy. The distance across 'our' arm is about 300 parsecs, the distance from one arm to the next is about 1,500 parsecs.

The second way of demonstrating the concentration of the material of the solar neighbourhood into a spiral arm is due to Guido Münch. This actually takes advantage of the fact that the light of a distant star is partially absorbed when it passes through the interstellar clouds. Münch's method depends on the absorption by gas, not dust, however. A distant star observed through both 'our' arm and the next arm is indicated in Fig. 53. If the gaseous matter is concentrated in the arms, absorption is not continuous over the whole of the distance from the Sun to the star but occurs over two sections of the track of the light, the two sections that lie within the arms.

230

Münch has found that the absorption is not continuous but is indeed concentrated in two sections, and in two sections that agree with the positions of the belts of blue giants found by Morgan, Whitford, and Code.

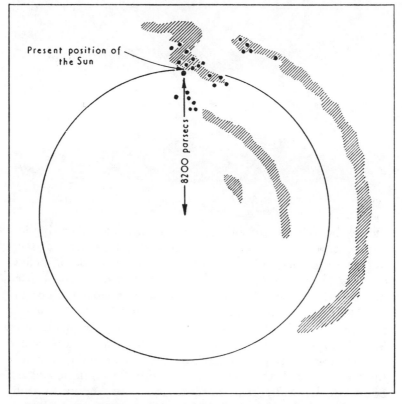

FIG. 52. Our Galaxy in plan. Regions of high hydrogen density shown by hatching, and groups of blue giants by dots. The Sun and planets move together in a clockwise sense approximately around the circle.

Even before these observations there was strong evidence for this coincidence from Baade's studies of M 31, since Baade had already established a marked association of both blue stars and clouds in the spiral arms of M 31. It was therefore probable that a similar association would be found in our Galaxy. The work of Münch goes far towards establishing this.

The final and decisive step in establishing the coincidence of
the gas clouds and bright stars in the spiral arms of our Galaxy
has come from a third line of attack along entirely novel lines.
It was suggested about ten years ago by van de Hulst that it

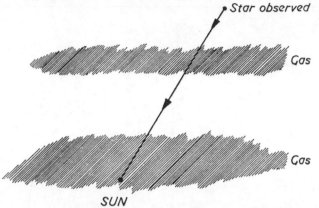

FIG. 53.   Observing through two lanes of gas (Münch).

should be possible to observe radio-waves emitted by low
temperature interstellar hydrogen gas. This was a most
important prediction because there was good reason for believ-
ing that large quantities of cool interstellar hydrogen existed
in interstellar space but up to that time no means of observing
cool hydrogen had been devised. Hydrogen near stars of
particularly high temperature had sometimes been observed
but this depended upon the hydrogen becoming greatly heated
by the stars. Since only a small percentage of the hydrogen in
the Galaxy is hot, the former observational technique was not
one of really widespread application. The important thing
was to have a way of observing the main tracts of cool hydrogen.

Van de Hulst's prediction of the emission of radio-waves
depended on there being two ways in which the electron in the
hydrogen atom can be attached to a proton. The radio-waves
are emitted through atoms switching between these two arrange-
ments. As with the light that is emitted when the electrons
in an atom alter their arrangement the radio-waves have a
definite wavelength, they form a spectral line. The wavelength
in van de Hulst's case is close to 21 centimetres, a value placed
conveniently for observation.

The prediction of the emission of radio-waves by cool hydrogen clouds was confirmed by Ewen and Purcell at Harvard University, and by Oort and Müller of the Leiden Observatory, and by Christiansen and Hyndman in Australia almost simultaneously. The situation was found to be exactly in accordance with van de Hulst's calculations.

This new development has provided a tool for surveying the Galaxy for dense clouds of cool hydrogen. The results so far achieved are also shown in Fig. 52. The hydrogen is seen to be strongly concentrated in the same arms as the blue giants of Morgan, Whitford, and Code. In addition there is important evidence of the existence of a second arm inside our own. In the next decade the further details of the hydrogen distribution will almost certainly be determined, so that the distribution of gas within our Galaxy will become known with considerable precision. This is a result that twenty years ago would have seemed impossible of attainment—an outstanding step in astronomy.

The detection of 21 cm. radio emission may also turn out to be a powerful tool for the investigation of cool hydrogen clouds in galaxies other than our own. So far only the Magellanic clouds have been examined. It has been found by the Australian radio-astronomers F. J. Kerr and J. V. Hyndman that both the Magellanic clouds contain considerable quantities of hydrogen. Also from this investigation it has become known that the two Magellanic clouds are in motion in orbits around each other, like the components of a double star system. The investigation of this motion depends on the displacements of the radio spectral line, the 'pitch' of the line being raised or lowered according as to whether the emitting masses of hydrogen are moving towards or away from us. It also appears that the clouds possess internal rotations within themselves.

No really systematic attack has yet been made on other galaxies however. But it can hardly be doubted that this will sooner or later—probably sooner—be turned into a major weapon of investigation. The main reason why apart from the Magellanic clouds little work has yet been done is that this branch of radio astronomy is still only about 5 years old. So rapidly is progress being made nowadays.

CHAPTER FOURTEEN

The Origin of the Stars in the Arms of Our Galaxy

The stars that we see in the sky belong mainly to the outer regions of our Galaxy. We do not normally see the profusion of stars that belong to the nucleus of the Galaxy. Partly because they are so far away and partly because they are much obscured by the clouds of dust that lie along the Milky Way, a large telescope is needed to distinguish the inner stars. But even without the vast aggregation of the nucleus there is no shortage of stars, as a glance at Plate XXV will show. These are all stars of the spiral arms, stars whose origin we shall now discuss.

It is an obvious suggestion that stars form out of the interstellar clouds of gas but the precise manner of their formation raises intricate problems. It used to be thought that a star could be produced by condensing a quantity of gas as an isolated system, each star forming as the outcome of a separate process. But this idea leads to very serious difficulties.

To see why, let us return once again to the great degree of concentration necessary to produce a star. If it were distributed at the normal density of the interstellar clouds of gas, the solar material would occupy a region that exceeded the present size of the Sun about ten million times, a region with dimensions of the order of a parsec. The gravitational field of such a large scale distribution would be very weak indeed. Consider the following comparison. A hypothetical man standing on the Sun as it is at present would have to throw a ball at nearly 620 kilometres per second for it to escape out into space. But if the Sun were expanded ten million times the ball would escape into space if the man were to throw at only one-fifth of a kilometre per second. This emphasises the dependence of

234

gravitating power on condensation, the less the concentration of material the weaker is its restraining field.

Now cosmically speaking, one-fifth of a kilometre per second is a very slow speed. The atoms of the interstellar gas are moving around at speeds more than five times greater than this. The atoms must therefore act like escaping balls. The Sun distended to the density of the interstellar gas clouds would have an insufficient gravitational field to control the motions of the individual atoms—they would simply evaporate away. Hence we may conclude with some certainty that stars like the Sun cannot originate singly out of the interstellar gas in a one at a time process, their gravitating power in the uncondensed state would not be strong enough.

The difficulty becomes less serious and may disappear altogether for a larger quantity of material. Whatever the internal motions of the atomic particles and whatever their density may be, a cloud can pull itself together by its own gravitational field *if it contains a sufficient quantity of material.* The masses required for condensation turn out to be very much greater than the Sun, however. At the density and temperature existing in the cool regions of the interstellar gas clouds the necessary mass turns out to be about 1,000 times that of the Sun. This is a typical mass for a whole interstellar gas cloud. Evidently then the interstellar gas clouds are aggregations that can hold themselves together by their own gravitational field. The situation is that a whole interstellar cloud can begin condensing but a small portion of it cannot condense alone.

At first sight there is an element of paradox in this. How then do the stars come to contain so little material? The answer is that stars are formed in groups. A large interstellar cloud condenses. As it does so the material of the cloud becomes more concentrated. This makes it possible for bits of the cloud to hold themselves together by self-gravitation. Indeed if the cloud condenses sufficiently the resulting concentration of material becomes so large that bits containing no more material than the Sun are then able to hold themselves together. We have already remarked that the gravitational holding power of a quantity of material depends on the degree of its condensation. We are now saying the same thing in a slightly different way. At maximum dispersion only the gravitational field of a whole interstellar cloud of gas can produce condensation. But as condensation gets under way separate regions inside the cloud develop gravitational fields that become strong enough for them to condense separately. And the more the main cloud condenses, the smaller the regions inside it that become capable of separate condensation, until regions containing no more material than the Sun can ultimately hold themselves together by their own gravitation. A shower of stars is thus produced inside the cloud.

The formation of stars in groups explains in a very satisfactory way the origin of open clusters such as the Pleiades (Plate XVII), for it is scarcely conceivable that the stars of these clusters originated separately and subsequently became associated together.

Dispersing star showers

Most stars are not members of clusters at the present time, however. But for consistency in our argument we must still demand that all stars were formed in groups. This forces us to argue that all stars form in showers the majority of which become disintegrated, only a minority preserving their association—this minority being just the open clusters.

Recent observational work by A. Blaauw goes far towards establishing the correctness of this view. It appears that most star-showers are self-disruptive. The first cluster to be examined in detail by Blaauw was the group of bright stars of which ζ Persei is a member. By a very careful analysis Blaauw has obtained the stellar motions shown in Fig. 54. The clear implication is that the stars of Fig. 54 are expanding outwards from a common centre. The cluster is about 30 parsecs in diameter at the present time and is about 300 parsecs away from us. The stellar velocities average about 12 kilometres per second. At this speed of expansion the cluster will increase significantly in size in a million years. We may accordingly conclude that the ζ Persei cluster is not much more than a million years old since the stars would otherwise have dispersed long ago.

It is not easy to repeat this work for other clusters. The number of very young expanding clusters is comparatively small, and only very young expanding clusters can be observed in the convenient compact state of the ζ Persei group. Not only

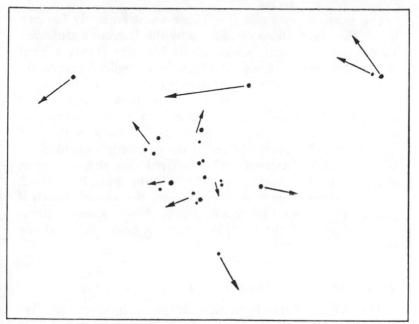

FIG. 54. Motions of the stars of the ζ Persei cluster.

this but a cluster has to be fairly close by if the motions of its constituent stars are to be measured with accuracy. Evidently we cannot expect to find many clusters that are both very young and very close to us. Indeed we are lucky to have found one in the ζ Persei cluster. A further investigation of expanding clusters must therefore depend on a new method of observation. Fortunately another method is available. An initially spherical group of expanding stars does not stay spherical, because after a time the constituent stars get pulled differently by the gravitational field of the Galaxy. The effect is to change initially spherical groups of stars into groups with characteristic ellipsoidal forms. It is possible to recognise expanding clusters from these characteristic forms. Blaauw has

237

found one such ellipsoidal group in the Scorpio-Centaurus region of the sky. This group is about 2,000 parsecs away and seems to be expanding at about 1.7 kilometres per second. Blaauw and Morgan have found another similar group in the constellation of Lacerta.

The existence of expanding clusters was correctly foreseen before the observations of Blaauw by the Russian astronomer V. A. Ambartzumian, whose arguments were closely related to what has just been said. Ambartzumian noticed that bright stars high on the main-sequence occur together in groups, in associations as he called them. From a study of the associations he suggested precisely the interpretation given above—that they are expanding clusters whose shapes have been distorted from an initially spherical form by the gravitational field of the Galaxy. Indeed Ambartzumian inferred that the velocity of expansion of the associations must lie in the range from about 1 kilometre per second to 10 kilometres per second, which is just the range found by Blaauw, the ζ Persei cluster being at one extreme and the Scorpio-Centaurus group being at the other.

The shrinkage of the interstellar clouds

The details of star formation remain to be discussed. We have still to explain why some groups of stars expand like the ζ Persei cluster, whereas other groups like the Pleiades stay together. There are other subtle problems to be solved. How is it that all the clouds of gas did not condense into stars long ago? Our Galaxy is some 5,000 million years old. How has so much gas been able to preserve itself over such a long period from condensing into stars?

Let us start by considering the last question. The interstellar gas sets off as if it intended to condense into stars, for the gas is widely condensed into clouds. The hesitation in the star-forming process sets in only after clouds have formed. The situation seems to be that the dense clouds are so opaque to radiation, especially to the infra-red radiation emitted by the material inside them, that their shrinkage is an extremely slow affair. The behaviour of a very dense cloud is rather similar to the behaviour of a star that lacks energy-generation by nuclear reactions. A temperature higher inside the cloud than outside produces an outward flow of energy that is radiated away by the surface. This steady loss of energy has to be made good by the cloud shrinking very slowly inwards, so that gravitation can maintain the pressure balance within the cloud. The time for an appreciable shrinkage to occur in this way must perhaps be reckoned in hundreds if not in thousands of millions of years.

The interstellar clouds are opaque to visible light because of the fogging effect of the dust particles—consider the great dark band of dust that can be seen in Plate XXVI. The clouds are opaque in the infra-red for a reason that also depends on the dust particles, although not directly through a fogging effect. Hydrogen atoms of the surrounding gas collide with the dust particles and sometimes stick to them. The dust particles accordingly come to possess a very thin film of hydrogen on their surfaces. The atoms in this film, being contiguous with each other, join up together to form molecules that subsequently evaporate off the dust back into the gas. In this way the gas comes to contain molecules as well as atoms. The hydrogen molecules then have decisive effects. They cause the cooling of the bulk of the interstellar gas down to very low temperatures —down to about 300 degrees of frost (degrees Fahrenheit). And together with other molecules—water, ammonia, they cause the dense clouds to become highly opaque to radiation in the infra-red.

Dust particles although they comprise only a small fraction of the mass of the interstellar clouds thus play an important part in controlling the properties of the gas. Indeed dust particles are so important that it seems worthwhile saying a few words about their origin, even though this is not very clearly understood at the present time.

Two entirely different dust forming processes have been suggested. One idea is that tiny solid particles condense out of the gaseous materials of the interstellar clouds, rather as water drops condense out of the vapour in our own terrestrial atmosphere. According to the work of Bates and Spitzer this might happen inside rather dense clouds. But the interstellar gas can only condense into clouds, particularly into dense clouds, if it is extremely cool. Molecules are required to produce cool gas, and dust is required to produce molecules. So the argument goes in a circle, the condensation of dust demands the presence of dust. In the entire absence of dust it seems unlikely that dust can form at all in this way.

The second suggestion is that dust particles originate in the atmosphere of stars of low surface temperature. It can be shown that at temperatures below about 2,000 degrees, carbon atoms in the atmosphere of a star will not remain gaseous but will condense into solid particles. It can also be shown that when the particles grow to about the wavelength of blue light—about one-hundred-thousandth of an inch—the radiation from the star pushes them outwards even in spite of the inward gravitational pull of the star.

This idea also has to face up to a criticism. In the majority of stars with atmospheres of low temperature the carbon atoms are linked with oxygen atoms to form molecules of carbon monoxide. And molecules of carbon monoxide do not form dust particles. A second difficulty is that a stellar source of dust requires stars to exist before the dust whereas our arguments would at first sight seem to suggest that dust must exist before stars, otherwise the interstellar gas would not become sufficiently cooled for clouds and stars to condense. Although for these reasons we might feel tempted to dismiss this second suggestion I am rather loath to do so because of a striking agreement with observation. The interstellar dust particles do in fact have a size of about one-hundred-thousandth of an inch. This as we have already noted is just the size at which a stellar source would blow them out into space.

Much remains to be understood but there are hints to show how it may perhaps be possible to resolve both the difficulties just mentioned. Exceptional stars are known that contain free carbon in their atmospheres, carbon atoms that are not linked with oxygen. Those are the so-called carbon stars. The carbon stars are also stars with cool atmospheres. Accordingly it seems that such stars if their surface temperatures should fall below 2,000 degrees must shower out a rain of soot.

It may also be possible to resolve the difficulty of the order of origin of dust and stars. In a later chapter we shall see that the stars in the central region of our Galaxy arise in a very different way from the stars of the spiral arms. Indeed we shall see that the stars of the nucleus arise in a way that demands the *absence* of dust. The origin of the central stars must therefore have preceded the origin of the dust. This would seem to remove the difficulty since we can appeal to the central stars to provide the first supplies of dust.

Fragmentation into stars

Now why does a condensing cloud of interstellar gas break up into a shower of several hundred or even perhaps several thousand stars, instead of shrinking as a whole into just one enormous star? Let us now try to answer this important question.

As the cloud shrinks gravitational energy is released. This causes the temperature inside the cloud to rise in the same way that the temperature rises inside a shrinking star. Sooner or later the temperature must become high enough for the molecules in the central parts of the cloud to become dissociated into their constituent atoms and for the dust particles to become evaporated into gas. Then something very remarkable indeed happens. The gas fragments by a process to be discussed in Chapter 17 into a shower of stars. The fragmentation is extremely rapid, taking no more than a few thousand years!

This spectacular development occurs when the temperature rises to about 3,000 degrees, a temperature that is attained when the cloud condenses to about one per cent of its initial size. Reckoning the initial size as 10 parsecs, the cloud therefore fragments into stars when it has shrunk to about one-tenth of a parsec. Shrinkage to this size increases the density a millionfold. Thus if initially the density was say 10 atoms per cubic centimetre (mostly hydrogen) the shrinkage preceding fragmentation increases the density to about 10 million atoms per cubic centimetre. Although this represents a very high concentration for the interstellar gas it is still much lower than the average density inside a star. The average density inside the Sun for instance amounts to about 1,000,000,000,000,000,000,000,000 atoms per cubic centimetre.

Evidently a further considerable concentration of material is still necessary after fragmentation has taken place before veritable stars are produced.

Calculations show that the initial masses of the stars lie in the range from about one-fifth up to about twice the Sun. At the time of their origin the stars lie on the main-sequence but they do not populate it to levels far above the Sun—only to about 20 times the brightness of the Sun. How then do the blue giants arise? By a further sweeping up of gas from the surrounding cloud. We must remember that it is only the heated innermost part of the cloud that fragments into stars. The stars at the time of their birth must therefore be surrounded by a cloud of comparatively dense gas with a density of about 10 million atoms per cubic centimetre. A star immersed in such a nutritive medium must grow rapidly by the tunnelling process discussed in Chapter 7.

The heating of the gas

As stars grow by tunnelling into blue giants their emission of radiation is greatly increased. And the proportion of the radiation that lies in the ultra-violet also increases very markedly. Now radiation in the ultra-violet is appreciably absorbed in the surrounding gas which must therefore become strongly heated. Eventually the temperature of the gas rises to a value comparable with the surface temperatures of the exciting stars themselves, say to a temperature of 20,000 degrees. Apart from in a few exceptional cases (to be mentioned later) the gas then evaporates away from the cloud into surrounding space.

It appears therefore that the building of blue giants is a self-terminating process. Sooner or later the blue giants simply blow the surrounding gas away, and tunnelling must then cease. This leads to a crucial point. Inside a newly formed cluster the stars possess motions but so long as all the original gas remains within or around the cluster the motions do not cause the stars to disperse, they simply move around among the other stars and among the gas. Once gas is evaporated however the motions cannot be controlled as readily as before because the restraining gravitational field has been weakened by the loss of the evaporated gas. Two cases now arise. One in which the velocities of the stars cause a swelling in the size of the cluster but not an entire dispersal. We associate such cases with the open clusters. We may regard the Pleiades and Praesepe as having originated in this way. In the other case the velocities are sufficient to disperse the stars entirely. We associate this second case with the expanding clusters of Blaauw and Ambartzumian. The velocities of expansion can be estimated. For a system with a diameter before expansion of one-tenth of a parsec (this is the order suggested by our considerations) and with a mass 1,000 times the Sun, the velocities of expansion of the stars must average about 3 kilometres per second. This is intermediate in the range inferred by Ambartzumian and measured by Blaauw, the range from 1 kilometre per second up to 10 kilometres per second.*

What is it that decides whether a cluster disperses or not? The answer probably lies in the proportion of the original cloud that becomes condensed into stars. In the case where only a low proportion is condensed most of the gravitational holding power of the cluster is originally supplied by gas not by the stars. When the gas is evaporated off most of the restraining gravitational field is then lost. We may expect a complete evaporation of the stars to occur in such a case. But if a high proportion of the gas becomes condensed into stars then the evaporation of the remaining gas will not weaken the restraining gravitational field very much. In such a case it is unlikely that a complete evaporation of the cluster will take place, although some degree of expansion must still occur.

Another possible variant may be mentioned. It might happen in exceptional cases that a cloud or a portion of a cloud shrinks to such a degree that in spite of the presence of blue giants the degree of heating of the gas is insufficient to evaporate it away from the cluster. The concentration necessary for this to occur is unusually large. A cloud with a mass 1,000 times the Sun would have to shrink to less than a tenth of a

* The present suggestions were put forward by the writer in lectures delivered at Princeton University in the Spring of 1953. The same idea was also put forward by Dr. F. Zwicky at a meeting of the Astronomical Society of the Pacific in June 1953.

parsec in order that the heating by very luminous blue giants should fail to evaporate it away. Two courses of evolution are then possible. One is that all the gas becomes swept up by the stars within the cloud. The other is that before the whole of the gas is swept up one of the bright stars within the cluster evolves to the supernova stage. The energy released by the supernova is so great that in this second case the remaining gas must become heated to a very high temperature, far higher than could be produced by the radiation of the brightest blue giants. Evaporation of the remaining gas can then no longer be delayed in spite of the strong restraining field of the cluster. Once the gas is gone the stars within the cluster become subject to expansion and dispersal exactly as before. But now the velocities of the stars are much greater than before. In a cloud one-thousandth of a parsec in size and with mass 1,000 times the Sun the expansion velocities of the stars can be as high as 100 kilometres per second. It is of particular interest that Blaauw and Morgan have recently identified a case of two bright blue stars, A E Aurigae and μ Columbae, that are moving outwards in nearly opposite directions from a common centre. The speeds of motion of both stars are close to 127 kilometres per second. It is difficult to see how such high velocities could arise in any other way except through the agency of a supernova.

It may be added that the explosion of supernovae inside exceptionally dense gas clouds is a process that may explain the origin of curious more or less spherical expanding clouds that are found in the Galaxy. These clouds look superficially like the products of supernovae, but they are expanding much more slowly than the gas from a supernova (hundreds rather than thousands of kilometres per second) and they contain considerably more material than could be derived from a supernova. A portion of one of these large slowly expanding clouds is shown in Plate XXX.

Recognising shrinking interstellar clouds

A shrinking interstellar cloud must be highly opaque to visible light. Even if the dust particles become entirely evaporated in the innermost parts of the cloud, dust in the outer parts must produce a high degree of opacity. So a shrinking cloud should be thought of as a roughly spherical opaque blob. Examples of dark blobs can be seen in the nebulosities shown in Plate XXXII. The blobs are detected only because they happen to be projected against bright clouds. A dark globule obviously cannot be seen by its own light.

The possible connection between dark globules and the process of star-formation was pointed out many years ago by Bok and Reilly, and has been elaborated by Spitzer and Whipple. This view has been opposed by Baade, who maintains that star-formation in the spiral arms of our Galaxy can have little to do with the dark globules. There is no known case of a globule in an intermediate condition between gas and stars.

It is possible that these apparently contradictory views can be brought into agreement. The lack of an observed connection between the dark globules and star-formation is an apparently strong point in favour of Baade's opinion. Yet it can scarcely be denied that the clouds out of which clusters of stars condense must look like dark globules in the pre-stellar stage. The resolution of the dilemma is probably that the great majority of the dark globules do not lie outside the large interstellar clouds, as the blobs that can be seen on Plate XXXII do. Most of them are tucked away inside the main clouds, where they are hidden from our view. It would then follow that star-formation would occur mainly inside the large clouds. In this way it is possible to reconcile Baade's view that star-formation occurs deep inside large clouds such as the Orion Nebula (Plate XI) and the Rosette Nebula (Plate XXXII) with the view that star-formation occurs as an outcome of the slow shrinkage and subsequent rapid fragmentation of dense masses of gas that in their early phases look like the globules that are occasionally found outside the clouds.

According to Baade star-formation is a process that in its actual occurrence is irrevocably hidden from us because it occurs deep inside large clouds where the dust in the general cloud (not only in the globules) prevents us from inspecting the process as it goes on. It is only after star-formation has occurred and blue giants have been produced that we have any chance of observing what has happened; for once they originate the blue giants blow the surrounding gas and dust away, to reveal a gap in the clouds where the new stars lie. So we only see things after the event. It is indeed just because we do not see these processes actually going on but only after they are completed that it has proved so difficult to understand how star-formation takes place.

Perhaps there is one exception to the statement that star-formation can never be observed. When bright stars are produced in a region of a large cloud such as the Orion Nebula they may happen to blow away sufficient of the dust from neighbouring regions to enable us to see into the cloud but without the gas being so completely evaporated that all star-formation ceases. This seems to be the case for the T Tauri stars (named after T Tauri the prototype star) which occur in large numbers in the Orion Nebula. Several hundred apparently growing T Tauri stars can be observed in this cloud. But the cases of intense 'star cookery' remain hidden from us. We see such groups as the ζ Persei cluster because the bright stars of this cluster have blown away the dust from their neighbourhood. Even if astronomers had lived over the last million years they would not have observed the early stages of formation of this cluster, for the reason that a veil of dust must initially have shielded the process of star-formation from view.

Gas pistons and gas bullets

It has been pointed out by Spitzer and Oort that the heating of the interstellar gas by the blue giants has many interesting consequences. Let us think about the whole interstellar gas, not about just one cloud. In some places the gas is heated to a high temperature (20,000 degrees). In other places the gas contains unevaporated dust and molecules and consequently is at a low temperature. The pressures developed in the high temperature regions cause the hot gas to push the cold gas around with some violence. Examples are shown in Plates I, XXXI, and XXXIII. In Plate I a cool opaque cloud containing dust, the horse's head, is being squeezed by surrounding heated gas. In Plate XXXI the long dark lane, the elephant's trunk, is similarly being squeezed. In Plate XXXIII a cloud of hot luminous gas is expanding like a bomb blast into cooler surrounding gas.

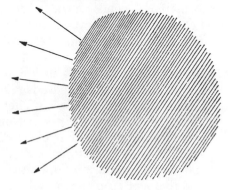

Particles evaporate due to heating by **BLUE GIANT**

BLUE GIANT

GAS CLOUD

FIG. 55.   Producing a gas bullet.

A blue giant can cause gas to be evaporated from a cloud even when the star itself does not lie inside the cloud. Radiation from the blue giant then hits the cloud from one side only, as is indicated in Fig. 55. In such a situation the cloud is impelled like a rocket, the one-sided evaporation of particles acting as a jet. As more and more of the gas is evaporated the residue of the cloud accelerates to greater and greater speeds. When 90 per cent of the gas has been evaporated the speed of the residue rises above 20 kilometres per second. When 99 per cent of the original material of the cloud has been evaporated the speed of the residue rises above 50 kilometres per second. Such speeds are quite exceptional. The random speeds of the interstellar clouds average about 8 kilometres per second. But clouds with speeds of 50 kilometres per second or more are sometimes observed. It is significant that they are always small.

This is indicative that their high velocities have been produced by the rocket-process shown in Fig. 55. Small clouds accelerated by the rocket-process become gas-bullets that may strike another cloud at high speed.

Star-formation as a cyclic process

The heating of the interstellar clouds by blue giants may cause cyclic changes in the process of star-formation. Star-formation depends on the existence of interstellar clouds of gas. Let the clouds be evaporated into a general gaseous medium and star-formation must cease. But once the blue giants have run their course, perhaps evolving to the white dwarf state in accordance with the discussion of Chapter 12, no more heating occurs. So a cooling phase is reached in which the interstellar clouds reform themselves. Then a new crop of blue giants arises, the interstellar gas becomes reheated, and the whole cycle begins afresh. The cycle need not be everywhere in the same stage of development. The cooling phase leading to star-formation may be operative in one part of a spiral arm, and the heating phase may be operative in another part. It is perhaps this variation that gives the 'string of pearls' appearance to the arms of the Andromeda Nebula (Plate XXI). The places where the star-forming phase has recently been operative show up as the bright regions of the arms, and the places where the blue giants have died as the relatively faint parts.

The cooling that follows the death of the blue giants may be a rather complicated process. It is probably not just a question of the reforming of molecules in gaseous layers on the dust particles, because in the expansion phase the dust particles themselves may be evaporated or blown clear of the spiral arms altogether. The cooling phase must then await a resupply of dust particles, possibly from the surfaces of giant stars with cool atmospheres.

The Magellanic Clouds (Plates XXII and XXIII) provide some evidence that star-formation is a cyclic process that includes a dust-free phase. The Large Cloud contains dust, gas, and extremely luminous blue giants. The Small Cloud contains gas but no dust, while the few blue giants in the Small

Cloud are not nearly so bright as those of the Large Cloud. This would suggest that the cyclic process in the Small Cloud is now at the phase in which the dust of the last star-forming period has been evaporated or blown clear away. The Large Cloud seems on the other hand to be at just the opposite phase, with plenty of dust, condensed gas, and with very bright blue giants. It is possible that a few million years hence the situation will have reversed, with the Small Cloud then containing the condensed gas and very bright stars, and with the Large Cloud going through a dust-free era.

The origin of multiple stars

Showers of several hundred stars at a time provide ideal conditions for the formation of multiple star systems. It is not at all improbable that in such circumstances one star will become linked with another in a double system, their distance apart being perhaps 100 times the radius of the Earth's orbit. After the general dispersal of the star shower in which they were born such a linked pair would stay permanently together. It may therefore be anticipated that a very appreciable fraction of the stars should be members of double-systems, an expectation that agrees with observation—more than half the spiral arm stars of our Galaxy apparently belong to double systems.

Next we must consider the possibility that two stars become linked together before their full condensation is complete. Then something remarkable occurs. The two components go closer together, and as they do so the orbits in which they move around each other become more and more circular. Suppose for instance that a continued sweeping up of gas raises the components from say half the mass of the Sun to 2.5 times the Sun. This fivefold increase causes the distance between the components to decrease to about one per cent of its initial value, so that if the initial distance was 100 times the radius of the Earth's orbit the increase of mass causes the separation to decrease to about the radius of the Earth's orbit. We thus obtain a rather close separation instead of the initial rather wide separation. Since the increase of mass must be different in the different cases this explains why considerable differences of separation exist from one double system to another.

The present theory also explains the origin of multiple stars containing more than two stellar components. Notable examples are the system of Castor to be observed in the constellation of Gemini, and the systems of ζ Cancri and ε Lyrae. Castor has six components arranged in three pairs, each pair being a close double. One of the pairs moves around a second pair in a time of just over 300 years, and the third pair moves around the other two in a period of more than 10,000 years. The system of ε Lyrae has four stars arranged in two moderately wide pairs that move around each other in a time of several hundred thousand years. The system of ζ Cancri also contains four stars arranged in two moderately wide pairs that move around each other in a time of about 1,000 years. A curious feature of ζ Cancri is that one of the four stars is invisible. It may be wondered how in this case we know of its existence. The answer is that one of the visible stars is observed to move around something that is invisible in a period of 17.6 years. It is inferred that this 'something' is a star, probably a faint white dwarf that is too distant to be seen.

The origin of these highly complex systems is probably quite simple. They are probably relics of open clusters. Open clusters tend to become disrupted by encounters with other clusters and with other stars. In the final stages of disintegration a few members of a cluster may be left. These few members may well form the sort of arrangement that is found in the system of Castor.

The possibility that a white dwarf is present in the system of ζ Cancri raises a curious point concerning the two dog stars, the brightest star in the constellation of the Large Dog, Sirius, and the brightest star in the Small Dog, Procyon. Both Sirius and Procyon are double systems. Both have a main star that is brighter than the Sun: the main star in Sirius has a mass about two and a half times the Sun, is about 25 times brighter than the Sun, and the main star in Procyon is about seven times brighter than the Sun. The companion star in both cases is a white dwarf. In Sirius the separation of the white dwarf from the main star is about 20 times the radius of the Earth's orbit,

and in Procyon the separation is about 13 times the radius
of the Earth's orbit. Now it is clear from the mode of origin of
a double system that the two component stars must be of
very closely the same age (this was a point already made use of
in the discussion at the end of Chapter 11). It follows that
evolution must have been more rapid in the white dwarf than
in what are at present the main components. In their early
history the relative importance of the components must have
been reversed, with the white dwarfs then the more massive
and luminous stars. This means that the white dwarf in Sirius
must at one time have been quite a massive star, more than 2.5
times the Sun. But the white dwarf component of Sirius has a
present mass of only 0.9 times the Sun. Hence the evolution
must have proceeded in such a fashion as to rid the originally
more massive and luminous component of most of its material.
A supernova explosion is clearly indicated. A similar argument
holds for Procyon. It appears likely therefore that the white
dwarf companions of both of the Dog Stars were at one time
supernovae, probably several hundred millions of years ago.

If Sirius was then as close to the solar system as it is now,
the supernova when viewed from the Earth must have been
about as bright as the full Moon—a most impressive sight.
Unfortunately the human species had not evolved when this
happened, and so man was not able to appreciate the spectacle.
It was presumably seen by the dinosaurs but I expect it meant
little to them.

The solar system again

The discussion of Chapter 6 was incomplete in an important
respect. It will be recalled that we had to postulate the presence
of a luminous blue star rather near the solar system in order
to explain how hydrogen at the outer edge of the planetary
disk came to be evaporated away from the gravitational
influence of the Sun. This was necessary to explain why the
planets Uranus and Neptune contain little hydrogen. In
Chapter 6 this step may have seemed rather artificial and
perhaps a little unsatisfactory. But the situation is now much
better. If the Sun was born among a cluster of several hundred

stars it is quite likely that a star of the required type was on hand during the early history of the solar system. It would be rather surprising if it were otherwise. So this apparent accident also disappears from the theory, and with it almost all element of arbitrariness. It seems as if our system of planets, instead of being in any way exceptional, is a thoroughly normal development of a thoroughly normal star.

CHAPTER FIFTEEN

The Galaxy as a Magnet

Whales can make progress through water either by wagging their tails up and down or from side to side. Light can travel through space in two ways, one like a tail moving up and down and the other like the tail moving from side to side. What of course wags in the case of light is an electric oscillation not a tail. These two ways of travelling are called the two directions of polarisation of light. When we receive light in which the two directions are equally represented the light is said to be unpolarised. When one direction is more heavily represented than the other the light is said to be polarised in the direction in which it is more heavily represented. If the intensity of the light in one direction exceeds that in the other by 1 per cent the light is said to be 1 per cent polarised, if by 10 per cent the light is said to be 10 per cent polarised, and so on.

The development of polaroid glass for automobile headlights is a practical case in which the polarisation of light is met with in everyday life.

Most sources of light, an electric light bulb or the Sun, emit unpolarised light. But as was discovered independently by Hall and Hiltner the light from some stars is polarised up to as much as 10 per cent. Of the stars examined by Hall and Hiltner some showed strong polarisation and others practically none. All those showing strong polarisation turned out to be cases where the light travels to the solar system along paths that pass through considerable clouds of dust, while those that showed no polarisation or only weak polarisation were the cases where little dust was encountered on the way to the solar system. This suggested that the phenomenon of strong polarisation is associated, not with the emission conditions at the surfaces of the stars, but with the passage of light through clouds of dust.

In order to produce polarisation the dust particles must

absorb one of the two types of light more strongly than the other. Large dust particles, such as those that float around in the Earth's atmosphere would not do this, but the tiny particles in interstellar space might (being mostly about one-hundred-thousandth of an inch in size). Such small particles will polarise light if they are of irregular shape. A needle-shaped particle for instance absorbs light more strongly when the electric oscillations wag in the direction of the needle than when they wag at right angles to it. So far so good. But to produce the observed polarisation large numbers of dust particles must be involved, and even if we grant that an appreciable fraction are needle-shaped, why should more of them point in one direction than another?

A magnetic theory proposed by L. Davis and J. L. Greenstein gives the best answer to this question. The needles turn around like propeller blades. And as a propeller turns around a shaft so we can think of a spinning needle turning around a shaft, albeit an imaginary shaft. The point of the Davis-Greenstein theory is that a sufficiently strong magnetic field causes all the shafts to have a systematic tendency to become parallel to the magnetic field. So if the Galaxy possesses a strong enough magnetic field the shafts will become so directed that the needles themselves never point along the direction of the magnetic field.

An analysis of the polarisation of the light of many distant stars shows that the observed results are consistent with this theory if the Galaxy possessed a magnetic field with an intensity about a hundred thousand times less than the magnetic intensity at the poles of the Sun, and if in our neighbourhood in the Galaxy the magnetic field points along our spiral arm. The acceptance of the Greenstein-Davis theory therefore leads to the inference that our Galaxy possesses a magnetic field. The intensity might at first sight seem rather low but we must remember the vast volume over which it is maintained. This demands an enormous flow of electric current. The largest current of which we have terrestrial experience is the surge of a lightning stroke, when a total flow of about 100,000 ampères is sometimes attained for a brief instant. In contrast, the total electric current that must flow continuously in the interstellar gas, amounts to some 3,000,000,000,000,000,000,000 ampères. Evidently then the inference to be drawn from the polarisation of starlight is a very far-reaching one. It leads to many important consequences that we shall now discuss.

The origin of the magnetic fields of the Sun and stars

It is also possible to appreciate the strength of the interstellar magnetic field inferred by Davis and Greenstein from a consideration of the magnifying effects that occur when a star condenses. The shrinkage of a magnetised gas enhances the field, for the reason that condensing material carries the lines of force of the magnetic field with it, thereby squeezing the field and increasing its intensity. A calculation along apparently straightforward lines suggests that the very large concentration necessary to produce a star would increase the magnetic field about ten million millionfold. So a field with the initial intensity indicated by the Davis-Greenstein theory would be magnified by the shrinkage into an intensity a hundred million times greater than the intensity actually observed at the poles of the Sun.

This enormous overestimate cannot be explained away by saying that deep inside the Sun the field is indeed of about the calculated intensity but that we do not observe it because it lies below an outer casing of weakly magnetised material. A very large internal field would make an important contribution to the pressure balance within the Sun. Such a magnetic contribution would be unlikely to possess the radial symmetry necessary to keep the Sun so accurately spherical in shape: the Sun would be appreciably squashed at its poles, flattened rather like the planet Jupiter is flattened by its rotation (see Plate VII)—the magnetic field indeed producing much the same effect as a rapid rotation would do. Since this is not observed it seems certain that no magnetic field anything like as high as that calculated can exist inside the Sun.

Nor can we argue that the Sun is an exceptional case, since the great majority of stars seem to be magnetically similar to the Sun. It is true that a number of exceptional stars do show comparatively high magnetic fields. These have been much investigated in recent years, notably by H. W. Babcock and A. Deutsch. The majority of them are stars of the main-sequence about 50 to 100 times brighter than the Sun, usually with surface temperatures in the range from eight to ten thousand degrees. These exceptional stars show magnetic fields about ten thousand times more intense than the field at the poles of the Sun, but even this is very much less—about ten thousand times less—than our calculated value. Well-authenticated cases consistent with calculation are extremely rare. The magnetic field found by H. W. Babcock for the supergiant component of the double-star system VV Cephei is one of the rarities. This double-system is a most remarkable one, with one component lying moderately high on the main-sequence (100 times the brightness of the Sun) together with an enormously swollen component possessing a brightness of from 10,000 to 100,000 times the Sun and with a radius some 1,000 times the Sun. The giant component of VV Cephei if swopped with the Sun would engulf the planet Jupiter and might even engulf Saturn. It is this giant component that shows the strong magnetic field. Apart from this case, however, and possibly one or two rather similar cases, there is no evidence from the magnetic fields observed in stars to support the apparently straightforward calculations based on the Davis-Greenstein theory of the interstellar polarisation of starlight. The observation that the Sun and certain other stars do possess magnetic fields can be taken as confirming the actual existence of an interstellar magnetic field but an interstellar field of one per cent, or even one-tenth of one per cent, of the strength required by the Davis-Greenstein theory would seem to fit better with our knowledge of the magnetic fields of stars.

Two possibilities for resolving the discrepancy may be mentioned, although it is not known at the present time whether either of them can be substantiated. One is that the aligning mechanism considered by Davis and Greenstein may be much more efficient than has hitherto been supposed. Comparatively little is known about the magnetic properties of very small particles such as comprise the particles of interstellar dust, especially if they are built up out of the type of molecule that chemists describe as a 'free radical'. If the process were an unexpectedly efficient one it could operate with a smaller interstellar magnetic field than that suggested by the work of Davis and Greenstein and this might reduce the magnetic fields inside stars to values that could perhaps be tolerated.

The second possibility is that the concentration of the magnetic field that accompanies the concentration of material when a star is formed is a much less efficient process than has hitherto been supposed. Certain assumptions are made (in order to avoid very intricate situations) in calculating the concentration of the magnetic field and one or other of these may turn out to be invalid. In particular it is possible that complicated effects arise in the late stages of the condensation. Indeed in Chapter 6 when we were discussing the origin of planets we saw how one such complication probably does arise. For myself, I am inclined to suspect that present calculations are indeed at fault at just this point: that stars possess subtle ways of getting rid of the magnetism of the gases out of which they form.

I am also coming to suspect that the curious magnetic effects that we observe at the solar photosphere and in the solar atmosphere may be the Sun's way of getting rid of the magnetism that it is still acquiring from the constant scooping up of interstellar gas (see Chapter 7), the rotation of the Sun playing an important part in the process. It is customary to suppose that these magnetic effects come from deep inside the Sun but so far this idea has met with very meagre success. Perhaps instead the fields really come from outside the Sun. The long-sought key to the origin of sunspots and to their cyclic waxing and waning may also lie here.

Cosmic rays and their origin

Further evidence for the presence of an interstellar magnetic field comes from an entirely different quarter, from the cosmic rays. Cosmic rays are highly energetic particles that for the most part enter the solar system from outside. Cosmic rays are emitted on occasion by the Sun but the main contribution comes it seems from interstellar space.

The physical nature of cosmic rays has been a puzzle for

many years. The incoming rays do not penetrate our atmosphere down to the surface of the Earth. They collide with the nuclei of the atoms of the terrestrial atmosphere, the collisions being of an extremely violent kind. Indeed collisions equivalent to even the mildest of them have been produced artificially in the laboratory only during the last few years, by means of the vast machines that have been built, notably at Brookhaven and at the Berkeley laboratory of the University of California. It will still be many years before it is possible to simulate artificially the most violent collisions of the cosmic rays with the atoms of our atmosphere. As an outcome atomic nuclei are smashed up and among the fragments are some particles that manage to penetrate down through the atmosphere to sea-level. Among them are the now well-known evanescent mesons. It was through these secondary particles that the earlier investigators received evidence of the entry of cosmic rays into the atmosphere.

This will explain the numerous errors that have been made in the identification of cosmic rays. It was first thought that the cosmic rays consisted of radiation of very short wavelength, γ-rays. This view was shown to be wrong when it was found that their intensity is not the same all over the Earth but is related to the local form of the Earth's magnetic field. Radiation would not have been affected by a magnetic field, so this immediately showed that the cosmic rays must be mainly material particles. The next idea was that the cosmic rays were electrons moving with very high speeds, speeds close to that of light itself. But after a time it was found that the effect of the Earth's magnetic field is inconsistent with this view. And with the accumulation of information concerning the nature of the secondary particles it became clear that an electronic component can be present only in very small proportion, if at all. In the next stage it was then supposed that the cosmic rays were almost entirely protons. Such was the state of affairs at the end of the late war.

Physicists at a conference held in Cambridge in 1946 scorned the suggestion that the cosmic rays probably contained the nuclei of atoms other than hydrogen. The incredulity was so great that nobody at the conference thought it worthwhile

258

to send up a balloon with photographic plates attached—a simple experiment that would at once have shown whether or not the nuclei of heavy atoms such as oxygen and iron were present among the incoming particles. In the event this experiment had to wait another two years before it was carried out by Bradt and Peters at Rochester. The nuclei of elements other than hydrogen were immediately found.

An initial assessment of the new observations led to the suggestion that the nuclei of all atoms are represented in the cosmic rays in about the same proportion as they are found in ordinary stars like the Sun. More recent work has cast serious doubts on this, however. Rather does it seem that the nuclei of the heavier atoms like iron, and of medium light nuclei like oxygen, are over-represented as much as tenfold.

A very remarkable possibility arises out of this situation: that at the time of their origin the cosmic rays consist entirely of heavy nuclei. The argument takes the line that all the protons, helium nuclei, and other light nuclei now found in the cosmic rays are the products of splintering of heavy nuclei in collisions. It can indeed be shown that splintering does provide a very plausible explanation of the observed distribution of the nuclei among the cosmic rays. There is thus much to be said in favour of the view that initially the cosmic rays are heavy nuclei. It has been urged against this view that if the light nuclei are splinter products then lithium, beryllium, and boron ought to be fairly strongly represented among the cosmic ray particles that enter our atmosphere. The experimentalists at Rochester claimed for some years that this is not the case but C. F. Powell and his colleagues at Bristol have confirmed the presence of these particular nuclei. While the controversy on this point may not be entirely settled the evidence seems to be swinging in favour of the Bristol point of view. The evidence while still not compelling is pointing very suggestively towards the conclusion just indicated, that the real primary cosmic ray is the heavy nucleus.

A complete understanding of cosmic rays cannot be forthcoming until we know how they originate. This was for long felt to be a very deep mystery but an important step towards a satisfactory theory was made by E. Fermi in 1949. The existence of magnetic fields in interstellar space is a basic supposition in Fermi's work.

A moving electric particle is deflected by a magnetic field. The local magnetic field possessed by a cloud of interstellar

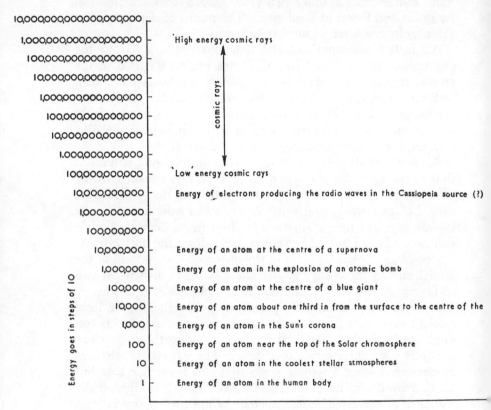

FIG. 56.

gas is able to deflect the motions of charged interstellar particles. If the clouds were at rest these deflection processes, or 'magnetic collisions' as we may call them, would not alter the energies of the particles. But if the clouds are in motion, and if different clouds have different motions, the particles gain energy as an outcome of the magnetic collisions. We are to think of particles wandering around in amongst a whole group

of clouds, the clouds themselves moving with different velocities. The gains of energy in the magnetic deflections are made
at the expense of the motions of the clouds.

But although all charged particles thus tend to pick up
energy from the clouds, the great majority simply fritter their
gains away. This they do by colliding with each other, with a
resulting loss of energy by radiation, notably radiation in the
infra-red. Indeed only a tiny minority, those that are moving
at very high speeds, manage to gain more from the magnetic
collisions than they lose by colliding with other particles.

The next point is perhaps best explained with the aid of
Fig. 56. Each step in Fig. 56 represents a tenfold multiplication
in energy, the unit being taken as the average energy of motion
of the atoms in the human body. It is seen that even the so-
called 'low' energy cosmic rays possess much more energy than
any other atomic particle found in nature. The low energy
cosmic rays possess a million times more energy than the
particles at the centre of the Sun, for instance. Now we come
to a crucial question. At what level in Fig. 56 would an interstellar particle gain more energy from magnetic collisions than
is lost by collisions with other particles? The answer depends
on the nature of the particle. For protons and heavy nuclei
the required level lies in the region of the low energy cosmic
rays. For electrons the level is still higher in the diagram.
Hence Fermi's ideas do not give a complete explanation of the
origin of cosmic rays. What is achieved is an explanation of
how still greater energies can be produced *if low energy cosmic
rays are already present among the interstellar particles*. It remains
then to discover the source of the low energy cosmic rays.

A likely possibility is that the low energy cosmic rays are
injected into the interstellar gas by stars. We have seen that on
occasion the Sun itself is a producer of cosmic rays. The rays
generated by the Sun belong to the lower part of the cosmic
ray distribution shown in Fig. 56. As they move outwards
from the Sun a small proportion are intercepted by the Earth
(and are hence detected) but the majority must travel out into
space where they augment the interstellar cosmic rays. Similar
processes on other stars, and in particular on stars having
stronger magnetic fields than the Sun, may very well be capable

of supplying the required low energy component of the cosmic rays.

The main problem now extant is to find out the process whereby the Sun and the stars produce their low energy cosmic rays. Many attempts to discuss this problem have been made but so far no satisfactory theory has emerged. My own impression is that the most likely process is one that works in an analogous way to the cyclotron invented by E. V. Lawrence. The cyclotron was the first of the machines employed by physicists for producing high energy particles in the laboratory. Its operation depends on a very careful adjustment between a magnetic field and the oscillations of an electric field. Unless this is accurately maintained particles do not get driven to high energies. Now several conditions have to be satisfied in order to preserve the necessary adjustment. For instance the accelerating particles must not be too numerous otherwise the driving process becomes overloaded. This may explain why heavy nuclei become accelerated and why protons and electrons do not. The protons and electrons in the atmosphere of a star are so very abundant that an attempt to drive them all would surely overload the accelerating mechanism. Heavy nuclei, particularly the very heavy nuclei, are much less numerous and would accordingly satisfy this condition best.

The magnetic stars

Observational evidence from the magnetic stars (the ones mentioned above with brightness some 50 to 100 times that of the Sun, and with surface temperatures from about 8,000 to 10,000 degrees) would seem to show that nuclei are indeed accelerated in stellar atmospheres. In these stars entirely anomalous abundances of heavy atoms are often found. In particular the elements described by chemists as the rare earths, of which the europium is an especially notable example, sometimes occur in quite unusual concentrations. Among medium heavy nuclei strontium is an important case. To this we may add the elements manganese, chromium, calcium, and silicon.

The best explanation of these exceptional abundances is

one given by G. Burbidge, M. Burbidge and W. A. Fowler, according to whom the most important nuclear process occurring in stellar atmospheres is one of exchange between neutrons and protons. A free proton collides with a heavy nucleus and is absorbed by it, a free neutron being emitted in its stead. The nucleus then returns to its original state by means of a β-process. To promote reactions of this sort either accelerated protons or accelerated heavy nuclei are required. According to the above argument the electro-magnetic acceleration of heavy nuclei must be considered the more likely of these two possibilities.

The neutrons so produced do not remain free for very long. They add themselves on to other nuclei in the atmosphere. They may add themselves to protons producing nuclei consisting of 1 proton and 1 neutron, namely nuclei of deuterium as the isotope H^2 of hydrogen is called. The deuterium of the Universe may well be produced in this way. The neutrons may also add themselves to nitrogen giving the unstable C^{14} discussed in Chapter 4. Addition of neutrons to other nuclei turns out to have some strange effects. Oxygen can only absorb 1 neutron. If it tries to absorb two it emits an He^4 nucleus and gets broken back to nitrogen. Neon and magnesium, on the other hand, tend to get built up into silicon but no further. Sulphur and argon are built into calcium but no further. Neutrons added to the isotope Fe^{54} (26 protons, 28 neutrons) produce an excess of manganese and chromium. Neutrons added to still heavier nuclei produce the excesses of such elements as strontium, the rare earths, and lead. We may add a most important point here. It seems possible that these neutrons, released as a consequence of electro-magnetic acceleration, may provide for the building of nuclei heavier than zinc. The origin of such nuclei was briefly touched on in Chapter 12, where we saw that they occur in very low abundances in the universe. The process of their formation must accordingly be a marginal one. Here we have a marginal process that may be added to that discussed on page 206.

The proton-neutron exchange process described above depends on the collison of the protons and heavy nuclei not being too violent. In cases of great violence the heavy nuclei, instead of emitting a free neutron, will tend to splinter, emitting a whole number of fragments. Such spalation reactions have been studied in the laboratory and are known to yield nuclei of the light elements, lithium, beryllium and boron. This is probably the process by which these particular light nuclei originate in the Universe.

The strange properties of these stars are enhanced by the variability of many of them. It is found that in some cases the magnetic fields change cyclically with time. Two explanations have been proposed by H. W. Babcock. One requires a genuine oscillation of the whole magnetic field of the star, such as might arise from a mechanical oscillation of the star itself. The second explanation is much simpler. The field of an ordinary magnet can be varied by turning the magnet round. The second suggestion is that the cyclic variations of magnetic field in the stars in question arise in a similar way, the stars acting like magnets that are turned round and round by rotation.

The work of Armin Deutsch has gone far towards establishing the correctness of the second of these two suggestions. The straightforward way to show this is to measure the times of rotation of the stars and to compare the result with the times of variation of their magnetic fields. If the two always agree then the evidence for a connection between the rotation and the variation of magnetic field becomes very strong. This has been done by Deutsch who has been able to show an identity of the rotation period and the magnetic period in many cases. One or two stars show unusual features but the agreement is impressive for the great majority of them.

Radio-astronomy

Our atmosphere provides a protective skin around the Earth. Besides supplying the air that we breathe, it shields us from all harmful radiations, particularly from γ-rays, X-rays, and ultra-violet light. But nothing is quite perfect in life, for this shielding is a great nuisance to the astronomer. It forces him to study the Universe in very limited ranges of wavelength. Indeed only two ranges of wavelength penetrate more or less freely down through the atmosphere. One is that of visible and near infra-red light, and the other is the radio-band. Until very recently astronomy had concentrated entirely on optical studies—on the visible light. The aim of radio-astronomy is to extend our studies of the Universe to the radio-band. Already in less than ten years so many new and entirely unexpected results have appeared that one cannot help wondering what aspects of the Universe might not be revealed if the whole range of wavelengths (set out in Chapter 3) were available for analysis. More and more astronomers are coming to think of remedying the defects of our present situation by making observations from above the atmosphere. It may be beyond present-day technical resources to mount a radio-controlled telescope on an artificial satellite moving round and round the Earth (completing a circuit every hour and a half) but it will surely not be beyond the resources of a future generation to do so. It is a reasonable prophecy that future developments will be directed more and more towards instruments that operate from positions located either high up in the atmosphere, or outside it entirely.

Radio-astronomy is conveniently discussed at this stage, because the preceding parts of the present chapter contain ideas that are important in radio-astronomy. The emission of radio-waves by cool hydrogen clouds has already been discussed in Chapter 13, so that we shall now be concerned with other features of the subject. It will be useful to give a list of the other known sources of radio-waves:

(i) the Sun;
(ii) clouds of hot hydrogen distributed along the Milky Way;
(iii) an emission extending outside the plane of the Milky Way but still coming from the Galaxy;
(iv) discrete sources of exceptional power within the Galaxy;
(v) discrete sources outside the Galaxy;
(vi) an emission from the central regions of the Galaxy.

These sources all differ in a very crucial respect from the emission by cool hydrogen. It will be recalled that the emission by cool hydrogen occurred at a definite wavelength of about 21 centimetres. In all the present cases, emission occurs at every radio wavelength. In terms of an analogy, we have the difference between striking a single note on the piano and depressing the whole keyboard simultaneously.

The present chapter will be confined to items (ii), (iii), (iv), and (vi), leaving (v) to be discussed subsequently. Item (i) has already been considered in an earlier chapter.

The observed distribution of intensity with wavelength is quite different in (ii) from what it is in (iii), (iv), and (vi). This contrast is shown in Fig. 57. The difference presumably arises from a marked dissimilarity in the mode of origin of the emission. It will be our main concern to trace what these modes of origin are. This is done more easily for (ii) than for (iii), (iv), or (vi). For simplicity we shall therefore consider (ii) first, even though this is perhaps the least important case.

Radio emission

A large proportion of the light emitted by stars high on the main-sequence is absorbed in surrounding interstellar gas, the absorption often serving to break the connection of the electron and proton in the hydrogen atoms of which the gas is mainly composed—the photo-electric effect again. After ionisation has occurred the protons and electrons are left free to wander around independently. In their wanderings the particles often collide with each other—that is to say they approach each other comparatively closely. Sometimes when this happens they become attached together again. Visible light may then be emitted. It is indeed through such recombinations that we can see the high temperature clouds of hydrogen. More usually however the colliding electrons and protons do not recombine. The radiation then emitted is not confined to any particular range of wavelength. Ultra-violet light, and blue, green, yellow, and red visible light is emitted, and infra-red also, and radio-waves. The fact that radio-waves are emitted in this way was first pointed out by Henyey and Keenan.

It has only been in the last year or so that radio emission by the hot hydrogen regions of the Galaxy has been detected.

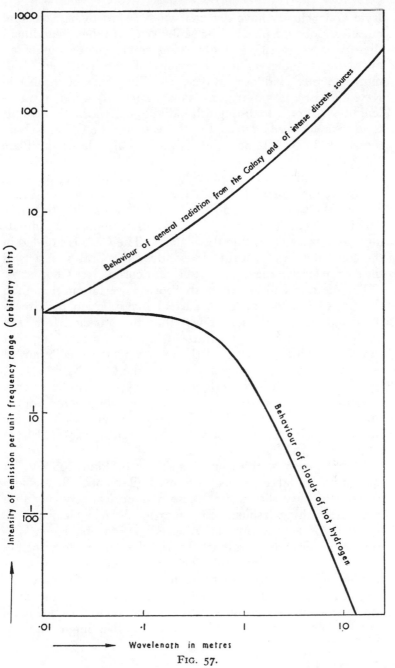

FIG. 57.

Ryle and Scheuer have detected what seems to be a general emission along the plane of the Milky Way. In their experiment there was no question of observing single clouds but of an averaging together of many regions of hot hydrogen. Still more recently Haddock, Mayer, and Sloanaker of the Naval Research Lab., Washington, have managed, using a wavelength of 9.4 cm., to distinguish individual clouds. Two clouds that have now been detected in this way are the Orion Nebula shown in Plate XI, and the Trifid Nebula shown in Plate XXXIV.

We now turn our attention to a quite different mode of emission, that associated with the items (iii) and (iv) listed above. We can perhaps do this best by considering (iv) first. The Crab Nebula (Plate XXVIII) is an example of an important discrete source within the Galaxy. The Crab is situated in the constellation of Taurus. It is indeed the Crab that acts as the source for investigating the Sun's far corona (see Chapter 7).

The discrete sources are vastly more powerful emitters than the hot hydrogen clouds. A careful investigation by Greenstein and Minkowski has shown that the emission from the Crab Nebula is about 100 times stronger than anything that can be explained in terms of the emission by the collisions of wandering electrons and protons. And the Crab Nebula is not by any means the strongest of the exceptional radio sources that have been observed. An exceptionally intense source situated in the constellation of Cassiopeia radiates at a rate that approaches a million times what might be expected from a hot hydrogen region.

A photograph of this source is shown in Plate XXXV. It appears as a large number of small filaments. Baade and Minkowski have shown that these filaments are moving in a most astonishing fashion. The sharply defined elements are found to be approaching us at speeds up to about 200 kilometres per second. The more diffuse filaments yield velocities very much higher than this, however. They are sometimes moving towards and sometimes away from us, the variation between the most rapid velocity of approach and the most rapid velocity of recession exceeds the enormous value of 4,000 kilometres per second. Even within a single filament variations of velocity of several thousand kilometres per second are found.

No completely convincing suggestion has yet been given of the origin of such a curious object. A clue is perhaps to be obtained from the radio data which shows that the emission is not by any means confined to the visible filaments but comes from a region of which the filaments are only a part. A possible explanation of the whole phenomenon was mentioned to me by Baade. This explanation is based on the supernova explosion as the most likely source of a considerable quantity of material moving at speeds of several thousand kilometres per second. The idea is that material from a supernova may be colliding with a dark cloud of gas and dust, the material from the supernova being on the far side of the cloud where we do not see it (because of the obscuring effect of the dust) except in places where it is spilling over the edge of the dark cloud.

It is to be expected that magnetic fields play an important part in controlling the motion of the filaments of Plate XXXV. If we accept the Davis-Greenstein value for the strength of the general interstellar magnetic field we must also accept the view that still more intense fields arise when two clouds of gases collide violently with each other, since it is to be expected that a considerable compression both of material and magnetic field will occur in the region of collision. The intensity in such a situation may rise to about one-thousandth of the field at the poles of the Sun. With a magnetic field of this order and with the very large velocities that are observed in the strong radio sources, it seems possible to explain the manner of emission of the radio-waves. The theory now to be outlined follows along lines suggested in 1950 by H. Alfvén and N. F. Herlofson.

The exceptionally high velocities play an important part. They serve to accelerate electrons by a process of magnetic collisions, a process similar to that proposed by Fermi for generating the high energy cosmic rays. The electrons so accelerated then emit radio-waves as they move in the magnetic field. The details of the emission are well known from laboratory observations of high speed electrons. The situation is that for electrons accelerated to the low energy end of the cosmic ray distribution, and for magnetic fields of the strength considered above, emission of radio-waves occurs at what (cosmically speaking) is an extremely rapid rate.

The requirement of large velocities (in order that the acceleration of electrons shall take place) seems to fit the results of Baade and Minkowski very well indeed. It has been found that all the strong radio sources contain gaseous masses with rapid internal motions. This is the case for example in the Crab Nebula where random motions of about 300 kilometres per second are found. The implication of the theory is that unless such motions exist, electron acceleration does not take place, and unless electrons with cosmic ray energies (at the low end of the distribution) are produced no strong emission of radio-waves can take place.

All this would suggest that the recipe for producing a strong cosmic radio transmitter is really a very simple one. It consists in taking a cloud of gas and in stirring it up with sufficient violence. We shall see in the next chapter that this recipe holds good when we pass from strong radio sources within our own Galaxy to sources outside the Galaxy.

All this does not exhaust the radio-waves received from our Galaxy—we still have to consider items (iii) and (vi) listed above. It used to be thought that the general radiation within our Galaxy came from scattered stars. Recently this view has been called into some question. Rather does it seem as if energetic electrons may be the source of the waves just as they are in the powerful discrete sources. But the electrons cannot be strongly concentrated in special clouds otherwise these clouds would be detected by the radio-astronomers as discrete sources. Possibly the electrons are produced in special regions, such as that of the Cassiopeia source, and then manage to escape out of their parent clouds thereby coming to form a general galactic stratum of emitting particles.

Perhaps we should add a remark by way of conclusion, on the intensities of cosmic radio sources. A terrestrial radio transmitter is reckoned to be fairly powerful if its output is as high as 1,000 kilowatts. The output of the strange source in Cassiopeia is some 1,000,000,000,000,000,000,000,000 kilowatts. As sources go within the Galaxy this is an intense one. But as sources go in the Universe it is quite modest. We shall meet still more powerful radio transmitters in the next chapter.

CHAPTER SIXTEEN

The World of Galaxies

The Local Group

In the last three chapters we have considered the structure of our own Galaxy. From time to time we have mentioned the Andromeda Nebula, M 31 (Plate XXI), and several smaller systems of stars such as the Magellanic Clouds (Plates XXII and XXIII). It is now our purpose to pass from these particular cases to a study of galaxies in general—their distribution in space, their physical forms, their internal properties.

It used to be thought twenty years ago that the majority of galaxies were quite separate from one another, that only a minority were members of clusters. In recent years there has been a marked swing of opinion towards an opposite point of view, for it is now believed that the normal state of affairs is for a galaxy to belong to a cluster. Lone galaxies arise only when they happen to be ejected from clusters, as galaxies do from time to time. A recent survey carried out by C. D. Shane and C. A. Wirtanen at the Lick Observatory, and analysed by J. Neyman and E. L. Scott, and C. D. Shane, lends strong support to this point of view.

Our own Galaxy is a member of a cluster, known as the Local Group. The other main member is M 31, the great galaxy in Andromeda. The next most notable number is M 33, found in the constellation of Triangulum and shown in Plate XXXVII. In all 19 members of the Local Group are known. They occupy a region of space about 1 million parsecs in diameter, with our Galaxy and the Andromeda Nebula on opposite sides of the centre. M 33 is a considerably smaller system than either of these two main monsters and many of the other members of the Local Group are considerably poorer systems still. After M 33 the only two that contain many highly luminous stars—

271

stars high on the main-sequence and supergiants—are the Large Magellanic Cloud and the system NGC 6822 (although a few rather bright stars are found in the Small Magellanic Cloud). The weakest systems are those to be found in the constellations of Draco, Sculptor and Fornax, which are not a great deal brighter in their total light than a globular cluster. Indeed as we shall come to see, poor systems of the Draco type are probably formed in the same process as that which gives rise to globular clusters. Intermediate systems are those of the satellite galaxies of the Andromeda Nebula, catalogue numbers M 32 and NGC 205, which are shown on Plate XXI. Compare M 32 and NGC 205 with the weak system of IC 1613 shown in Plate XXXVI. It is seen that M 32 and NGC 205 are much more concentrated, the weak system being very 'loose'.

Because of their comparative nearness, because our Galaxy is immersed in the Local Group, the other members appear scattered over the sky; some such as the Andromeda Nebula being visible from the N. hemisphere of the Earth, and others such as the Magellanic Clouds being visible in the S. hemisphere. Because of the obscuration produced by the dust lying along the plane of the Galaxy any faint members of the Local Group that happened to lie in directions along the Milky Way would probably escape detection. It is possible that the Local Group possesses three or four faint members that have not been observed for this reason.

It should now be said that the Local Group of galaxies is a bound system. Just as the planets are bound to the Sun and move together with the Sun around the centre of our Galaxy, so the galaxies of the Local Group are to be considered as a single connected physical system. The relevance of this remark will become much clearer when in a later chapter we come to consider the expansion of the Universe. The Local Group is not expanding.

A word may also be said about the total amount of matter in the Local Group. Outstanding contributions come from the Galaxy and M 31. Between them these two monsters contribute about 400,000 million times more material than is present in the Sun. But the volume occupied by the Local Group is so vast that even this enormous mass of material if it were spread uniformly through the Local Group would yield only the minute average density of some 60 parts in a million million million million million of the density of water.

The distribution of galaxies in space

Next beyond the Local Group come a few other small clusters of galaxies, in one of which the beautiful spiral M 81 (Plate XXIV) is particularly outstanding. M 81 is at a distance of about 2,500,000 parsecs. The first of the great clusters is reached at a distance of about 10 million parsecs.* This is the huge cloud found in the constellation of Virgo, the cloud shown in Plate XXXVIII. A particularly important individual member is shown in Plate XXVII. The Virgo cloud contains upwards of 1,000 *visible* galaxies. It may also contain a large number of systems like those of Fornax and Sculptor which would be far too faint to be seen.

Although the Virgo cloud is incomparably richer than the Local Group, it is not a great deal bigger. The Virgo cloud is about twice the size of the Local Group.

Beyond the Virgo cloud large numbers of clusters can be distinguished. Because of their relation to the discussion of later chapters a few of them will be mentioned explicitly. In Plate XXXIX we see the central regions of the Coma cluster, a cluster also with upwards of 1,000 members. Owing to the increased distance the galaxies of this cluster appear smaller than those of the Virgo cloud, although of course in actual size they are much the same. The Coma cluster, one of the richest of all known clusters, is probably at a distance of about 50 million parsecs. This distance is much beyond the range of the methods of measurement discussed in previous chapters. How such very great distances are inferred will form a topic of discussion in a later chapter.

Another special cluster, that in the constellation of Corona Borealis, is at the even greater distance of about 150 million parsecs. This is shown in Plate XL. At still greater distances the number of clusters is very great, so that only one

* The estimates of very large distances given in this book are rather unorthodox, being greater than the values that are usually quoted. My reasons for accepting the present values are given in Chapter 19.

or two representative cases can be mentioned. One that has played an important part in astronomical measurements is shown in Plate XLI. This lies in the constellation of Hydra at a distance of some 400 million parsecs. By now the distance is so great that the structural details of the galaxies can no longer be distinguished, by now we must identify a galaxy either on the basis of a fuzziness of outline or of a lack of spherical shape.

Even the galaxies shown in Plate XLI are not the most distant that can be photographed with the 200-inch Hale reflector. What a galaxy looks like near the ultimate limiting distance to which the 200-inch telescope can penetrate is shown in Plate XLII. To assist the identifications bracketing marks have been drawn on the plate. It is seen that there is no shortage of these very distant galaxies. Indeed when the limit of faintness is reached more galaxies can be seen on many plates than can stars of our own Galaxy. The faint galaxies shown in Plate XLII are probably at distances of about 1,000 million parsecs, or about 20,000,000,000,000,000,000,000 miles away. Somewhere between 100 and 1,000 million galaxies can be seen with the 200-inch telescope. The total number of galaxies within 1,000 million parsecs must, however, be much greater than this. We have seen that our Local Group contains 19 identified members. Yet only six or seven of them could be seen at a distance of 10 million parsecs, and only two could be seen at distances approaching 1,000 million parsecs; these being our Galaxy and the Andromeda Nebula.

From what has been said it will be realised that there is a considerable variability between different clusters. Some, probably the majority, are rather poor specimens like the Local Group. Others are extremely rich like the Coma cluster. An astronomer's life might be more interesting if we lived in the Coma cluster, but perhaps we should then get a somewhat false impression of what the average situation in the Universe is like.

The structural forms of the galaxies

Next we shall consider the forms of the galaxies. The basis of the present discussion will be a system of classification introduced by Hubble. We first distinguish cases in which no dust clouds are observed. These can be fitted into the elliptical sequence shown in Fig. 58. It will be seen that the polar diameter remains much the same along the entire sequence. Different degrees of rotation cause the differences in the equatorial diameter. For instance an Eo galaxy would be changed to the elongated form of an E7 galaxy if it were endowed with a sufficiently rapid rotation. The polar diameter often has a length of about 1,000 to 1,500 parsecs, while in a galaxy of type E7 the equatorial diameter may be as great as 5,000 parsecs. Galaxies fitting into the scheme of Fig. 58 are called elliptical galaxies. The two satellites of the Andromeda Nebula (Plate XXI) are elliptical galaxies. Other examples are shown in Plate XLV.

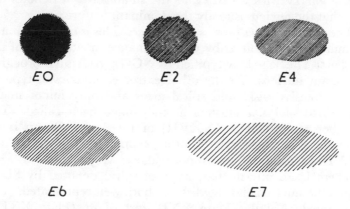

FIG. 58. The elliptical sequence. The members E1, E3 and E5 are not shown.

When we turn to galaxies that contain dust clouds we find a curious situation. Dust is scarcely ever found in the central regions but only in a flattened outer part. The nucleus of such galaxies if taken by itself could very well be classified in the sequence of Fig. 58. The nucleus of the Andromeda Nebula might be classified as an elliptical galaxy of perhaps type E3. It almost seems as if galaxies containing dust consist of two parts, a central nucleus of the elliptical type with an outer disk attached. A case where it is difficult to resist the impression that we are looking at just such a two-part system is that of the 'sombrero hat', the galaxy NGC 4594 shown in Plate XXV. The nucleus in this case would correspond to an elliptical nebula of about type E3. This plate illustrates the important point that dust is a constituent of the disk, not of the nucleus. Where the disk comes in front of the nucleus the light from the nucleus is blotted out by a great equatorial band of obscuring material.

When a galaxy possesses an outer disk, spiral arms are almost invariably observed. In cases where the nucleus is very large and the disk comparatively small, as in NGC 4594, the galaxy is said to be of type Sa. Galaxies with disks are referred to as 'spirals' to distinguish them from those without disks—the ellipticals. The letter S in the designation Sa denotes a spiral (i.e. a galaxy with a disk) and the small letter a denotes the fact that the nucleus is really the dominant feature.

The spiral galaxies possess a sequence. This is not determined so much by rotation as by the dominance or otherwise of the nucleus. The Sa galaxy typified by NGC 4594 has a thoroughly dominant nucleus. At the other extreme, galaxies of type Sc have extensive disks and spiral arms and only minor nuclei —glorified globular clusters as they have been called. The member M 33 (Plate XXXVII) of the Local Group is an example of an Sc spiral. Another example is shown in Plate XLVII. This is the 'whirlpool' galaxy, M 51.

There is an intermediate type of spiral denoted by Sb in which the nucleus and the disk are both well represented. The Andromeda Nebula (Plate XXI) and M 81 (Plate XXIV) are examples of Sb galaxies. Our own Galaxy is also probably of type Sb.

When we look at such photographs as those of the galaxies NGC 4594 and M 51 it is difficult to resist the impression that the outer disk has grown out of the nucleus. One is insistently reminded of the magnetic effects discussed in connection with the origin of planets, in which a disk of gas is pushed away from the Sun by a magnetic twisting process. The discussion given in the previous chapter in favour of the existence of a strong magnetic field in the disk of our own Galaxy adds point to this view. At a later stage we shall consider whether the whole phenomena of spiral arms may not have its roots in the action of magnetic fields.

It must now be said that while this classification into E and S galaxies deals with most of the cases that are actually observed, it does not include every known galaxy. We have seen that in the Local Group the majority of systems are very faint objects such as the system of IC 1613 shown in Plate XXXVI. These loose systems are so feeble that even though they may be the most frequent type of galaxy only those of our Local Group can be observed. These systems have the appearance of weak elliptical galaxies that have not yet managed to take up the concentrated forms shown in Fig. 58. In the following chapter we shall see that all galaxies may at one time have been in a similar loose condition but that in systems containing much more material and many more stars than is the case in IC 1613 a process of concentration has occurred to produce the E and S galaxies.

In addition to the probably very numerous weak loose systems, there are two other groups of galaxies that fall outside the classification so far discussed. One is the class of irregular galaxies. The Magellanic Clouds are examples. Others are shown in Plate XLV. Although they are rather displeasing to the eye, we must realise that these irregular galaxies are not loose formless structures like IC 1613. They contain dust, which the loose systems apparently do not, and they are characterised by a bar-like feature. This has suggested to many astronomers that the irregular galaxies may have a connection with the second group that falls outside the above classification. This second group is denoted by the letters SB, S for spiral, and B for a barred characteristic.

The general forms of the SB galaxies are in many ways similar to those of the S galaxies but whereas the spiral arms of the S galaxies emerge directly from the nucleus, in the SB galaxies the spiral arms emerge from a bar that extends across the nucleus, as in Plate LVI. Just as the S galaxies possess the subdivision Sa, Sb, Sc, so the SB galaxies possess the subdivisions SBa, SBb, SBc, with the same connotation of decreasing importance of the nucleus. This is illustrated in Plate XLVIII. A very odd feature of these barred spirals is that their nuclei often contain an inner set of spiral arms. This is perhaps the most puzzling of all the problems that are raised by the observed shapes of the galaxies.

The difference between elliptical and spiral galaxies

Why do some galaxies possess an outer disk and others not? An important step towards answering this query has been made by Baade and Spitzer who point out that one galaxy must collide with another from time to time. Galaxies move about relative to each other. The galaxies of a cluster move around inside the cluster and may collide with one another.

The effect of a collision is not so drastic as might be thought at first sight. The stars of one galaxy do not hit the stars of the other, because interstellar distances are very large compared to the sizes of the stars themselves. Think of the stars as ordinary household specks of dust. Then we must think of a galaxy as a collection of specks a few miles apart from each other, the whole distribution filling a volume about equal to the Earth. Evidently one such collection of specks could pass almost freely through another.

This free interpenetration does not hold good, however, for any gas that the two galaxies may contain. Gas clouds of one galaxy must collide violently with gas clouds of the other. Such collisions produce high temperatures within the gas. Indeed if the velocity of collision is large enough the temperature must become so high that a considerable proportion of the gas gets evaporated entirely away from the parent galaxies. What may be an actual collision of two galaxies in progress is shown in Plate XLIX.

We can now relate the elliptical and spiral galaxies. We say that all galaxies at the time of their birth possess the means of developing into spiral galaxies, they possess a nucleus and a residue of gas that could grow into an outer disk. But because of collisions several alternative lines of evolution arise. First a galaxy might lose its gas through collision *before* any disk developed, in which case an ordinary elliptical galaxy would be produced, belonging to the sequence Eo to E7 of Fig. 58. Second a galaxy might suffer a collision *after* an outer disk had developed. In such a case we would expect to find a structure similar to NGC 4594, but without the dark band of the sombrero—the collision of the gas would also strip out the dust, since the dust is mixed with the gas. Such galaxies are known. They were classified by Hubble as So galaxies. It was indeed just the existence of So galaxies that led Baade and Spitzer to suspect the importance of collisions between galaxies. The third possibility is that a galaxy does not suffer a collision at all in which case it retains its gas, a disk grows, and the galaxy becomes a spiral.

An observational test can be applied to these ideas. We should expect fewer spirals in proportion to ellipticals in those places where collisions are frequent. This expectation agrees with observation. A low proportion of spirals is found near the centres of dense aggregations such as the Coma cluster, where collisions must be comparatively frequent. The proportion of spirals increases quite markedly towards the outside of the dense clusters. This is also in accord since the probability of a galaxy suffering collision is much less in the outer parts of a cluster than it is in the much more congested central regions.

The greatest radio transmitters in the Universe

When two galaxies containing large tracts of gas interpenetrate each other the motion of the colliding gas masses must be unprecedentedly violent. Remembering the conclusion reached from our discussion of the origin of radio-waves emitted by the intense sources within our own Galaxy (it will be recalled that violent gaseous motions were thought to be the recipe for producing an intense radio source), we may expect an outstandingly strong radio emission from colliding galaxies. This agrees with observation, for the most powerful known radio emission comes from two distant colliding galaxies in the constellation of Cygnus. These galaxies being at great distance are faint objects even when seen in a large telescope. They are the ones shown in Plate XLIX. The identification of these galaxies as the most powerful known source of radio-waves came about partly from the radio observation of F. G.

Smith and partly from the optical investigations of Baade and Minkowski.

The emission of radio energy by these galaxies is rather greater than their emission of visible light, a situation that no one would have guessed to be possible only a few years ago. The radio power output of the Cygnus galaxies amounts to about 1,000,000,000,000,000,000,000,000,000,000,000 kilowatts.

Other examples of encounters between galaxies are known but none so extreme as the Cygnus case, probably because the Cygnus case represents the head-on collision of two exceptionally large spirals—like ours and the Andromeda Nebula. When an elliptical galaxy collides with a spiral the gas that is present in the latter certainly gets a fair measure of stirring up, sufficient to make it a moderately strong emitter but nothing like the situation that arises when both galaxies are spirals, both containing large quantities of gas. The case shown in Plate LI is probably an example of the collision of an elliptical galaxy and a spiral galaxy.

Quite apart from radio emission arising from collisions between galaxies a much weaker emission of radio-waves occurs in other galaxies, just as it occurs in our own. An observer in the Andromeda Nebula could detect the radio emission from our Galaxy and in a like manner an observer in our Galaxy can detect the Andromeda Nebula. This was in fact first done by Hanbury-Brown and Hazard at the University of Manchester. This work followed the discovery by Ryle at Cambridge of what were at one time called 'radio stars'. These were discrete sources of radio-waves identified in various places in the sky. The first survey revealed about 50 such sources. The first discrete source to be identified was that of the Crab Nebula, the identification being due to J. G. Bolton. The Andromeda Nebula was next identified by Hanbury-Brown and Hazard. Then Ryle soon added about four more galaxies as identified sources.

Three or four years ago there was serious uncertainty about the nature of the majority of the 50 or so discrete sources then known (by now the work of Ryle has increased this number to about 1,800). It was first suggested that they might be very nearby unidentified objects within our own Galaxy—hence the

now discarded term of 'radio stars'. The approximate uniformity of their directions (they were found more or less
equally in all directions) precluded any distant sources within
our own Galaxy, since such sources would be distributed along
the Milky Way not uniformly over the sky. A drastic alternative to the purely local radio star hypothesis was proposed by
Gold even before the identification of the Andromeda Nebula.
He argued that the uniformity of directions could equally well
be explained if most of the sources were very far off, far outside
our Galaxy, and he proposed for consideration the view that
the majority of the discrete sources were simply galaxies other
than our own. The balance of evidence now favours this interpretation.

After this historical digression let us return for a brief
moment to the ordinary galaxies as emitters of radio-waves—
not the colliding galaxies. By now a considerable number of
nearby galaxies have not only been identified but several of
them have had their rates of emission accurately measured. A
curious situation emerges. So long as we keep to Sb and Sc
galaxies there seems to be a simple proportionality between
the emission of radio energy and the emission of visible light: if
one galaxy emits x times as much visible light as the other then
it also emits x times the amount of radio-waves—the two
keeping step together. This relationship holds good for M 31
(Plate XXI), M 81 (Plate XXIV), and M 51 (Plate XLVII).

The two types of stars

We come now to important new concepts that we have been
skirting around for some time. The main idea can be put very
briefly. The stars in the elliptical galaxies and the stars in the
nuclei of the spirals are old stars like the stars of the globular
clusters. In contrast, the highly luminous blue giants and supergiants are young stars. Young stars are found only in the arms
of the spirals.

This discovery due to Baade cleared up a serious difficulty.
Until 1944 it had not been possible to distinguish any individual
stars in the nucleus of even the comparatively close Andromeda
Nebula, although individual stars had been resolved by Hubble

in considerable numbers in the spiral arms. This was a curious situation, particularly as much of the light of M 31 comes from the nucleus.

When in 1944, equipped with a new type of photographic plate specially sensitive to red light, Baade succeeded in resolving the individual stars in the nucleus of M 31 it became plain that the puzzle lay in differences between the stars of the nucleus and the stars of the spiral arms. To emphasise their differences Baade called the latter 'stars of Type I' and the former 'stars of Type II'. The elliptical galaxies, globular clusters, and the nuclei of the spiral galaxies are of Type II, while the stars in the arms of the spiral galaxies are of Type I.

A more detailed understanding of the situation can be got by returning to Fig. 16 where a schematic evolutionary sequence for the stars of the globular clusters is shown. The stars of the elliptical galaxies and of the nuclei of the spirals are believed also to follow much the same sequence. At the great distance of M 31 the only stars that Baade could distinguish in the nucleus were those in the upper part of the giant sequence near the point C of Fig. 16. In contrast to this situation for the nucleus, the stars that Hubble had previously been able to distinguish in the spiral arms of M 31 belong either very high on the main-sequence in the territory of the blue giants or to the region of the supergiants. They were all extremely luminous stars, considerably brighter than the stars at C of Fig. 16.

It may be wondered how we can be sure that the stars of the nucleus of M 31 follow much the same sequence as the stars of the globular clusters when only the tip of the M 31 sequence was thus detected. Part of the answer is that Baade has found that when the stars of the nucleus of M 31 become separately distinguished, so do the stars lying in the globular clusters that belong to M 31. No important difference between the resolved stars of the nucleus of M 31 and of the associated globular clusters can be found. A second argument in favour of the uniformity of the star distributions of Type II comes from the two elliptical galaxies M 32 and NGC 205, the satellites of M 31. The brightest stars of these satellite galaxies are indistinguishable both in brightness and in colour, from the resolved stars of the nucleus of M 31.

The same situation holds for the Fornax galaxy which possesses three associated globular clusters: the resolved stars of the Fornax system are closely similar to the stars of the three globular clusters. The agreement now becomes more complete, because the Fornax system is appreciably nearer to us than the Andromeda Nebula and can therefore be resolved down to intrinsically fainter stars—more of the evolutionary sequence of the stars can be distinguished, not just the tip of the sequence as in the case of M 31.

The Large Magellanic Cloud contains a predominantly Type I population but the Small Cloud contains both Type I and Type II stars. The Small Cloud also possesses globular clusters. It accordingly provides an ideal place to test the similarity of the Type II sequences in globular clusters and in galaxies. Indeed the Small Cloud is sufficiently near to us for the identity of the two sequences to be established nearly down to their junction with the main-sequence, i.e. down to about the point A of Fig. 16. An even more comprehensive identification could come from an analysis of the stars in the nucleus of our own Galaxy. This is a somewhat ticklish project since observations towards the centre of the Galaxy must of necessity be made through dust clouds. But in the opinion of such an experienced observer as Baade the practical difficulties of such a project can be overcome.

The upshot of our present discussion is that there are two populations of stars, those of Type I belonging to the arms of the spiral galaxies, and those of Type II belonging to the elliptical galaxies, the globular clusters, and the nuclei of the spiral galaxies. Now what is the physical basis of this classification into two stellar populations?

The outstanding point is that all stars of Type II are old stars. In an earlier chapter we saw that the globular clusters in our Galaxy are probably older than 4,000 million years and younger than 8,000 million years—we saw that 5 or 6 thousand million years was about the most likely estimate. Other Type II stars are similar enough to the globular cluster stars for us to be sure that they all possess a comparable antiquity. The Type I stars, on the other hand, are not all old stars. A Type I population contains stars of variable ages ranging from stars like the Sun, which with an age of about 4,000 million years is almost as old as the Type II stars, to stars high on the main-sequence with ages of not more than a few million years.

The reason why a Type I population contains both old and young stars is clear. The arms of spiral galaxies contain clouds of gas and dust that are always available for the making of new stars. It is out of these clouds that the highly luminous stars we observe in the spiral arms have recently been born. In contrast the elliptical galaxies, the globular clusters and the nuclei of the spirals do not contain gas and dust and consequently no new stars are being born there.

An interesting and important inference is that the exhaustion of the supplies of gas in the nuclei of the spirals, in elliptical galaxies and in the globular clusters must have become almost complete at an early phase of their histories. Gas must originally have been present in order to form the Type II stars themselves but the gas did not persist in any great degree after the Type II stars were formed. This suggests that in the early history of a galaxy there was something of the nature of a star-forming catastrophe. In the earliest phase of the history of a galaxy all the material presumably was gaseous. But the gas did not condense into stars steadily. Rather was there one process in which stars were produced wholesale. In the case of a galaxy such as our own or the Andromeda Nebula this wholesale process must have yielded not only the stars that now make up the nucleus but also the stars of the globular clusters and those of the huge halo enveloping the whole system. The stars of the halo of our Galaxy (see Fig. 26) are also stars of Type II.

More about the origin of the elements

There is a further difference between the two types of star, one that is often used for distinguishing them. Stars of Type I contain an appreciably higher proportion of metal atoms than those of Type II. This difference was first found by Schwarzschild and Spitzer, whose observational work on this question has recently been extended by Greenstein, who finds that the difference in metal content may be as much as a factor of 20. The Sun as a Type I star contains about $\frac{1}{4}$ per cent by mass in the form of metals. Greenstein finds Type II stars in which the metal content may be as little as $\frac{1}{100}$ of a per cent.

The method of establishing this depends on observations of nearby stars of our own Galaxy. Stars of the halo move in orbits that occasionally take them through the disk of the Galaxy. We may expect that a small number of such stars may be plunging through the part of the disk in the neighbourhood of the Sun at the present time. These visitors from the halo can be recognised from the high velocities with which they appear to be moving: their orbits around the centre of the Galaxy are not at all similar to that of the Sun, or to those of the other stars that belong to the disk of the Galaxy, so that the difference of velocity between a halo star and the Sun is usually very large. The visitors when so distinguished are found to have the low metal content mentioned above.

The reason for this marked difference of composition is readily understandable in terms of the discussions of Chapter 12. We saw that elements other than hydrogen are built up by nuclear reactions occurring inside evolving stars. Such elements are constantly being blown out into the interstellar gas by the exploding stars. Now those stars that originated before this manufacturing and distributing process got well under way must be poor in their heavy element content. Those that originated later must contain progressively more and more heavy elements. So we see that the heavy element content of a star can be interpreted as a measure of its age. Old stars are very poor, while young stars are comparatively rich (only to the tune of a per cent or so in metals though).

The interpretation just given of the differences of heavy element content found in the stars implies that there should be a continuous variation from the very oldest stars to the very youngest stars. There should be no question of just two groups, heavy-element-poor-stars, and heavy-element-rich-stars. This seems to be in accordance with observation, so far as observation has gone. Among the stars that are genuine residents of the disk of our Galaxy there is, in addition to the normal stars of Type I, a group of stars that seem to be intermediate between Type I and the Type II stars. The normal Type I stars are often referred to as a 'spiral-arm' population, while the intermediate class of star is said to constitute a 'disk-population'. The metal content of the disk population is about a third of the metal content of spiral arm population. Besides possessing a lower metal content than the spiral arm stars, the disk population has other distinguishing characteristics. The proportion of them that are double stars is considerably less than the proportion among the spiral arm population, a point already noted by J. H. Oort many years ago.

Now how should we refer to the disk-population? Are they to be classed as Type I or as Type II stars? No definite answer has been agreed on this question. The properties of the disk population, properties of age and composition, suggest they should be classified as Type II stars. They are old stars, older than the Sun, as can be seen from their lower metal content. Yet their position in the outer part of the Galaxy, in the disk of the Galaxy, conflicts with the simple idea that Type II stars are those belonging to the nuclei of the spiral galaxies and to their halos, to the elliptical galaxies and to the globular clusters, while the Type I stars are those that belong to the disks of the spirals. This conflict has led some astronomers to refer to the disk population as 'intermediate' or as 'late' Type II or 'disk' Type II. No one is really satisfied with this sort of compromise, and some more powerful system of classification is needed.

Remarks about the arms of the spiral galaxies

The disk population does not contain blue giants or any supergiants. These extremely luminous stars are confined to the regions containing gas and dust, to the spiral arms. It is indeed because the bright blue stars are confined to the spiral arms that the arms stand out so well on plates sensitive to blue light. When plates sensitive in red light (but not in the blue) are used the spiral structure largely disappears. It is a curious thought that if we possessed instruments that were only sensitive to very red light we should probably be unaware of the existence of spiral structures. This emphasises the importance of developing observational methods that transcend the present limited ranges of wavelength. Probably it will be necessary to go outside our terrestrial atmosphere. A telescope on an artificial satellite is a high priority astronomical requirement.

Now why is a spiral type of structure almost invariably found whenever a galaxy possesses an outer disk (exceptions in the case of galaxies of type So)? Although it is the light of bright stars that cause spiral arms to show up so prominently the issue is not a stellar one. The problem is to explain why gas and dust become concentrated in spiral arms, for wherever the gas and dust go the bright stars are sure to follow. The realisation that the spiral arm problem is a gas and dust problem not a stellar problem is most important because it allows forces other than gravitation to play a part, pressure forces and magnetic forces. But in spite of this undoubted step forward no convincing explanation has yet been given of why gas and dust should become concentrated in spiral arms. So we can only discuss possibilities.

A 'coffee-cup' theory has been suggested by Weizsaecker. Stir black coffee vigorously with spoon. Then take the spoon out of the cup leaving the coffee swirling around. Lastly pour on a few drops of cream near the centre. A species of spiral galaxy will be produced. What happens is this. The cup drags back the outer part of the liquid causing it to take longer to move in a circuit around the cup than the liquid nearer the centre. The drop of cream gets drawn out into a spiral just because the coffee on the outside is subject to this dragging effect.

Weizsaecker's argument is that at the time a galaxy originates the gas that goes to form the outer disk will not usually possess exact symmetry: it might for instance have the sort of shape sketched in Fig. 59(a). If the outer parts are rotating more slowly than the inner parts (this is a very likely supposition) then a coffee-cup effect will arise causing the gas to be drawn out into a form reminiscent of spiral structure (see Fig. 59(b)). The essence of the argument lies in a denial that any really important reason is required to explain spiral structure: the plausible assumption that the outer parts of a galaxy rotate more slowly than the inner parts (take longer to complete a circuit of the centre, that is), together with the further plausible supposition that at the time the galaxy forms the gases that go to make the disk do not possess exact symmetry (any more than the clouds that form in the sky possess exact symmetry) are regarded as being sufficient to explain the observed forms of the galaxies.

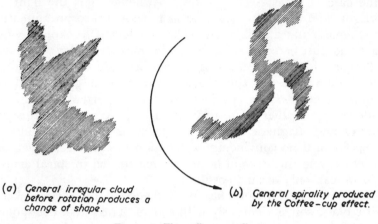

(*a*) *General irregular cloud before rotation produces a change of shape.*

(*b*) *General spirality produced by the Coffee-cup effect.*

FIG. 59.   The coffee-cup effect.

It is to be doubted whether this is so. The coffee-cup effect certainly produces a tendency towards a general spiral effect, what Baade terms 'spirality', and it is true that in some galaxies little more than a general spirality is found. But in other cases, such as M 81 and M 51, the spiral structure seems too well formed to be attributed to accident. Besides it is difficult to resist the impression when we look at such cases as the 'sombrero hat' (Plate XXVI) that the disk of a galaxy grows out of the nucleus, just as the arms of M 51 seem to grow with an almost exact symmetry out of the nucleus. Some other powerful controlling process seems as if it must enter the problem. This is not to say that rotation may not play an important role in 'winding up' the arms of a galaxy, but the chance shape of a mass of condensing gas hardly seems to provide an adequate basis for the origin of spiral arms.

Other attempts to explain the origin of spiral arms have been numerous but unsuccessful. The problem is a tantalising

LI—NGC 5128, PROBABLY A COLLISION OF TWO GALAXIES,
A GLOBULAR GALAXY AND A SPIRAL

This is another strong transmitter of radio-waves.

Mt. Wilson and Palomar Observatories

LII—A Group of Galaxies in the Constellation of Leo

Notice the way the two galaxies at right-centre influence one another.

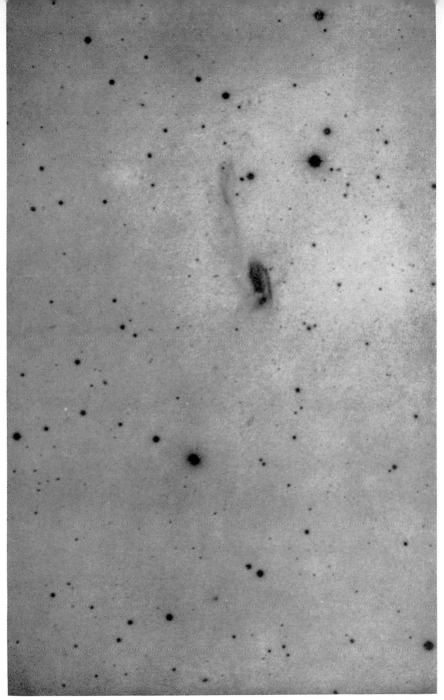

F. Zwicky

LIII—Bridges between Galaxies

This photograph in negative form shows the lanes of stars that sometimes stretch between galaxies. An obvious bridge is seen in the upper central part of the photograph. The hard circular images are local stars of our own Galaxy.

LIV—THE GALAXY M 74, AN SC SPIRAL

LV—THE GALAXY NGC 7217, AN EXAMPLE OF 'SPIRALITY'

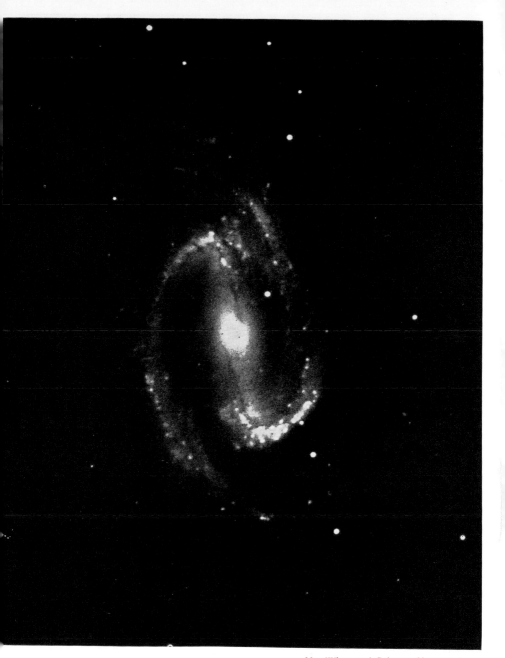

LVI—NGC 1300, a Fine Example of a Barred Spiral

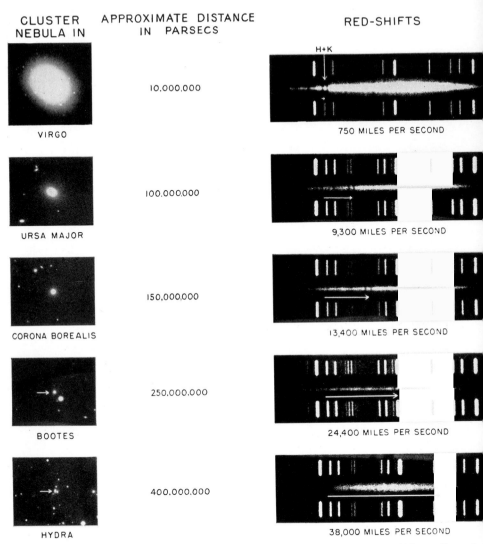

CLUSTER NEBULA IN	APPROXIMATE DISTANCE IN PARSECS	RED-SHIFTS

H+K

VIRGO — 10,000,000 — 750 MILES PER SECOND

URSA MAJOR — 100,000,000 — 9,300 MILES PER SECOND

CORONA BOREALIS — 150,000,000 — 13,400 MILES PER SECOND

BOOTES — 250,000,000 — 24,400 MILES PER SECOND

HYDRA — 400,000,000 — 38,000 MILES PER SECOND

Mt. Wilson and Palomar Observatory

LVII—THE RED-SHIFT EFFECT

Observational evidence for the expansion of the Universe.
1 parsec equals 19,200,000,000,000 miles.

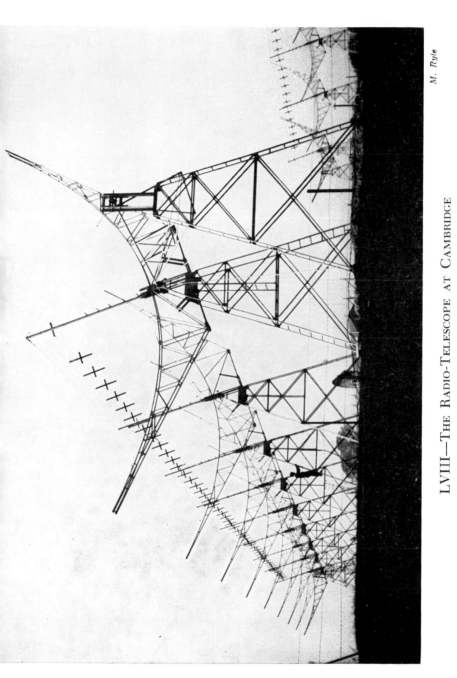

M. Ryle

LVIII—The Radio-Telescope at Cambridge

This instrument is used for observing cosmic transmitters of radio-waves. It operates at a wavelength of 3.7 metres, and covers about an acre of ground.

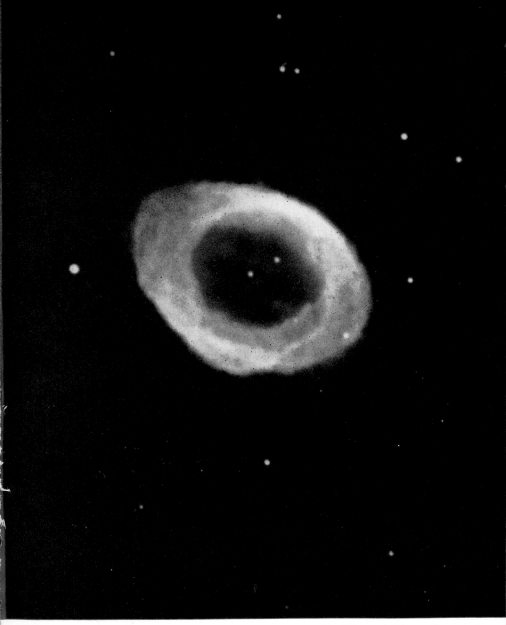

Mt. Wilson and Palomar Observatories

LIX—THE RING NEBULA

A shell of gas surrounding a star at a late evolutionary stage (beyond the Zwicky-Humason stars). The gas has presumably been expelled from the star.

one. The formation of spiral arms seems to be universal in all galaxies that possess outer gaseous disks, so widespread indeed as to make it certain that some quite decisive process must be at work. Yet no idea as to how the process operates has been suggested that compels even lukewarm support—the coffee-cup idea might perhaps be accepted as a plausible contributory factor but not as the main process.

In view of the long series of failures in attempts on this problem I think it is tempting to suppose that we simply have not been getting hold of the right end of the stick, that an entirely novel idea is required. The present hope is that the accumulation of knowledge about cosmic magnetic fields may supply the missing clue, for opinion is coming somewhat insistently to the point where magnetic fields are being thought of as playing a key role. But exactly how a magnetic field might cause spiral arms to be formed is still far from clear.

For myself, I incline to the view that the galaxies may possess magnetic fields that are not entirely internal in origin —that electric currents flowing in intergalactic space may serve to connect one galaxy to another. In Plate LII we have a case where one galaxy apparently influences the structural form of another. It used to be thought, on slender grounds, that the influence is gravitational but I think that a magnetic effect is more likely to prove correct. Cases are known where a spiral arm connects two galaxies. Plate LIII shows an extreme example observed by F. Zwicky in which an arm extends as a bridge between two galaxies. It would seem that if spiral arms are a manifestation of a galactic magnetic field then the bridge shown in Plate LIII should be considered as evidence of the presence of a supragalactic magnetic field. There is some evidence that these intergalactic bridges may be powerful emitters of radio waves. This would support their association with magnetic fields.

CHAPTER SEVENTEEN

The Formation of Galaxies

Stars by the million

The discussion of star-formation in Chapter 14 was entirely concerned with the origin of spiral arm stars, with stars of Type I. We must now extend our discussion to include the origin of the Type II stars. Some of our former arguments retain their cogency in this new context, particularly the argument that stars cannot condense one at a time. Yet the Type II stars in the nucleus of a spiral or in an elliptical galaxy do not seem to be arranged in separate clusters. How do we explain this? By what might seem a staggering answer, by saying that the nucleus of a spiral (or an elliptical galaxy) is itself just one gigantic cluster. We say that the Type II stars of a galaxy were all formed in a common process. In this way we explain at a stroke how it comes about that the Type II stars of a galaxy are of closely similar ages, why they are all old stars. But other questions remain to be answered. Why are Type II stars produced by millions at a time, whereas Type I stars are produced by only a few hundreds at a time? What is the cause of the Type II star-making cataclysms?

Two significant hints can be used to attack these questions. We have already noticed in Chapter 14 that a cloud can always pull itself together by its own gravitation if it contains a sufficient quantity of material. The amount required depends on the temperature of the gas. The higher the temperature the greater the mass of the cloud must be if condensation is to take place. And the greater the mass the larger the number of stars into which the cloud will eventually fragment.

The second hint points to the same conclusion. We have seen that the galaxies seem to be enveloped by extended halos of Type II stars. Presumably the halo stars were formed along with the rest of the Type II stars in the same gigantic process. Star-formation must therefore have taken place throughout the whole vast volume of the halo. Remembering that the halo surrounding a galaxy may be of two or three times the size of the galaxy itself, it is clear that the original gas cloud must have contained the whole galaxy. Evidently the origin of the galaxies themselves is closely associated with the formation of Type II stars. This gives us a plan to work on. We must now consider how the evolution of a galaxy out of a huge cloud of gas can be related to the formation of the Type II stars.

Supragalactic clouds

Let us first give attention to the density and temperature that the material of a supragalactic cloud is likely to possess. The density is easily discussed. We know fairly accurately what the average density in our Local Group of galaxies amounts to. It is about 60 parts in a million million million million million of the density of water. It must have been from material with this sort of density that the galaxies in our Local Group condensed. And since more distant galaxies seem to be very similar to those of the Local Group it is reasonable to suppose that the galaxies in general condensed from densities of about this amount.

It is much more difficult to decide what temperature the cloud is likely to have. To produce an enormous shower of stars a rather high temperature is necessary. This demands an initial absence of dust, for dust would cause molecules to be formed and molecules would produce an unduly low temperature, just as molecules produce low temperatures in the comparatively tiny interstellar clouds that lie in the spiral arms of the Galaxy (Plate XI). This requirement is not at all troublesome, however. Rather would it be very surprising if dust were not initially absent, for dust could neither be spontaneously generated by condensation from the gas at the low densities now in question, nor could any dust be produced by stars because no stars were present initially. We may suppose therefore that hydrogen atoms were the only important constituent of our supragalactic cloud.

Atomic hydrogen is unable to lose much energy by radiation unless its temperature rises above 10,000 degrees centigrade. But above 10,000 degrees, collisions between particles of the gas cause electrons to be knocked out of an increasing fraction of the atoms. The radiating power of the hydrogen then becomes quite strong.

Now a considerable amount of energy must be released by the gravitational field that causes the contraction of the very large clouds out of which whole clusters of galaxies form. This energy must heat up the gas. The degree to which the temperature of the gas will rise depends in part on the rate that energy is supplied to it and in part on the radiating properties of the hydrogen. Perhaps the most instructive way of presenting results is in terms of the curve of Fig. 60. It is seen that the energy requirement rises very steeply for temperatures between 10,000 and 25,000 degrees. This steep rise is mainly due to the strong emission of radiation that sets in when hydrogen is heated above 10,000 degrees. Comparatively little extra energy is required to lift the temperature from 25,000 to 100,000 degrees. But significantly greater quantities of energy are required to generate temperatures of millions of degrees.

It may be noted that the energy scale in Fig. 60 depends on the time taken for our supragalactic cloud to condense. Estimating this at 3,000 million years the unit of energy in Fig. 60 comes out at 100 kilowatts for every gram of material in the cloud*. For a typical cloud this would amount to a total of some 1,000,000,000,000,000,000,000,000,000,000,000, 000,000,000,000,000, kilowatts for the whole cloud. For comparison the total amount of energy consumed by the human species throughout the whole of its history is a mere 300,000, 000,000,000,000,000 kilowatts.

The energy supply is not likely to be so small that the initial temperature lies below 10,000 degrees. Nor does it seem likely that the temperature can be higher than 1 million degrees since this would require an implausibly large energy supply. Nor are all temperatures between 10,000 degrees and 1 million equally probable. The range from 25,000 to 150,000 degrees, B to C in Fig. 60, is an improbable range since it is most

*Properly, the unit of energy should here be written as the kilowatt-second, not the kilowatt.

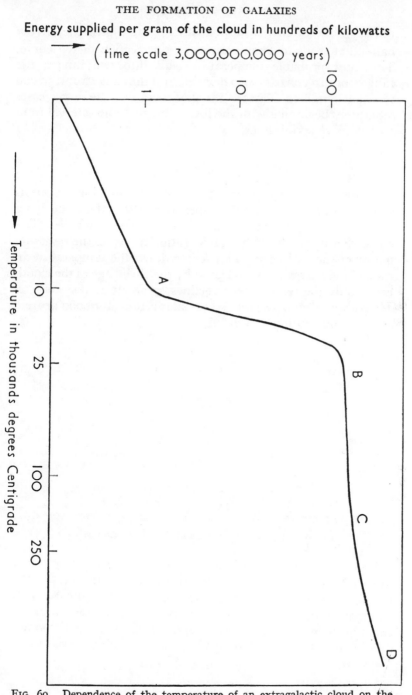

Fɪɢ. 6o.   Dependence of the temperature of an extragalactic cloud on the initial supply of gravitational energy.

unlikely that the energy supply will happen to fall in the narrow band that leads to temperatures in this section of the curve. The most probable temperatures fall into two ranges, the range from 10,000 to 25,000 degrees, and the range from 150,000 to about 1 million degrees. We shall deal with these two cases separately beginning with the lower interval, the interval from 10,000 to 25,000 degrees.

Fragmentation into galaxies of a moderate size

Consider then a supragalactic cloud condensing under its own gravitation, the initial temperature inside the cloud lying somewhere in the range from 10,000 to 25,000 degrees. The rise of density produced by condensation increases the radiating power of the hydrogen. This forces down the temperature in spite of the energy that is released by the shrinkage of the cloud. Eventually the temperature declines to about 10,000 degrees. Thereafter the temperature stays balanced near 10,000 degrees as the cloud continues to shrink.

(a) Thermal motion   (b) Aerodynamic motion

FIG. 61. In actual cases (a) and (b) are superimposed.

Equipped with this information we can now carry out a most relevant calculation. We can determine the proportion of the energy released by gravitation that goes into random thermal motions of the atomic particles (Fig. 61a) and how much goes into general aerodynamic motions inside the cloud (Fig. 61b). The answer depends on how much material there is in the condensing cloud. For a mass about 10,000 million times the Sun it turns out that a moderate degree of condensation supplies roughly equal contributions to the thermal motions and to the aerodynamic motions. But for appreciably larger masses—such as we may suppose our supragalactic cloud to possess—almost all the energy released by gravitation goes into the aerodynamic motions. Now this energy is not radiated away from the cloud like the energy of the temperature motions. This means that only a small proportion of the energy supplied by gravitation during the shrinkage of our cloud is lost by radiation, most of the energy is simply stored inside the cloud as aerodynamic motions. This storage prevents the cloud from shrinking to any great degree—for unless a shrinking gas cloud can get rid of an appreciable fraction of the energy released by gravitation the shrinkage cannot be permanent, the aerodynamic motions simply re-expand it. So apparently we arrive at the conclusion that a very large gas cloud cannot shrink permanently. It might shrink temporarily but a re-expansion would occur.

What then happens to a very large cloud of gas? The answer is simple. A large cloud of gas cannot shrink as a whole but it can shrink in bits. A portion of the cloud containing a mass perhaps 10,000 million times the Sun can shrink permanently to a moderate degree, say to about a third of its initial dimensions, for in this case an appreciable fraction of the energy released by gravitation does go into the thermal motions of particles and is radiated away and lost from the system. The aerodynamic motions are then insufficient to cause any important re-expansion. So we see that an extremely large cloud, even though it cannot evolve by shrinking as a whole, can evolve by breaking up into sub-systems each of which can shrink to a moderate extent. The sub-systems have masses of about 10,000 million times the Sun. This is a typical galactic mass, being comparable with the mass of M 33 (Plate XXXVII) and with the masses of M 32 and NGC 205, the two satellites of the Andromeda Nebula. We see then that a large cloud must break up into a group of sub-systems each with a typical galactic mass. We can say that the large cloud fragments into a cluster of galaxies.

These arguments give the beginning of an explanation of why galaxies have masses in the general neighbourhood of 10,000 million times the Sun, and of why a cloud with mass much greater than this must condense into a cluster of galaxies instead of into one single aggregation. Many subtleties still remain however. We have still to explain how monster galaxies like the Andromeda Nebula and our own Galaxy are produced. The monster galaxies have masses about 100,000 million times the Sun, ten times our present estimate. In the other direction there are many dwarf galaxies with masses probably no greater than 300 million times the Sun. The dwarf galaxies certainly cannot originate in the processes we have just described because at the density and temperature at present under discussion, sub-regions of a cloud with masses as small as those of the dwarf galaxies do not possess sufficient self-gravitation to shrink at all. So although our arguments are beginning to make some important things clear, we are still far from a thorough understanding of the whole process of formation of galaxies. At a later stage we shall see that a more complete understanding comes from thinking about clouds with temperatures in the high range from 150,000 to 1 million degrees. Since we have still to consider this case it is scarcely surprising that our present arguments do not give a complete description of the origin of galaxies. Before we discuss the high temperature range it will, however, be useful to continue the present discussion through to the stage where Type II star-formation takes place.

The formation of the Type II stars

Calculation shows that the shrinkage of a galaxy with a mass about 10,000 million times the Sun can proceed only to a moderate degree, perhaps to about one-third of the initial size. The gravitational energy released in any further contraction then goes nearly all into aerodynamic motions not into thermal motions. So no further permanent shrinkage can take place—the aerodynamic motions cause re-expansion just as they did with the original supragalactic cloud. And what happens next is similar to what happened before. The increase of density produced by the first moderate permanent shrinkage of the galaxy allows sub-regions within the galaxy to condense permanently. So the galaxy instead of continuing to condense as a whole, fragments into perhaps four or five sub-regions. The experience of each of the sub-regions is then entirely similar to that of the galaxy itself. The sub-regions can only shrink permanently by a moderate amount before they themselves again run into the same aerodynamic situation. Each of

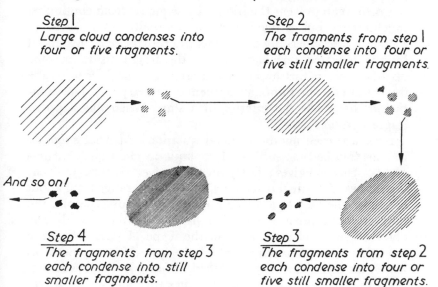

Step 1
Large cloud condenses into four or five fragments.

Step 2
The fragments from step 1 each condense into four or five still smaller fragments.

And so on!

Step 4
The fragments from step 3 each condense into still smaller fragments.

Step 3
The fragments from step 2 each condense into four or five still smaller fragments.

FIG. 62.   The hierarchy sequence.

the sub-regions must then fragment into four or five sub-sub-regions. The experience of each of the sub-sub-regions is then entirely similar to that of the sub-regions—and so on. Evidently we have to do with a step-by-step process along a hierarchy sequence. This is illustrated in Fig. 62.

Here we reach an important point. The times required for the steps of Fig. 62 grow less as we pass along the sequence. The time for stage (ii) is about one-quarter of the time for stage (i), and the time for stage (iii) is about one-quarter of the time for stage (ii), and so on for further stages. This may be expressed by saying that the time required for a whole series of steps (i), (ii), (iii), (iv), (v), (vi), (vii) . . . is only 25 per cent longer than the time required for step (i) alone. At each stage the fragments decrease in mass and size to about one-fifth of the mass and size at the previous stage.

Now does this hierarchical sequence go on indefinitely until the fragments become of negligible mass and size or does it stop after a more or less definite number of steps, and if so why? It appears that only a decline in the radiation emitted by the fragments can prevent the hierarchy sequence from continuing indefinitely. But a decline does eventually occur, because sooner or later the rising density within the fragments produced by the repeated shrinkages cause the fragments to become opaque. When this happens radiation can no longer escape freely from the interior of a fragment out into space. The situation becomes like the interior of a star. When this happens fragmentation stops.

Now we reach another crucial question. At what stage do the bits thus become sufficiently opaque to radiation? Fortunately calculation gives a fairly precise answer. It turns out that the masses of the final fragments must lie in a range from about 0.3 times the Sun as a lower limit up to about 1.5 times the Sun as an approximate upper limit. This is exactly the observed range of the masses of the Type II stars. We have now dug through to the root of the cataclysmic process in which the Type II stars are formed. We see how thousands of millions of stars can be formed in one stroke and we see moreover just why the Type II stars must have the individual masses that we observe them to possess.

We are not yet quite at the end of our consideration of the details of star-formation, however. It is in the very nature of the fragmentation sequence that a 'loose' system of stars is produced, not a closely condensed system like those of the elliptical galaxies or like the nuclei of the spirals. But this is no disadvantage, since we have to provide for the origin of the very extensive halos of stars that surround the galaxies. We now say that the halo of a galaxy is simply the volume occupied by the loose hierarchical system at the end of the fragmentation process. Then by encounters between different members of the loose structure a central condensation of stars is gradually built up. The members of the loose system tend to fall inwards towards a common centre. In the congestion that then arises near the centre the hierarchical system gets broken up and in its place a central amorphous mass of stars is formed. The process is illustrated in Fig. 63. Calculation gives about 1,000 parsecs for the diameter of the inner amorphous region—in excellent agreement with the dimensions of the satellites of the Andromeda Nebula. The uncondensed residue in such a case as that sketched in Fig. 63 forms the halo surrounding the galaxy.

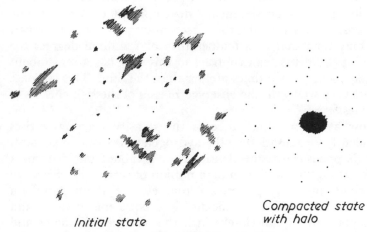

Initial state   *Compacted state with halo*

FIG. 63. The compacting of a Galaxy.

One point needs adding. Any rotation possessed by our original cloud must become particularly exaggerated during the formation of the inner condensed amorphous region. Rotational velocities and rotational forces always become more exaggerated as a system condenses. All supragalactic clouds may be expected to possess rotation even though in some cases it may be only slight. The gravitational field of one cluster of galaxies can endow another cluster with rotation. This is probably the main source from which the galaxies derive their rotations, although even within a particular cluster the gravitational field of one galaxy can endow another with a small degree of rotation. The effect of rotation is indicated by the elliptical form given to the central condensation of Fig. 63. The degree of the flattening will of course vary from one galaxy to another.

Monster galaxies

Our next step must be to consider the second of the two temperatures cases, the high temperature range from 150,000 to 1 million degrees. In this case radiation by the hydrogen does not become important until the supragalactic cloud has condensed to a very considerable degree. During this first contraction there is no significant development of aerodynamic motions. Consequently this first contraction is permanent. We may note that at a temperature of 1 million degrees the smallest cloud that can contract in this way has a mass about 100,000,000,000,000 times greater than the Sun. This estimate agrees very well with the observed masses of the rich clusters of galaxies.

Now as contraction proceeds the density eventually rises sufficiently for radiation by the hydrogen to become important. This happens when the density rises to about one part in a hundred million million million million of water. At this stage the cloud probably possesses a diameter of about 2 million parsecs. It is again significant that both this density and diameter agree quite closely with the observed diameter and average densities of the rich clusters of galaxies.

We reach a dramatic situation. Once radiation thus becomes important, a swift fall of temperature down to about 10,000 degrees takes place. Further contraction then produces fragmentation on an enormous scale. Because of the higher density produced by the first phase of shrinkage it turns out that the fragments are smaller and less massive than before. A calculation shows that they possess a mass some 300 million times the Sun, about a thirtieth of the former value. So our large supragalactic cloud breaks up into about 30,000 small galaxies each with about 300 million times the mass of the Sun.

The situation for each of these small galaxies follows along lines that are in some respects similar to those already discussed. Stars form by just the same sort of cataclysmic accelerating fragmentation process. If each loosely built system could be considered as an isolated system the final stages of development shown in Fig. 63 would again occur for each system separately. But now we have to consider the development, not of just one loose hierarchical structure but of a whole cluster containing as many as 30,000 systems. It seems that compacted amorphous masses of stars may form not out of one loose galaxy but out of many by addition. In this way monster galaxies containing upwards of 100,000 million times the mass of the Sun can be formed, requiring the compacting together of perhaps two or three hundred of the smaller galaxies. The view that the very large galaxies are formed by the compacting of many sub-systems is supported by the attachment of several hundred globular clusters to such monsters as NGC 4594 (the 'Sombrero'), to M 31—the Andromeda Nebula, to M 81, to our own Galaxy, etc. The globular clusters represent fragments that in themselves become separately compacted and so become attached to the monsters but without being absorbed by them. On this basis we might say that the Local Group was at one time composed of loose systems such as IC 1613 and the Fornax and Sculptor system, of perhaps 1,000 of these systems. The Andromeda Nebula and our Galaxy were then formed in a mopping-up operation, an operation in which several hundred loose smaller systems were aggregated together. The smaller members of the Local Group are simply debris that have survived from the mopping-up operation.

In this way it seems possible to explain both the existence of many small loose galaxies and of the monster galaxies.

The gaseous residue and the origin of magnetic fields

Some gas is likely to be left uncondensed. Indeed at each stage of the hierarchy sequence only those parts of the gas where the density is higher than average are likely to condense; the low density regions of a cloud do not condense. The uncondensed gas in a galaxy at the time of its formation might perhaps be as great as 30 per cent of the total mass.

It is from such an uncondensed residue that the outer disks

of the spirals are probably derived. The formation of the disk of a spiral may well be connected with the development of a magnetic field within the gas. An initially very small magnetic field can be built up into a large field by an appropriate general motion of the gas. This problem has been examined by Batchelor and independently by Biermann and Schlüter who all find that the type of motion, turbulent motion, that we may expect the gas masses to possess causes them to act like a dynamo. It is very likely in this way that the magnetic fields we have so often discussed originate—the magnetic fields that generate cosmic rays and intense radio-waves, the magnetic fields that may be of importance in the origin of spiral arms, the magnetic fields that are passed on to the Type I stars when they condense, the magnetic fields that probably play a key role in the origin of planetary systems.

We may sum up by itemising the important stages in the formation of a monster spiral galaxy such as our own: fragmentation of most of the material of a cloud into an assembly of 'loose' Type II star systems; a concentration of the loose systems into a nucleus; a concentration of the gaseous residue; a magnetic field generated within the gaseous residue as an outcome of turbulent motions; a disk of gas growing out of the nucleus probably through the agency of the magnetic field. To this we may add the possibility of the gaseous material of the disk developing spiral arms.

We are now concluding a cycle of argument that began with Chapter 13. For now we have seen in a brief outline how a galaxy such as our own can originate, a galaxy possessing a nucleus of perhaps 100,000 million stars, with an outer gaseous disk, with a magnetic field, possibly with spiral arms (our starting point in Chapter 13), with a surrounding halo of stars, with hundreds of attached globular clusters, and belonging with other galaxies to a cluster.

One point remains to make the chain complete. It seems unlikely that a second phase of star-formation will arise in the arms of the spirals until a supply of dust becomes available to cause a cooling of the gaseous residue. Where does this dust come from? We can probably guess the answer correctly. From the Type II stars of the nucleus and of the halo. The cooling produced indirectly by the dust (indirectly through molecule formation) concentrates the gas of the spiral arms and allows it to condense into the interstellar clouds that we have so often discussed. A second phase of star-formation then occurs within the interstellar clouds by just the processes that we considered in Chapter 14. These are the Type I stars. So it seems that the Sun and our planetary system came into being.

CHAPTER EIGHTEEN

The Expanding Universe

The Universe is everything; both living and inanimate things; both atoms and galaxies; and if the spiritual exists as well as the material, of spiritual things also; and if there is a Heaven and a Hell, of Heaven and Hell too; for by its very nature the Universe is the totality of all things.

There is a general impression abroad that the large scale aspects of the Universe are not very important to us in our daily lives—that if the Earth and Sun remained all else might be destroyed without causing us any serious inconvenience. Yet this view is very likely to prove wildly wrong. Present-day developments in cosmology are coming to suggest rather insistently that everyday conditions could not persist but for the distant parts of the Universe, that all our ideas of space and of geometry would become entirely invalid if the distant parts of the Universe were taken away. Our everyday experience even down to the smallest details seems to be so closely integrated to the grand scale features of the Universe that it is wellnigh impossible to contemplate the two being separated.

Olbers' paradox

Let us start with an everyday question, one so trivial that probably few have ever bothered to ask it, and yet one that has the most profound connections with the distant parts of the Universe. This is a question first asked by Olbers in 1826, and recently revived by H. Bondi.* Why is the sky dark at night? To appreciate the depth of this strange query suppose the Universe to be uniformly populated with clusters of galaxies. Draw a sphere with a large radius, anything you please say 1,000 million parsecs. Then draw a series of larger spheres, all

* *Cosmology*, Cambridge Monographs in Physics, 1952.

304

with the same centre, the difference in radius between one and the next being always the same, say 1,000 parsecs. The regions between successive spheres form the skins of an onion but of an infinite onion; they extend out indefinitely—however many spheres we draw, we can always draw one more. Now the volume of the successive skins increases proportionately to the square of the radius. Then since for a uniformly populated Universe the number of stars that fall in a particular skin must on the average be proportional to its volume, we see that the number of stars in successive skins increases as the square of the radius. But the intensity of the light that we receive from any individual star is proportional to the inverse of the square of its distance away from us—double the distance and we receive only a quarter of the light. So we have the following situation: each skin of the onion contains on the average a number of stars proportional to the square of its radius, while the intensity of radiation from each star—as measured by an observer at the centre of the system—is inversely proportional to the square of the radius. So the total intensity of the radiation received at the centre from all the stars of a particular skin does not depend at all on its radius—the increase in one factor simply cancels the decrease in the other. But since the number of skins can be made as large as we please, this means that the intensity of the light at the centre can also be made as large as we please—or at any rate large to the point where one star blocks out the light of another, and this does not arise until the whole sky becomes everywhere as bright as the disk of the Sun (taking the Sun to be a typical star). This requires the light and heat received from the Universe by the Earth to be about 6,000 million times greater than the intensity of full sunlight. Well, we don't receive this amount of radiation, otherwise we should be instantly burned up.

Obviously something has gone very wrong with the argument. The question is where? The immediate temptation is to doubt our starting assumption that the Universe is uniformly populated. The paradox would not arise if the material of the Universe were to exist in an isolated region of space, since in such a case the contributions of the skins could not be continued indefinitely. This was indeed the way that the scientists of the nineteenth century sought to escape from the dilemma. According to nineteenth-century views our Galaxy was to be regarded as isolated in space with nothing outside it. As late as the beginning of the present century a great controversy took place at an international conference of astronomers. On the one side, championed notably by R. A. Proctor, was the view that large numbers of galaxies exist outside our own, stretching away into the depths of space. On the other side, at that time the victorious side, the view was still expressed that the Universe consisted of our Galaxy only. Other galaxies were interpreted as local nebulosities lying within our own. The protagonists of this latter quite erroneous view based their case on a thoroughly wrong-headed argument, namely that no galaxies are observed in directions along the plane of the Milky Way. This was thought to prove the association of the galaxies with the Milky Way. But Proctor argued, just as we do today, that this apparent absence of galaxies is simply due to the absorbing effects of dust along the plane of the Galaxy. But the majority of astronomers in the first two decades of the present century could not accept this view for the reason that most of their researches on the structure of our Galaxy had proceeded on the assumption that dust was not a serious obscuring agent. It was not until about 1925 that these views became discredited, and the suggestions of Proctor became thoroughly vindicated. Notably as a result of the work of J. H. Oort and B. Lindblat it became realised that the structure of our Galaxy is radically different from what had formerly been thought, and that the older views were wholly in error due to the neglect of the obscuring effects of the interstellar dust particles. At about the same time it was established beyond question by E. P. Hubble that the galaxies are great independent star systems similar to our own and lying at enormous distances from us. In a few years Hubble took man's conception of the Universe from a localised region of a few thousand parsecs in dimensions out to unprecedented distances of hundreds of millions of parsecs; for not only did Hubble show that the galaxies are unquestionably great star-systems, as the Galaxy is, but he showed that out to distances of hundreds of millions of parsecs there is no evidence that we live in a purely localised aggregation of matter. The galaxies stretch away from us farther and farther into space and by the time they are lost to view (through faintness due to great distance) some 100 million or more of them are accounted for.

Since this decisive reorientation of man's outlook on the Universe—one of the most important scientific revolutions of thought of all time—no one has thought fit to suggest that the distribution of matter is localised in space. Rather has the opposite point of view come to gain general credence, that apart from local variations—the presence of a cluster of galaxies in one locality rather than in another, there are no marked spatial fluctuations in the distribution of matter on the large scale, that regardless of what the special position of the observer happens to be the Universe presents the same large scale aspects in the distribution of galaxies. It follows that Olbers' paradox is reinstated. It cannot be answered in the manner that scientists of the nineteenth and early twentieth centuries attempted to answer it.

A more sophisticated attempt to defeat Olbers' paradox depends on a time argument instead of a space argument. If all the stars of the Universe were younger than a definite age our former considerations would become invalid, since light from sufficiently distant skins of our onion would not yet have reached us. The process would have to be 'cut off' at a certain distance, the distance from which the transit time of light equalled the ages of the oldest stars. No light from still more distant skins could yet have arrived into our locality. This would invalidate our procedure of adding together equal contributions from as many skins as we please. Only a limited number could be reckoned as contributing to the light of the night sky.

Now we saw in Chapter 9 that the stars in our Galaxy are probably all younger than about 6,000 million years, and the similarity of the stars of neighbouring galaxies with those of our own suggests that they too are probably not much older than about 6,000 million years. So there is a measure of observational support for the present line of escape from Olbers' paradox. What we are now saying is that the Universe, although not constructed in such a way that its material content is confined to a particular spatial locality (and indeed although it may be spacially unlimited) is limited in time.

But this is a view that we must consider with some caution. There is a suspicious similarity between the nineteenth-century attempt to localise the material content of the Universe in space and the present suggestion of confining the existence of matter (or at any rate of stars) in time. In the case of spacial limitation the old views were supported by the finite spacial extension of our Galaxy. Now we are supporting the time limitation by the finite ages of the stars of our Galaxy. The two processes are logically similar in character and one of them having proved disastrously wrong we must be a little chary of accepting the other.

When the proposition is generalised from the statement that all stars are younger than a definite age to the proposition that the Universe is younger than a definite age I am inclined to be still more sceptical. What is implied by this view is that at a certain definite time in the past—say 6,000 million years ago, the laws of physics suddenly became applicable. Before this time physics was not applicable. After this time physics dominated the behaviour of the Universe. The transition between no-physics and all-physics was instantaneous.*

One has to be particularly cautious in accepting this sort of view because the human brain apparently possesses a kink in these matters that only too readily leads to serious mistakes. Europeans of the eighteenth century used to believe that the Universe came into being about 6,000 years ago! When this view was shown to be utterly wrong it was then said that the Universe was 20 million years old, then 100 million years, and so by a series of steps up to the 6,000 million years mentioned above.

Such arguments carry one no further, however, than the stage of suggestive speculation. But what does go further is a staggering discovery made by V. M. Slipher and by E. P. Hubble and M. Humason. If a singular origin of the Universe were the only escape from Olbers' paradox we should be well-

---

* Expressed in mathematical terminology, that the equations of physics possessed singularities about 6,000 million years ago, and that the equations cannot be continued through these singularities.

nigh forced to accept it. But the discovery just alluded to provides an escape along entirely unexpected lines. The existence of such a very strange resolution of the paradox greatly increases my doubts of the correctness of a finite temporal origin of the Universe.

The Universe is expanding. This is the purport of these discoveries. It is important to say right at the outset that the expansion is on the large scale, not local. The distances in our own solar system are not expanding, nor are the distances in our Galaxy, nor the distances in the Local Group. But beyond the Local Group, beyond about half a million parsecs, expansion begins. The giant galaxy M 81 (Plate XXIV) at a distance of 2,500,000 parsecs is moving away from us, its distance is increasing at about 80 miles per second. The galaxies of the Virgo cloud at a distance of perhaps 10 million parsecs are moving away from us at a speed of about 750 miles per second. The Corona cluster of galaxics (Plate XL) is moving away from us at rather more than 13,000 miles per second, while the Hydra cluster (Plate XLI) at a distance of some 400 million parsecs is increasing its distance every second by a further 38,000 miles. It may be of interest to compute how much farther away the Hydra cluster is now than it was at the moment when you began to read this chapter.

The red-shift

Now how is this known? In Chapter 13 we saw how motions towards or away from the observer can be determined by a study of the pitch of spectral lines emitted by a source of light. Our present sources are whole galaxies. It is thus found that all galaxies outside the Local Group are steadily moving away from us. Before examining Plate LVII, which illustrates these observations, we should notice that spectral lines can occur in two forms, as bright lines or as dark lines, the two cases being rather like the negative and positive of a photograph. When the atoms of a gas emit spectral lines the lines are bright. For example the lines emitted by a hot interstellar gas cloud are bright. When on the other hand light of all wavelengths without spectral lines is produced by a hot source—e.g. by the photosphere of a star, and when the light then passes through a comparatively cool cloud of gas, the cool gas often absorbs light at just the same characteristic wavelengths that it would emit if it were hot. In such a case the light that comes through the cool cloud is weakened at these characteristic wavelengths, which therefore appear as dark lines. The light from the Sun contains dark lines rather than bright lines, because the light from the photosphere passes through the slightly cooler material in the lower parts of the solar atmosphere. This is also the situation for most other stars. Dark lines are not of invariable occurrence, however. Very hot stars, stars very high on the main-sequence, emit bright lines. And some very cool stars also emit bright lines, as if particular patches on their otherwise cool surfaces become heated to comparatively high temperatures.

The relation of all this to the measurement of the red shifts— the displacement of lines in the direction of decreasing wavelength—is that because the great majority of stars show dark lines, the combined light of all the stars of a galaxy also shows dark lines. Several of the classic measurements by M. Humason are shown in Plate LVII, the lines employed being the H and K lines of calcium. In Plate LVII it is the somewhat hazy central band that represents the emission of the galaxy, wavelength increasing from left to right. The strong upper and lower lines were produced by terrestrial atoms. These were also photographed for comparison purposes.

The great discovery that galaxies far off are increasing their distances much more rapidly than the comparatively nearby galaxies is clearly shown by the examples given in Plate LVII. It may be noted that the distances marked in Plate LVII do not represent the original measurements of Hubble but have been modified to take account of more recent estimates to be discussed in the next chapter. The dependence of recessional velocities on the distances of the galaxies is shown in a more direct form in Fig. 64. The outstanding feature of this representation is the line that can be drawn through the observed results, showing that the expansion of the Universe takes place in a linear fashion—double the distance of a galaxy and the rate at which its distance is increasing also doubles. This

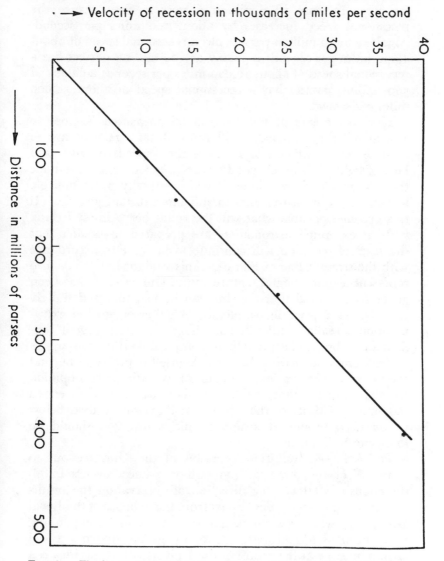

FIG. 64. The linear relation between distance and speed of recession (dots refer to actual observations).

311

result can be expressed in more precise form by saying that for every increase of a million parsecs in the distance the recessional speed increases by about 100 miles per second. A galaxy at 10 million parsecs has a recessional speed of about 1,000 miles per second; a galaxy at 100 million parsecs has a recessional speed of about 10,000 miles per second; a galaxy at 500 million parsecs has a recessional speed of about 50,000 miles per second.

The fastest rate of recession so far measured is close to 40,000 miles per second. Still more distant galaxies are so faint that it is difficult to measure their speeds because of a lack of light. There are good grounds, however, for the hope that by improved techniques it will eventually prove possible to extend the measurements to still more distant galaxies. If this becomes possible what will the result be? Almost I think without exception astronomers are prepared to predict that the rates of recession will continue to increase in accordance with the straight line of Fig. 64. This straight line is taken to represent a fundamental feature of the Universe. It has been generally accepted that the line can be extended indefinitely to distances as great as we please. Whether or not this extrapolation is really justified is something that needs urgent confirmation, but unfortunately a complete verification up to speeds comparable with that of light itself is probably beyond the power of observation. In conformity with general opinion we shall assume that the line of Fig. 64 can be extended indefinitely. Many of the arguments that will be used below would need serious alteration if this assumption should be found to be in error.

The observed uniform expansion of the Universe out to distances of the order of 400 million parsecs occurs in all directions. Whatever the direction of observation the results are always the same. That apart from the galaxies of the Local Group the whole system of galaxies seems to be expanding away from us has suggested to many people that our Local Group must be at the centre of the Universe. But this idea is a logical *non sequitur*. Imagine a pudding containing raisins being steamed in an oven. Let the raisins represent the clusters of galaxies. Suppose that the raisins do not expand as the pudding cooks, but that the pudding itself swells steadily. Then in the swelling every raisin moves away from every other raisin: an observer attached to *any* raisin would see the others all receding away from him. Moreover if the pudding were to swell uniformly (in such a way that its material remained of a uniform consistency) the raisins would have the linear property shown in Fig. 64—the greater the distance between two raisins the greater the rate at which their distance apart increases—double the distance and the rate of increase also doubles.

Of course it can be said that a pudding has a centre but we judge the centre of a pudding from the shape of its boundary. To give a parallel with the Universe we must imagine the pudding not possessing a boundary, but being an infinite pudding. The word 'infinite' should cause no conceptual difficulties. It simply means that however much of the pudding we consider there is always more of it.

Olbers' paradox again

It is now necessary to relate all this back to Olbers' paradox. It will be recalled that Olbers' paradox arose from dividing space up by a series of spheres thereby forming a series of skins. It turned out that the contribution of the stars in a particular skin to the light received at the centre was always the same no matter what the radius of the skin happened to be. This property depended on the number of stars in a skin increasing with the radius of the skin in a way that just compensated for the weakening by increasing distance of the light received from each star. Now this cancellation no longer occurs when the clusters of galaxies are receding from each other. This is a most important and significant point. It turns out that expansion causes a further weakening of the light, an additional weakening that destroys the cancellation, and which completely resolves Olbers' paradox.

This further weakening of the light is very small for galaxies that are near to us, such as the galaxies of the Virgo cloud. But the effect becomes stronger as the distances increase. At the greatest distance to which red-shift measurements have

313

been made (the galaxies of the Hydra cluster at about 400 million parsecs) the weakening is to about ⅔ of the intensity that the light would have if no expansion were occurring. At the maximum distance of about 1,000 million parsecs to which the 200-inch telescope at Palomar Mt. can penetrate (Plate XLII) the light is weakened to about ⅓ of what it would be if no expansion were occurring. The situation becomes even more drastic at still greater distances (assuming the extrapolation of the line of Fig. 64). Indeed at a distance of about 2,000 million parsecs, where the rate of increase of the distance comes up to the speed of light itself, the light is weakened to nothing at all! No light emitted by the stars in a skin with a radius greater than about 2,000 million parsecs can ever reach us. There is an absolute cut-off at this distance. So our former argument that the number of contributing skins can be made as large as we please is no longer valid. Hence the amount of light received cannot be made extremely great and Olbers' paradox is resolved. Indeed the amount of light that we can receive can be worked out from the known distribution of galaxies. It turns out to be very small, much less than the sunlight scattered by the gases that lie within our own planetary system and which contributes to the glow of the night sky. The effect of the very distant galaxies on this glow is therefore very small. *The sky is dark at night because the Universe expands.* This is the unexpected resolution of the puzzle—so unexpected that it never occurred to the scientists of the nineteenth century. We started the present chapter by saying that everyday matter of fact observations are deeply related to the grand scale features of the Universe. Here we have an illustration of this statement.

Did the Universe have a singular origin?

At an earlier stage we considered the possibility of avoiding Olbers' paradox by assigning a definite origin in time to the Universe. Now that Olbers' paradox is resolved in a far subtler way it would be natural to discount entirely the idea of a singular origin were it not that the expansion of the Universe apparently gives support to it from an unexpected direction.

Expansion takes the clusters of galaxies apart from each other. Space is therefore (it seems) getting more and more empty as time goes on. Space must accordingly (it seems) have been more densely occupied in the past than it is today. Indeed if the Universe has always been expanding as it is at present, space must (it seems) have been jammed tight with matter not so very long ago.

Let us formulate the argument a little more precisely. Suppose we take the distance of a particular cluster of galaxies and divide by the rate at which its distance is increasing. Because of the linear property of Fig. 64 the result is essentially the same whatever cluster we elect to use for this purpose. The result is a period of time known as the Hubble constant—constant because it is the same for all clusters. Perhaps the best value consistent with all present-day knowledge is about 7,000 million years. The determination of this particular value will be discussed in the next chapter. Now let us imagine ourselves going backwards in time for 7,000 million years (not a fantastic piece of theorising; the Earth is some 4,000 million years old). Then if the clusters of galaxies have always had their present rates of recession the manner of derivation of Hubble's constant requires all the clusters of galaxies to have been jammed on top of each other at that time, giving a density of matter in space that rises inordinately high, indefinitely high, infinitely high. This state of affairs represents, according to the view of some astronomers, the singular start of the Universe. On this view such important features of the Universe as its expansion and its large scale uniformity of composition were impressed on the Universe at the start by the manner of creation. Creation could have occurred quite differently, matter might have been distributed lopsidedly without large scale uniformity, but it isn't because it wasn't created that way. Indeed the Universe might have been created in any of an infinity of other ways but it wasn't. It was created to have just the properties of expansion and of uniformity that we observe. If we ask why so, no answer can be given.

At the time of creation the density of material was very high, much higher than the density of water. As expansion proceeded the density became steadily less: it decreased to the density of water; then steadily down and down until it reached a millionth of the density of water; then steadily further down to a million millionth of the density of water; down and ever down to a million million millionth of the density of water; further down and still further down to a million million million millionth of the density of water; and so down to about a thousand million million million millionth of the density of water, when at long last something happened—the clusters of galaxies were formed, presumably as a result of some such process as was described in the previous chapter. Once the clusters of galaxies had condensed, the expansion continued by way of increasing the distances between the clusters, this being the stage of the proceedings that we now observe.

Let us see whether this argument is really an inescapable one. What are the alternative possibilities? One alternative is to deny that the Universe has always been expanding. This can be done in a consistent way by postulating that the real nature of gravitation differs from classical Newtonian ideas. Instead of requiring attraction always to occur between two particles as in the Newtonian theory it can be argued that attraction occurs only if the distance between two particles is not too great, otherwise attraction is replaced by repulsion. And if instead of considering just two particles we consider a whole cloud of matter the modified situation is that gravitation produces a condensation of the cloud only if its density is sufficiently high, otherwise a general repulsion and dispersal occurs. The densities at which repulsive gravitation thus becomes operative are so low that there is no question of the ordinary attractive form of gravitation being appreciably modified in our solar system or in the Galaxy or in other galaxies.

Similar arguments can be applied to the Universe at large. If the average density in the Universe is less than a certain critical value (fixed by hypothesis) then the Universe will start to expand even if it is not expanding to begin with. If on the other hand the average density in the Universe is just equal to the critical value, the Universe remains static if it is initially static. But this state of balance is unstable—give the Universe a slight expansion and it continues to expand with ever increasing speed, give it a slight contraction and it contracts with ever increasing speed.

The object of thus altering the law of gravitation is to explain the observed expansion of the Universe without any need for an initially explosive state. On this view when we go back into the past the density of matter does not pile up indefinitely because the expansion was then slower than it is now; and sufficiently back in the past there was no expansion at all because the Universe started from the balanced state just described.

A special feature of this theory is that it provides a better way of forming galaxies. It can be shown that clusters of galaxies could condense in the balanced initial state. Although on the very large scale it must be supposed that some unknown cause disturbed the Universe in such a way as to set it off expanding instead of contracting, in local regions the reverse situation might have occurred—local regions might have started contracting instead of expanding, thereby forming clusters of galaxies. In the explosion theory the formation of clusters of galaxies has to be introduced as an *ad hoc* process that takes place for no good reason at just the stage where the density of matter falls to a thousand million million million millionth part of the density of water (or perhaps somewhat less than this). But in a theory with gravitation modified along the lines indicated above the origin of the clusters of galaxies is afforded a more natural explanation. A state of balance implies the possibility of the balance being tipped in localised regions towards contraction.

To end the present chapter a second flaw in the argument for a superdense singular explosive origin of the Universe will be discussed. Without any modification of gravitation of the sort contemplated above it is still incorrect to argue that expansion necessarily implies a superdense singular explosive origin of the Universe. This inference is not valid unless all the matter now in existence was also in existence in the past.

It is therefore important to examine the idea that many of the atoms now in existence were not in existence in the past, and that many of the atoms of the Universe that will be in existence in the future are not in existence today. This idea requires atoms to appear in the Universe continually instead of being created explosively at some definite time in the past. There is an important contrast here. An explosive creation of the Universe is not subject to analysis. It is something that must be impressed by way of an arbitrary fiat. In the case of a continuous origin of matter on the other hand the creation must obey a definite law, a law that has just the same sort of logical status as the laws of gravitation, of nuclear physics, of electricity and magnetism. This distinction is very important and is worth a rather more detailed exposition.

The laws of physics are expressed by mathematical equations. The symbols that appear in the equations are related either directly or indirectly to quantities that can be determined by observation. The logic of classical physics is very straightforward. If the observable quantities are known at one particular instant of time, the equations must enable us to determine their values at all other times. That is to say the laws of physics allow us to proceed from a known situation to a *prediction* of what is going to happen in the future. It is because of the ability to make correct predictions that physics has come to play such a dominant role in our modern civilisation. Past societies of men are referred to as the stone-age, the bronze-age, and the iron-age. The civilisation of the present day might perhaps most appropriately be termed the age of physics. In the past there has been no shortage of prophets and necromancers, but it is physics that has proved the first really reliable agent in human experience for the making of predictions.

Now what decides the laws of physics? What decides the form of the mathematical equations that refer to the phenomenon of gravitation for instance—the equations that determine how the planets move around the Sun? What decides the form of the mathematical equations that refer to the propagation of radio-waves? The answer to these questions is very simple—the success of the predictions that are made by the equations. The laws of physics are governed by a process of intellectual natural selection. When they make correct predictions they survive. When they make incorrect predictions they become extinct. Physicists then look for new laws that do not make incorrect predictions.

By now we are in a position to appreciate the difference between the two views on the origin of the material of the Universe. In the case of an explosive origin of the material, the origin is expressed by the starting conditions, not by the laws of physics themselves. In the case of a continuous origin there is no possibility of expressing the creation as a starting condition, since creation happens all the time. A continuous origin must therefore be expressed in terms of equations whose properties can be worked out by the processes of mathematics, and whose predictions can be confirmed or disproved. In one case the origin is assigned to an arbitrary fiat and no modification of the laws of physics is required. In the other case there is no arbitrary fiat but a modification of the laws of physics has to be made. The origin of matter thus becomes susceptible to treatment on a similar footing to the phenomena of gravitation, of electro-magnetism, and of the forces that bind the atomic nuclei together. We shall have more to say on the divergence between these two points of view in the last chapter. For the present it is sufficient to realise that a theory of the continuous origin of matter must face up to the challenging issue of determining a mathematical law that serves to control the creation of matter. Let it be said at once that no thoroughly satisfactory way of devising such a law has yet been found. All the attempts that have yet been made are clearly susceptible of improvement, and one can now be fairly sure of the direction that the improvements are likely to take. This again is an issue that we shall take up in the last chapter. For the present it is enough that imperfect as the equations no doubt are they are good enough to enable a number of very interesting results to be obtained.

The first is that the Universe must expand. The steady origin of matter forces the Universe to expand. The effect of the origin is to cause a stretching of space that takes the clusters of galaxies apart from each other. The stretching of space takes the part of the swelling of the pudding in the analogy we used above. The steady potentiality for new atoms to appear in space gives space active physical properties, it is no longer an inert something in which matter resides.

The origin of matter not only forces the Universe to expand

but the rate of expansion is determined. If the Universe were expanding initially at some arbitrary rate, then the origin of matter causes the rate either to increase or to decrease according to the initial conditions until a definite value is reached, after which the rate is steadily maintained. The expansion rate so reached has the same value irrespective of the initial state of affairs, a value such that the average density of matter in space is maintained constant. The steady origin of matter in space does not therefore lead to space becoming fuller and fuller of material. Nor does the expansion of the Universe lead to space becoming more and more empty. The rate of expansion is forced to come into step so as to compensate exactly for the steady origin of material. It is the appearance of this remarkable balance as a *consequence* of the theory that gives one of the strongest reasons for regarding the continuous origin of matter as a serious possibility whose consequences demand just as careful consideration as those of the two other types of theory that were discussed above. It should be explained here that a somewhat different outlook on the whole problem of the continuous origin of matter has been put forward by Bondi and Gold. Bondi has described this in detail in a recent book *Cosmology*.* The present development expresses my own outlook, which has been also influenced by the work of W. H. McCrea and by F. Pirani.

The maintenance of a constant average density of matter in space has led to the concept of the steady-state universe. Since the average density of matter in space is the same at all times, the present and the future should be just as good for the condensation of clusters of galaxies as the past was. So the theory suggests that clusters of galaxies should not only have formed in the past but should be forming at present and should go on forming in the future. This is in sharp distinction to the other two types of theory, which require all galaxies to have condensed about 6,000 million years ago. The steady-state theory suggests that although expansion leads to the distances between the centres of clusters of galaxies increasing, new clusters of galaxies condense at such a rate that the average number within a fairly large region of space remain effectively un-

* H. Bondi, *op. cit.*

altered with time. In this way we arrive at a Universe in which the individuals—the clusters of galaxies—change and evolve with time but which itself does not change. The old queries about the beginning and end of the Universe are dealt with in a surprising manner—by saying that they are meaningless, for the reason that the Universe did not have a beginning and it will not have an end. Every cluster of galaxies, every star, every atom had a beginning, but not the Universe itself. The Universe is something more than its parts, a perhaps unexpected conclusion.

CHAPTER NINETEEN

Observational Tests in Cosmology

Was there ever a superdense state?

It is a suspicious feature of the explosion theory that no obvious relics of a superdense state of the Universe can be found. One might have expected for instance that galaxies of very high average density would have been formed during the early stages of expansion. But this did not happen. The average densities actually occurring in the galaxies are very low, amounting to no more than one million million million millionth part of that of water. What is the explanation of this? Why are there no galaxies with an average density of one million millionth of water? Why did the Universe apparently wait until the average density of matter in space sank below one million million million millionth part of that of water before any condensation occurred?

An ingenious answer has been offered to these questions by George Gamow, who argues that during the early phases of a superdense Universe radiation was the predominant form of energy, not matter. According to Gamow's theory the importance of radiation decreased as expansion proceeded until the main source of energy eventually came to be resident in the matter. It was not until this stage was reached that clusters of galaxies could condense.

As an aside, we may ask why the energy carried by radiation declines as the Universe expands. What happens to the energy of the radiation? It goes into expanding the Universe. This also answers a question often asked about the radiation that is constantly being emitted by the stars in all the galaxies. What happens to the radiation of a star as it travels out into space? Where does it go to? It does not travel indefinitely without modification, since it experiences the red-shifting process. This means that the electric vibrations of the light go slower and slower the farther the light travels. The red-shift process thus causes the light to lose energy. This is just the Olbers paradox again—or rather this is just the cut-off process that saves us from Olbers' paradox. The energy lost by the light goes into expanding the Universe. But we must not make the mistake of supposing that the light from present-day stars provides the main cause of expansion. It amounts to less than a hundredth of one per cent of what is required to drive the Universe at its observed rate of expansion. The effect is a small one.

Returning now to our main argument, although the reason why we do not observe superdense galaxies can be explained away in the manner suggested by Gamow it is a little suspicious that it should be necessary to explain it away. It is strange that events have conspired to hide from us all direct evidence of the existence of a state as spectacular as an explosive creation of the Universe must certainly have been, if it ever existed.

Until recently it seemed as if the elements other than hydrogen might be taken as evidence in favour of a superdense state. According to views developed by Gamow, Alpher, and Herman all the elements were built up from free neutrons (neutrons decay into hydrogen) during the earliest phases of the existence of the Universe—in the first 20 minutes or so: according to Gamow's phrase 'in less time than it takes to cook roast duck and potatoes'. So on this basis it could be said that relics of the superdense state do exist, namely the elements other than hydrogen.

If this view were correct we should expect all stars to contain the same proportion of metal atoms; for if the process that led to the origin of heavy elements were a universal one there should be no local variations of composition. But this is not so. We have seen that the earliest stars to form in the Galaxy possess very low concentrations of heavy elements; and that through the building of heavy elements in stars, and through their distribution in space by the supernovae, stars possess more and more heavy elements in proportion to hydrogen the later the stage at which they are born. This gives such a good account of the observed differences between young and old stars that it can scarcely be maintained any longer that the building of all heavy elements belongs to the earliest moments of a superdense universe. The best that can be argued is that a small proportion of the elements, the small proportion found in the oldest stars, might be associated with the superdense state. But this is such a serious weakening of the original proposition that it must be considered to point quite strongly against the concept of the superdense state. The argument could to some extent be saved if the presence of comparatively small proportions of heavy elements in the oldest stars could not be explained in any other way. But it can be explained in another way, very readily by the steady state theory. This point is worth considering at some length, especially as it offers the answer to a question that was left over from Chapter 12.

So far in our discussion of the continuous origin of matter we have said little about its composition at the time of origin. We now introduce the assumption that it is the simplest of all substances, hydrogen. Neutrons might seem an equivalent choice, since neutrons decay by a β-process into hydrogen atoms. But neutrons represent a higher energy state than hydrogen atoms, so we shall suppose that matter originates as hydrogen atoms, choosing the lower energy condition of these two possibilities. The hypothesis that matter originates throughout space as hydrogen does not mean that a galaxy must consist entirely of pure hydrogen at the time it condenses however. This would only be correct if there were no pre-existing galaxies. But in the steady-state theory there are always other galaxies that pre-exist any particular galaxy, and these will already have produced heavy elements. Some of the heavy elements thus generated will certainly remain trapped inside the interstellar gases of their parent galaxies but a proportion must escape altogether, not only from the parent galaxy but even from the cluster of galaxies of which it is a member. This is especially so for elliptical galaxies which contain very little gas wherewith to trap the heavy elements. So we see that space is not only populated by the hydrogen atoms that originate in space but also by heavy elements that are thrown off by exploding stars in the galaxies, although of course the latter contribution is very small compared with the former. But it is large enough to account for the low concentrations of elements that are found in the oldest stars of our Galaxy.

It should be possible to check this argument by observation. If the elements present in the oldest stars of our Galaxy were produced in a superdense state of the Universe, while the majority of the heavy elements present in young stars are produced by exploding stars, then we should expect that the relative proportions of one heavy element to another should be different in the two cases—for the reason that two entirely different processes of origin of the heavy elements must be reflected by considerable differences in their relative abundances. If on the other hand the heavy elements present in the 'first' stars to form in a newly condensed galaxy were produced by the supernovae of previously existing galaxies, as the steady-state theory requires, then there should be no notable differences in the relative abundances of heavy elements in young and old stars—the absolute concentrations should be different but not the relative proportions of one element to another. Here then is a definite means of testing the two theories. Within a few years definitive results should be available. The observations although difficult to make should be within the range of what is possible.

Before leaving this question of heavy elements it may be noted that the presence of heavy elements, even in low concentration, in very old stars is a strong point against the second type of theory that was discussed above, the theory that depended on modifying the nature of gravitation. In such a theory all galaxies form at the same time and if the material that they form out of is hydrogen then the 'first' stars should consist of pure hydrogen—previously existing galaxies cannot be invoked in the same way as in the steady-state theory, nor is there any superdense state in which to build an initial supply of heavy elements.

The value of Hubble's constant

Hubble's constant was introduced in the previous chapter, where its most probable value was given as about 7,000 million years. It is desirable, because of its subsequent importance, to see how this value is obtained before we go on to discuss further ways of testing the different cosmological theories. To obtain Hubble's constant from observation it is necessary first to choose a cluster that is sufficiently distant for any purely random motions that the galaxies inside it may possess to contribute only negligibly to the red-shift measurement. This is the case for example with the Hydra cluster, which is found to be receding from us at a speed of about 60,000 kilometres per second. So if the distance of the Hydra cluster can be found we have only to divide the distance by 60,000 kilometres per second to obtain Hubble's constant. The question therefore turns on the determination of the distance of this cluster, or of some other suitable cluster.

Now a determination of distance cannot be made with the aid of any of the standard headlights discussed in earlier chapters, since no single star except possibly a supernova can be separately distinguished at the distance of the Hydra cluster. Only a whole galaxy can serve as a standard headlight at this distance. It is at this stage of the argument that great caution must be exercised. The galaxies of the Local Group and other nearby galaxies vary very considerably in brightness from one to another. Which should we regard as typical?

Perhaps the best procedure that can be adopted at the present time is to assume that the brighter galaxies in all clusters are closely comparable in their luminosities. This would make the brighter galaxies comparable with M 31, our large companion in the Local Group. It is true that the majority of galaxies are considerably fainter than M 31, but these are not the galaxies that we see at great distances—great distance forces us to give attention only to the brightest galaxies.

The case for choosing the Andromeda Nebula as a standard headlight is not as arbitrary as this brief statement might suggest. In the first place the three galaxies M 31, M 81 (Plate XXIV) and our own Galaxy, turn out (with the new distance measurements discussed in former chapters) to be of very similar brightnesses as well as of very similar masses, so similar as to suggest that all three belong to a group of more or less standard galaxies. This view is supported by the determinations of the average masses of the galaxies in the Virgo cloud and in the Coma cluster made some years ago by Sinclair Smith and by F. Zwicky. These determinations yielded average masses quite close to that of the Andromeda Nebula, as indeed has the recent determination by Thornton Page of the average mass of double galaxies. Double galaxies are galactic systems that move around each other as the two stars of a double star do.

The argument for regarding M 31 as a typical member of the brighter class of galaxy accordingly seems to be a strong one. The headlight method for determining distances can be used on this basis, since the intrinsic brightness of M 31 is now known with considerable accuracy, thanks to the work of Baade and of Erik Holmberg. It turns out that the distance of the Hydra cluster is rather more than 400 million parsecs, and Hubble's constant is about 7,000 million years.

Now this value is very much greater than the 1,800 million years quoted a few years ago, so much greater that a short comment on the reasons for the change is worthwhile. The former estimate of 1,800 million years was based on two seemingly erroneous steps: one a fourfold underestimate of the intrinsic brightness of M 31, and the other the curious assumption that M 31 is the brightest galaxy in the Universe, being some 4 times more luminous than the brightest galaxies in any of the great clusters—surely an unlikely supposition.

That the new determination of Hubble's constant is much more likely to be correct than the old value is shown by an entirely independent argument. In Chapter 12, when discussing the Crab Nebula (Plate XXIX), we saw that distances can also be determined by what we called the method of the standard yardstick: that when the actual size of an object is known a measurement of its apparent size enables the distance to be calculated. Now the actual size of M 31 is known with a considerable degree of accuracy. So if we assume that other galaxies of structurally similar form, other Sb galaxies that is to say, have the same size as M 31 their distances can readily be determined. Distances obtained in this way confirm that Hubble's constant must be as great as 7,000 million years— indeed the yardstick method suggests that 9,000 million years might possibly be a better value.

Criteria depending on Hubble's constant

Hubble's constant plays an important but different part in each of the three theories at present under review. In the superdense theory the ages of all the galaxies must be comparable with, but less than, Hubble's constant. This requirement can only be tested with reasonable accuracy in the case of our own Galaxy. With the age of the Galaxy at about 6,000 million years and with Hubble's constant at 7,000 million years the requirement is evidently well satisfied. In the second theory with the modified form of gravitation, the ages of the galaxies should all be greater than Hubble's constant. The case of our own Galaxy would thus seem to contradict the second theory. In the theory based on the continuous origin of matter the galaxies should *on the average* have ages that are comparable with, and probably somewhat less than, Hubble's constant but there is no special requirement on the age of a particular galaxy (such as our own for instance). The third theory is not therefore exposed to any serious test on this particular point, although it is satisfactory that our Galaxy comes out to have an age not much different from the average for all galaxies.

Hubble's constant does have a further deeper significance in the third theory however. We have seen that in this theory the rate of expansion of the Universe is determined by the rate of the origin of matter—Hubble's constant is determined by the rate of origin of matter that is to say. We can now ask the question: what rate of origin is required to explain a value of 7,000 million years for Hubble's constant? The answer is that one hydrogen atom must originate every second in a cube with a 160 kilometre side; or stated somewhat differently: that about a quarter of a million hydrogen atoms originate every second in a volume of space equal to the volume of the Earth, or about one atom every century in a volume equal to the Empire State Building. Although this might seem very small, it is not small when added up throughout the whole 'observable' Universe. The 'observable' Universe is defined to be just the part of the Universe within the Olbers' cut-off distance at some 2,000 million parsecs. Within this region of space matter originates at about a hundred million million million million million tons per second.

In the steady-state theory the average density of matter in space does not decrease with time, as in the other two theories. It remains constant at a value that depends on the rate of origin of matter. For the rate just quoted the density is about 3 parts in a hundred thousand million million million million of the density of water, or about one atom of hydrogen to a good sized suitcase. Contrast this with the interior of a supernova where a good sized suitcase would contain several million tons of material.

In the steady-state theory we expect expansion to cease wherever the density exceeds the average more than two or threefold. Any localised region in which this occurs then forms a 'bound' system. On the steady-state theory we accordingly expect that 'bound' regions can exist at all densities greater than this. We expect the density of matter within the clusters of galaxies to vary from one cluster to another but never so as to fall below two or three times the average for the whole Universe. This requirement of the theory is strikingly confirmed by observation as the following remarks will show.

The Local Group is an example of a particularly weak cluster, so that the observed density in the Local Group can be regarded as giving an estimate for the density of the weakest bound systems. Now it turns out that the density within the Local Group is indeed about two or three times greater than the theoretical average density for the whole Universe, the one corresponding to a value of 7,000 million years for Hubble's constant. The agreement of theory and observation is excellent.

It has been supposed by some supporters of the steady-state theory that the change in Hubble's constant from the old value of 1,800 million years to 7,000 million years is a pity—for the reason that a value of 1,800 million years presented such a severe age difficulty to the superdense theory as apparently to place it entirely out of court. What was not perceived in this view however was that 1,800 million years for Hubble's constant would also be in flat disagreement with the steady-state theory. Such a value for Hubble's constant would imply an average density of matter in the whole Universe some 15 times greater than the value given above. This would place the density within the Local Group *lower* than the average density in space and would require the Local Group to expand apart, which it is not doing. It needs a value of 7,000 million years for Hubble's constant to explain why the Local Group remains a bound cluster.

Remarks on the formation of new galaxies in the steady-state theory

Only those features that are self-propagating can exist in a steady-state Universe. The formation of galaxies is an example of a feature that must be self-propagating, one generation of galaxies giving rise to the next generation—as with humans. We may think of the galaxies as possessing a reproduction factor, defined as the factor by which the average space density of galaxies in one generation exceeds that in the previous generation.

Now on a very general argument the only possible average reproduction factor is 1. The reason for this rests on the infinitely large number of generations that have occurred in the past (infinitely large simply means greater than any number you care to mention). Thus if in the past the average reproduction factor had been less than 1 the density of galaxies would have grown less generation by generation, until after a sufficiently large number of generations no galaxies at all would have been left—which we observe not to be the case. If on the other hand the average reproduction factor had been greater than 1 the space density of galaxies would have grown greater generation by generation until by now the density would have become infinitely great—which also we observe not to be the case. So we see that the only possible average factor is 1. What reason can we give for this?

The best explanation is a very simple one: that the density of galaxies is limited by the availability of material. Suppose that the reproduction factor is greater than 1 when plenty of material is available. Then the density of galaxies will increase steadily until a shortage of material does eventually arise, as it must sooner or later since the average total density of matter in space is fixed, (the total density includes both condensed and uncondensed material). The reproduction factor must then fall back to 1 and stay thereafter at 1.

The argument is entirely analogous to the discussion by Malthus of human populations. With human populations the average reproduction factor is greater than 1 when ample supplies of food are available. The population increases generation by generation until a shortage of food arises. The resulting increase in the mortality rate then cuts the reproduction rate back to 1. In our own time Malthus has been foolishly discredited on the basis that his predictions have been falsified in Western civilisation. The reason for the falsification is that supplies of food have risen to a degree that Malthus never anticipated. But no mathematician can have the slightest faith in the arguments of the opponents of Malthus. Rising food supplies must sooner or later (the word *must* is unqualified) fail to keep pace with rising populations so long as the reproduction factor is greater than 1. It may be added by way of ending this comparison between our human society and the galaxies that whereas a human generation is reckoned at 30 years, a galactic generation must be reckoned in terms of Hubble's constant, 7,000 million years!

Tests of the steady-state theory

We have now amassed sufficient information to apply another test to the steady-state theory, but we must be careful to get the conditions of the test correct. It is not a valid conclusion from the above remarks that the material of the galaxies spread smoothly throughout space should equal the average total density in the Universe. To see why not, consider the following further results yielded by the mathematical form of the theory.

The average age of material in the Universe is equal, not to Hubble's constant, but to $\frac{1}{3}$ of Hubble's constant. Only some 5 per cent of material is as old as Hubble's constant, only about $\frac{1}{4}$ of a per cent is as old as twice Hubble's constant, only about $\frac{1}{100}$ of a per cent is as old as three times Hubble's constant. This decreasing proportion of material with age arises from the expansion of the Universe, which spreads out material more

331

and more thinly as it ages. The explanation of the seemingly paradoxical remarks of the previous paragraph is now clear. All material condenses into galaxies but the condensation takes a time of the order of Hubble's constant. We must allow time for a supragalactic cloud of gas to condense, for stars to form, for the initially loose structure of galaxies to compact. Only then do we observe a cluster of galaxies. This means that the condensed galaxies should comprise only a few per cent of the material of the Universe. What in fact is observed? That the average density given by smoothing the observed galaxies through space is a few per cent of the average total density calculated from the steady-state theory. Within the uncertainties of the observations, the agreement between observation and the theory is again excellent.

An entirely decisive confirmation of the steady-state theory would be obtained if clusters could be detected at an early stage of formation, before their constituent galaxies compacted. But unfortunately observations on this point are very difficult to make, for reasons that can readily be appreciated. Suppose that we distributed the Type II stars of M 31 throughout a vast halo, say 100,000 parsecs in diameter, and then removed the whole structure to a distance of 5 million parsecs. The resulting object would be extremely difficult to detect, since all that could possibly be observed would be a very faint glow in the sky. Yet this is how even a large galaxy newly forming at a comparatively moderate distance outside the Local Group would look. So although there may be quite a number of galaxies now condensing within a distance of 10 million parsecs it is not surprising that they have as yet escaped detection.

The position is a good deal more hopeful if instead of attempting to detect the early 'loose' structural form of a newly forming galaxy we consider the situation after the majority of the Type II stars have concentrated into a central amorphous nucleus. The problem is then no longer one of structural detection, since the galaxy now has a normal concentrated form, but of distinguishing a young Type II assembly from older Type II assemblies. Of the possible ways of distinguishing a young condensed galaxy probably the most effective will turn out to depend on the distribution of the total light of the galaxy with respect to colour. But as this possibility will take much the longest to discuss, it is best to consider another interesting possibility first.

The gaseous residue left over from the Type II star-formation process must become very considerably agitated during the concentration of a galaxy from an initially loose form. Now we have seen in previous chapters that the agitation of gas seems to be strongly correlated with the emission of radio-waves. It is possible therefore that galaxies might be detected during the concentration phase by strong radio emission, not of course so strong as when two galaxies collide as in the case of the two galaxies in Cygnus (Plate XLIX) but considerably stronger than a fully formed galaxy. In support of this view cases are known of galaxies that are not colliding with any other galaxy but which are unusually strong radio emitters. M 87 (Plate XXVII) is a spectacular example. Strong radio emission comes from the whole volume of this galaxy, which is also peculiar in possessing an enormous number of globular clusters and a jet of gas inside the main distribution of stars, the jet seemingly being emitted from near the centre of the system. One cannot help wondering whether M 87 might not be a galaxy of comparatively recent formation. A photo-electric examination of the extent of the halo of this galaxy might well prove of interest, as indeed might be the case for all those galaxies that show exceptionally strong radio emission and which are not collision cases.

A subtle criterion

It may eventually prove possible to obtain a precise determination of the age of a Type II star system from the distribution of colour within the total light emitted by the stars. To see how this might be done we note that most of the light of a Type II assembly comes from stars that are evolving off the main-sequence, and we may anticipate that its colour distribution must depend on what particular point of the main-sequence the stars are evolving from. Now this depends on the age of the system, so the colour distribution will therefore depend on the age of the system. It follows that by measuring the colour distribution it should be possible to infer the age in a straightforward way.

This would almost certainly be so if we knew just how the evolutionary tracks depend on the point of emergence from the main-sequence. The best way to obtain this information would be by direct observation. But the only complete evolutionary tracks so far determined by observation are for Type II star assemblies belonging to our own Galaxy and since these are of nearly the same age we only obtain the evolutionary tracks as they branch off rather a narrow range of the main-sequence. With one or two exceptions other galaxies are too distant for the important parts of the evolutionary track of their Type II stars to be obtained through the observation of individual stars. The exceptions are the Magellanic Clouds and one or two of the nearby loose systems of the Local Group. So far no measurements on these are available.

The alternative to an observational attack on the problem is to determine the evolutionary tracks by theoretical analysis. Although this project is being strenuously followed up, the theoretical results so far achieved are very far from being precise enough to be yet used in this context. So we see that as things stand at present there is no possibility of a direct inference of the age of a Type II star system from the colour distribution of its total light. This does not prevent a more limited observational programme from being applied, however. For example it is possible to find out whether the Type II star systems in the galaxies all have light with the same colour distribution. If so we should have a strong indication that all galaxies are of almost exactly the same age, thereby contradicting the steady-state theory. If on the other hand appreciable differences are found, we should have a strong indication that there are differences of age, although just what differences it would be impossible to tell until either the observational or theoretical knowledge discussed above becomes available.

This more limited programme has been started by Stebbins and Whitford. The results so far achieved will now be described. The distribution with respect to wavelength of the light received from the elliptical galaxy M 32 (Plate XLV), one of the satellite galaxies of the Andromeda Nebula, is shown in

334

Fig. 65. Two wavelengths are marked in this figure at A and B. The ratio of the amount of light received at B to the amount at A determines what is known as the index of colour for M 32. Although it gives a very incomplete representation of the shape

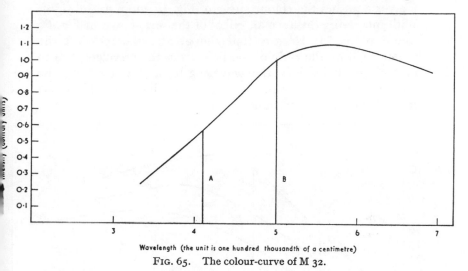

Wavelength (the unit is one hundred thousandth of a centimetre)

FIG. 65. The colour-curve of M 32.

of the whole curve this index is often used in observational work because its measurement is accomplished much more readily than the measurement of the whole colour-curve.

Now observations of colour index for a number of nearby elliptical galaxies and for the nuclei of a number of nearby spirals have shown a remarkable degree of constancy from one galaxy to another (although not agreeing with the Type II stars in the globular clusters it may be noted). This has been interpreted as indicating that all Type II systems in nearby elliptical galaxies and in the nuclei of the nearby spirals have colour curves of the same shape as that shown in Fig. 65. Such a view is perhaps a plausible one but it cannot be regarded as certainly established since only measurements for the whole range of wavelengths can settle the matter beyond question, and this has not yet been confirmed.

Accepting, however, the identity of the colour-curves in our immediate region of the Universe, it was at first argued that all

335

elliptical galaxies everywhere would probably also possess the same curve. If this were so then a very simple way of estimating red-shifts without any detailed measures of spectral lines would be available. The red-shift effect due to the expansion of the Universe pushes the colour curve of Fig. 65 more to the right. With increasing distance an effect of the sort shown in Fig. 66 would occur. It is clear that the greater the red-shift the greater will be the ratio of the light from the wavelength B to that of the light from the wavelength A. Or inverting the argument, the measurement of the colour index would enable the red-shift to be determined.

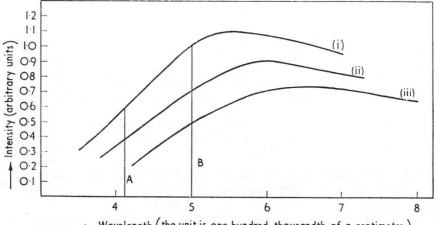

FIG. 66. (i) Unshifted colour-curve, (ii) curve shifted by a recessional speed of 20,000 km. per sec., (iii) curve shifted by a recessional speed of 40,000 km. per sec.

When this method was employed by Stebbins and Whitford it was found that the red-shifts estimated from the colour measurements were inconsistent with the red-shifts measured by the change in the position of spectral lines. Not only this but the disagreement was progressive, the greater the red-shift (i.e. the greater the distance) the greater was the discrepancy, the discrepancy being in the sense of an overestimate of the red-shift by the method described above. The certain inference is that the elliptical galaxies do not all possess the same colour curve. This in itself is perhaps not particularly surprising.

But what at first sight seems surprising is that the colour curves of the elliptical galaxies should change in a systematic way with distance. If we accept this conclusion and if further we reject the idea that our own locality in the Universe has the distinguishing feature of being placed in some special spacial sequence with respect to the colour curves of the elliptical galaxies observed by Stebbins and Whitford, then we seem to be left with only one argument. The systematic effect must apparently be due to the increasing time required for light to travel to us as the distances of the galaxies increase. We see a distant galaxy not as it is at the present time but as it was at the time the light set out on its journey across space to us. This idea leads to even more surprising conclusions when we follow its implications a little further.

The time required for light to travel to us from the most distant of the galaxies observed by Stebbins and Whitford is only some 1,000 million years. This is short compared to the times of evolution of the Type II stars in our own Galaxy—these have evolution times of about 6,000 million years. Apparently then the track of the evolving Type II stars (most of the light comes from the evolving stars) must change in some very pronounced way in a time of only 1,000 million years, even though the time for the whole evolution must be about 6,000 million years. At first sight this seems impossible but a detailed consideration of the problem suggests one somewhat implausible loophole. The index of colour depends on the ratio of the light received at two wavelengths. It certainly seems impossible that an appreciable change should occur in only 1,000 million years in the light received at the longer wavelength, B of Fig. 65, the light at this wavelength being emitted mainly by the stars in the ascending part of the evolutionary track N to O of Fig. 15. But a change of the index of colour could equally well arise from a change in the light received at the shorter wavelength A of Fig. 65. There is an appreciable contribution (if we accept information from the globular clusters) to this shorter wavelength range from stars that are placed late in the evolutionary track, from P to Q of Fig. 15. Perhaps the difference lies in these stars. So little is yet known about their detailed structural behaviour that we are not in a position to deny the assertion that the disposition of these stars may change appreciably in as little as 1,000 million years.

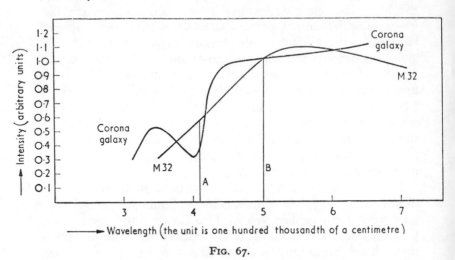

FIG. 67.

By observing at six different wavelength ranges instead of only two, Whitford and Code have recently confirmed that the differences of the colour curves do indeed lie at the shorter wavelengths. The nature of the differences found by Whitford and Code is shown in Fig. 67, where the colour curve of M 32 is given together with that of an elliptical galaxy in the Corona Borealis cluster (which is at about half the maximum distance to which Stebbins and Whitford carried their original measurements). The wavelength positions A and B are also marked in Fig. 67. It is seen that these particular wavelengths happen to be in positions that exaggerate to the full the difference between the ratios B to A for these two galaxies. If the wavelength A had been placed at a somewhat shorter wavelength no difference in the index of colour would have been measured, and if A had been placed at a still smaller wavelength the colour index would have been altered in an opposite sense, the galaxy in the Corona Borealis cluster would have seemed bluer instead of redder than M 32. This somewhat arbitrary feature of the method of measuring an index of colour has emphasised the importance of examining the whole colour curve, rather than just two portions of it.

But these remarks do not alter the situation that a systematic change of the colour curve, in the sense of an increasing ultra-violet emission with increasing distance, does seem to exist. Now let us move helter-skelter to a dramatic conclusion.

Such a distance effect, depending on time differences of only 1,000 million years—and for galaxies at moderate distances on times appreciably shorter than this, would be entirely masked if there were intrinsic age differences as great as 1,000 million years between the galaxies. Hence all the galaxies must have identical ages to within a few hundred million years. This conclusion, if we accept it, destroys the steady-state theory at once.

Indeed it turns out that only the superdense theory in the form advocated by Gamow can survive the present interpretation of the observations of Stebbins and Whitford. In Gamow's exposition the galaxies all condensed at the particular stage of the expansion of the Universe at which the average density in space was comparable with the average densities now found in the galaxies. The galaxies are supposed to be localised regions that at a certain stage of the general expansion failed for some unknown reason to continue in the expansion. The material of the Universe after expanding from the super-dense state is supposed to have suddenly gone into blobs that did not continue themselves to expand, the expansion becoming confined to the distances between the blobs. In this way the ages of the galaxies can be made coincident within a few hundred million years, as the Stebbins-Whitford measurements apparently require. But this theory has the serious weakness that it fails to explain why the galaxies are concentrated in clusters, and the existence of weak clusters like the Local Group seems to be entirely beyond explanation.

The impasse now reached is a serious one in which all three types of theory seem in one way or another to be in serious contradiction with observation. In these circumstances it seems worthwhile considering whether we were justified in dismissing at the outset the alternative possibility that the clusters of galaxies in which Stebbins and Whitford carried out their observations—the Local Group, the Virgo Cloud (Plate XXXVIII), the Corona Borealis cluster (Plate XL), and the Boötes cluster (Plate LVII) form a sequence with respect to age. Is it possible that the times of travel of the light from these various clusters has nothing at all to do with the matter; that it is the clusters themselves that are of grossly different ages? The degree of coincidence required is not very great. We require the Local Group and the Virgo Cloud to be of about the same age, then the Corona Borealis cluster must have a shifted age, and the Boötes cluster must have an age shifted still more in the same direction (at this stage of the argument we do not have to specify whether older or younger). It has been pointed out by Gold and Sciama that a graduation both as regards size and population exists between these same clusters, the Virgo Cloud being larger and containing more galaxies than the Corona Borealis cluster and the Corona cluster being larger and containing more galaxies than the Boötes cluster. In view of these differences, why not a graduation with respect to age also?

Another point that requires emphasis is that Stebbins and Whitford found elliptical galaxies to be the only ones showing systematic effects. Spiral galaxies showed no systematic effects presumably because of the presence in spirals of bright young stars of Type I. Now in some degree the distinction between elliptical galaxies and spiral galaxies is not an entirely clearcut one. In Chapter 15 we saw that the ellipticals predominate in the clusters probably because they are stripped of gas by collisions with one another. When we observe an elliptical galaxy two ages are really relevant, one is the age of its Type II population, and the other is the interval since it lost its gas by collision. This latter age is important because it affects the issue as to what Type I stars might still be left even though all the gas has been lost. A galaxy that lost its gas say 2,000 million years ago might well still contain sufficient of the not too bright Type I stars that condensed 2,000 million years ago (before the gas was lost) for its emission of blue light to be much affected. Another galaxy might have lost its gas say 5,000 million years ago in which case the Type I stars might contribute only negligibly to the blue light. The chance of a

340

galaxy losing gas by collision inside a cluster is much affected by the richness of the cluster, so we see how a variation in the population of clusters might well play a role in affecting the colour curves of its constituent galaxies, even of those that are apparently of an elliptical type.

These two additional possibilities, one a gross difference of age between the clusters examined, and the other a complication through contamination of some apparent elliptical galaxies with Type I stars, seem inherently more plausible than the interpretation in accordance with a strict similarity of ages. This is not only because of the impasse reached in the above argument but also because so far no explanation is available as to how a time as short as 1,000 million years can appreciably affect the colour curve of any old Type II distribution of stars. There is also what seems a crushing argument that has so far been held in reserve. Stebbins and Whitford found considerable variations in the index of colour from one elliptical galaxy to another within the Virgo Cloud. Differences in the time of transit of light cannot be used here, so that we must of necessity fall back on inherent differences. The steady-state theory, in that it requires the material of the Virgo Cloud to have condensed from an initially more dispersed state, leads to the conclusion that differences of ages amounting to several thousand million years should occur within one and the same cluster. This is in accordance with observation. On the explosion theory there should be no differences.

The upshot of this discussion is that an observational examination of the colour curves of the elliptical galaxies provides the possibility of a powerful attack on the problem of the ages of the galaxies. We have seen that the interpretation of the observations is still fraught with great uncertainties but it does seem as though this type of work should be able to answer the question posed by the steady-state theory as to whether the galaxies are of variable age or not. This should go far toward making a definite choice between the three types of theory. If matters still seem very uncertain it must always be remembered that clearly sign-posted roads are not to be expected at a pioneering frontier.

CHAPTER TWENTY

The Continuous Origin of Matter

The origin of matter as a law

It remains in this last chapter to discuss more of the details of the continuous origin of matter and of the cosmological theory based on it. There is an impulse to ask where originated material comes from. But such a question is entirely meaningless within the terms of reference of science. Why is there gravitation? Why do electric fields exist? Why is the Universe? These queries are on a par with asking where newly originated matter comes from, and they are just as meaningless and unprofitable. The dividing line between what can validly be asked and what cannot depends on the organisation of science, in particular on the role played by the laws of physics. We can ask questions quite freely about the consequences of the laws of physics. But if we ask why the laws of physics are as they are, we shall receive only the answer that the laws of physics have consequences that agree with observation. If further we ask why this agreement exists, we enter into the territory of metaphysics—the scientist at all events will not attempt any answer. Newton's law of gravitation can be used to predict when and where the next total eclipse of the Sun is going to occur, and you may depend on it that events will fall pat in accordance with prediction. But we must then be satisfied. We must not go on to ask why.

It follows that when the origin of matter becomes a law of physics it is completely protected from such prying questions as: where does matter come from? An impregnable shield against such questions is provided by law, scientific law, the *modus operandi* of science. This does not of course mean that the continuous origin of matter is protected from all attack. It means that the attack must come from a different quarter. It

342

must come from a comparison of the consequences of the law with observation. And this is just what the preceding chapter was about.

The present situation is not new. When a neutron changes to a proton by a β-process an electron is disgorged. The electron originates. It did not exist before the process, after the process it does. Yet no one ever seems to have been worried by the question of where the electron comes from. We say that it originates in accordance with the laws of β-disintegration.

It is time now that we came to the law of the continuous origin of matter itself. Matter is capable of exerting several types of influence—or fields as they are usually called. There is the nuclear field that binds together the atomic nuclei. There is the electro-magnetic field that enables atoms to absorb light. There is the gravitational field that holds the stars and galaxies together. And according to the new theory there is also a creation field that causes matter to originate. Matter originates in response to the influence of other matter. It is this latter field that causes the expansion of the Universe. The distances over which the several fields operate are in an ascending scale—the nuclear field has the smallest range, although within this range it is easily the most powerful; next come the electro-magnetic influences which have their main importance over the range of size from atoms up to stars (the range in which we humans lie); then the gravitational field is dominant over all sizes from planets and stars up to the clusters of galaxies; and lastly comes the universal field, the creation field, dominant in the largest aspects of the Universe.

We can pull off an important stroke at this stage. Because the creation influence is mainly determined by very distant material it cannot vary much from point to point. The proximity of the Sun does not produce any enhanced influence here on the Earth, nor does the fact that we happen to lie in the Galaxy. It may well be this smooth distribution of the creation influence that is responsible for the large scale spatial uniformity of the Universe.

Mach's Principle and the General Theory of Relativity

It is curious how even the most everyday incidents are intimately related to the large scale aspects of the Universe. The darkness of the sky at night is one example. The winds are another. The winds have a general prevailing direction from west to east. Every air-traveller knows that because of the winds it takes longer to fly from London to New York than from New York to London. The meteorologist explains this in terms of the Earth's rotation, by saying that the Earth is turning around on its polar axis in such a way as to rotate from west to east. If the Earth rotated the opposite way the winds would blow from east to west, and the East Coast of the U.S. would then have a climate like Mediterranean Europe, N.W. Europe would be frozen out, and the British Isles in particular would take up a climate similar to that of Kamchatka.

Although there is little doubt that these prognostications would prove correct, the argument—good enough as it is for ordinary purposes—does not pass muster in a strict logical test. It is not really correct to talk of a body as spinning around (although we have often done so in earlier chapters!). There is no such thing as a spin pure and simple. We can talk with precision of a body as spinning around *relative* to something or other, but there is no such thing as an absolute spin: the Earth is not spinning to those of us who live on its surface and our point of view is as good as anyone else's—but no better. So it is really quite wrong to speak of the winds as blowing on the Earth from west to east because the Earth is spinning round from west to east. We can only say that the winds blow predominantly from west to east because the Earth is turning relative to something or other. Now turning relative to what? Turning relative to an observer on the Moon (i.e. turning as seen by an observer on the Moon)? Turning as seen by an observer on the Sun? Turning as seen by an observer on Sirius (assuming such an observer could see the Earth)? Turning as seen by an observer in some globular cluster? Turning as seen by some observer in the Andromeda Nebula? Turning as seen by an observer in M 87?

These questions may have a monotonous aspect, but they

344

are all very relevant. Every one of the observers would arrive at a different answer if they could measure the rotation of the Earth accurately, although several of the measurements would be extremely close to each other. The situation that the measurements would disagree with each other by however small a margin makes it extremely implausible that we should answer any one of the questions in the affirmative. If we did so, if we said for instance that it is the rotation relative to the observer on Sirius that sets the winds blowing on the Earth, we should then have to face up to the demand for an explanation of why this one observer should be so privileged and not the others. Rather than attempt to meet such a seemingly impossible demand we must agree that it cannot be the rotation of the Earth relative to any of these observers that is the single determining factor. Rather does it seem preferable to say that it is not the rotation of the Earth relative to any one body or particle that is decisive but that some average rotation has to be determined, a rotation averaged in some manner with respect to all the material in the Universe. In such an average we may expect that material at great distances from the Earth will dominate, just as it must in the law of the continuous origin of matter. So we can perhaps best answer the question of what makes the winds blow on the Earth by saying that it is rotation relative to the really distant material of the Universe, material at distances comparable with the Olbers limit, about 2,000 million parsecs, 40,000,000,000,000,000,000,000,000 miles away.

This is an astonishing conclusion but one I think that can scarcely be gainsaid. It was first enunciated in 1893 by the Austrian philosopher Ernst Mach, and is usually referred to as Mach's principle. One of the original aims of Einstein in the formulation of his general theory of relativity was to give precise mathematical expression to Mach's principle. In the outcome the general theory of relativity contains a curious dichotomy. From one point of view it does give precise expression to Mach's principle. From another point of view it contradicts Mach's principle. This dichotomy is worth considering.

If it is assumed that matter is distributed uniformly on a large scale then the relativity theory allows one to prove Mach's principle. But this highly satisfactory result is much tempered

345

by the situation that when we do not assume the material in the Universe to be uniformly distributed on a large scale a corresponding result cannot be proved. There is indeed a very simple case in which the theory leads to an absurdity. The theory permits us to think of a 'universe' that contains *only* the Earth and the Sun with no other material present at all. In such a universe the forces that control the terrestrial winds can be made (according to the theory) to do anything we please, to drive the winds just as they actually occur if we wish, or even if we feel so disposed to make the winds blow in the opposite direction from east to west. According to Mach's principle it should only be the rotation of the Earth relative to the Sun that has significance in such a universe. Yet the theory of relativity admits rotary forces that are in no way connected with the rotation of the Earth relative to the Sun. This notable failure of the theory is characteristic of any discussion of a 'universe' containing only a spatially localised distribution of material.

Two entirely different points of view have been put forward to meet this situation. One argues that the material of the Universe does in fact seem to be distributed uniformly, and that in this case the relativity theory satisfies Mach's principle. This first point of view makes no claim to answer the question of why the material of the Universe is uniformly distributed on the large scale. Instead it is supposed that the uniformity of the Universe is a property derived from the manner of its creation—the Universe was started uniform and has been approximately that way ever since. This is the view of the protagonists of the superdense cosmology. On this view we are obliged not only to attribute such general cosmic manifestations as the expansion of the Universe and the large scale uniformity of matter to the way that the Universe started off, but also the forces controlling such literary mundane matters as the winds on the Earth.

In spite of the unsatisfactory character of a theory that is obliged to place its crucial processes beyond the range of both observational verification and of tests of theoretical consistency, a number of physicists have expressed themselves as not in disagreement with this procedure. The disposition to fall back in so many essential features on the way the Universe was started off is presumably due to a common situation in physics; that the behaviour of a localised system always depends on starting conditions. But the starting conditions in such a case are simply a way of giving precise exposition to how the system in question happens to be localised. Manifestly the Universe is not a localised system, by definition the Universe is synonymous with 'everything there is'. Consequently there is no real parallel between the problems of everyday physics and problems that concern the whole Universe. I am strongly of the view that the difference is a crucial one and that all starting conditions should be eschewed in cosmology. If this opinion is accepted the above argument must be entirely abandoned, and a quite different approach to the cosmological problem must be sought.

The direction that such a new line of attack should take was already foreshadowed in our discussion of the relation of the relativity theory to Mach's principle. The implication of this discussion would seem to be that the theory is not wrong but incomplete, that components are missing that would make an important difference in the case where the theory is unsuccessful but which would make no important difference in the successful case. It is at just this point that the mathematical expression for the creation influence becomes important. The theory of relativity can be modified in an interesting way by the inclusion of the creation field in its equations. The new terms lead to the continuous origin of matter and to the expansion of the Universe. It is on the resulting mathematical theory that all previous statements about the steady-state theory have been based.

The position in this respect of the steady-state theory is worth emphasising. Assuming a general spatial uniformity, it is found that if at a particular time the average density of matter is less than a certain critical value, space will become fuller and fuller of material until the density rises to the critical value, after which the density is maintained constant. Conversely if the average density of matter were initially greater than the critical value the Universe would expand so fast that the density would fall back to the same value as before, after

347

which it would again be maintained constant. The Universe accordingly possesses uniformity with respect to time. This suggests a penetrating question: must the Universe also possess a general uniformity with respect to space? Is it the case that if at one time the material in the Universe were not distributed uniformly with respect to space that sooner or later it must come to be so distributed? If this could be shown, subject to one essential proviso, the outstanding problem of cosmology would have been solved.

The proviso just mentioned is that the theory must not establish spatial uniformity too strongly, otherwise condensation leading to the formation of clusters of galaxies could not occur. The requirement is one of very large scale uniformity but not of complete uniformity. This is an important and probably crucial aspect of the problem. To appreciate its significance we may consider in general terms the process by which new clusters of galaxies are supposed to form. As with humans, one generation of galaxies impresses its pattern on the next. The basic idea, due to Sciama, is that processes occurring inside already existing clusters lead to portions of the clusters breaking away from the main group. These evaporated fragments move out from their parent clusters into newly originated material where they act as condensation centres for the formation of new clusters. This idea is undoubtedly correct, in that fragments must certainly evaporate away on occasion from already existing clusters, and they must then act as new condensation centres. But the requirements of the steady-state theory are far more stringent than this. Because in the steady-state theory we have to deal with an indefinitely large number of generations the population of galaxies must have a reproduction factor from generation to generation exactly equal to 1. And in addition to the total population of galaxies the average spatial size of the clusters must also be reproduced from generation to generation. If the reproduction factor for size were less than 1 clusters would eventually die out and all galaxies would become single. If on the other hand the reproduction factor were maintained greater than 1 the size of the clusters would grow indefinitely and the large scale uniformity of the Universe would ultimately be destroyed.

What then controls the reproduction factor for cluster sizes? Shortage of material may be the answer, as it probably is in the case of the total number of galaxies. But it is difficult to resist the impression that subtler effects are at work. It seems perhaps most likely that above a certain size the large scale unifying requirement of the Universe becomes dominant. The suggestion is that if the average cluster size were less than a critical value the reproduction factor for cluster sizes would be greater than 1 and the average size of clusters would grow from generation to generation until the critical value was reached, at which stage the tendency towards uniformity would cut the reproduction factor back to 1. A stable situation would then be reached with the average cluster size neither growing larger nor smaller. Perhaps the central problem facing the protagonists of the steady-state theory is to demonstrate the correctness of this proposition.

Epilogue

It is now time to give a general summing up of the discussion of both this and the two preceding chapters. It will be clear that the aim of the steady-state theory is to dispense with arbitrary conditions: arbitrary starting conditions leading to expansion and large scale uniformity, arbitrary conditions leading to the formation of galaxies. Instead of attributing the main features of the Universe to arbitrary fiat it is proposed that nothing less should be possible than a demonstration that all the main features of the Universe are consequences of the laws of physics, entirely independent of any starting conditions.

The conventional outlook of present-day physics is that all physical laws are to be discovered by an examination of very small scale happenings in the laboratory, by the examination of the properties of atoms with particular reference to the nuclei of the atoms. Yet we have an example of a law of physics that was not discovered by experiments in the laboratory and whose relation to the field of atomic physics is still not understood. This is the law of gravitation. What we know about gravitation was discovered from a study of phenomena on the scale of our own solar system (this statement applies both to the work of Newton and of Einstein). Are we then to suppose that no further additions to the laws of physics are to be obtained through the study of the Universe on a scale larger than the solar system? The distance to Olbers' limit is more than 100,000,000,000,000 times greater than the distance of the Earth from the Sun. Is the study of the Universe on such a tremendous scale to be no more than an exercise in the application of what we have already learned on the Earth and within the solar system? We should certainly doubt whether this is so were it not for the fact that a great deal of what happens on a larger scale is very readily explicable in terms of our extremely locally derived knowledge. The behaviour of the whole of our Galaxy, of the stars in it, of their formation from gas clouds, of the motions and properties of the gas clouds, all appear entirely explicable in terms of locally derived knowledge. It is only when we come to phenomena on an extragalactic scale, on a scale greater than the clusters of galaxies, that we arrive at a situation where our locally derived knowledge apparently breaks down—for it seems fair to describe a recourse to a whole set of arbitrary starting conditions as a break-down. The suspicion is that what we ought to be deriving as consequences of the laws of physics we are being obliged to accept as conditions arbitrarily imposed for no reasons that we understand. This procedure is quite characteristic of the outlook of primitive peoples, who in attempting to explain the local behaviour of the physical world are obliged in their ignorance of the laws of physics to have recourse to arbitrary starting conditions. These are given credence by postulating the existence of gods, gods of the sea who determine the arbitrary starting conditions that control the motion of the sea, gods of the mountains, gods of the forests, of the air, of the seasons of the year, of the Sun, of the Moon, and so forth. There is a strong hint that what modern man has tried to do with the Universe is no better than what primitive man did with problems whose nature we now find simple but which once no doubt seemed just as complicated as the problems that remain unsolved today. In principle arbitrary starting conditions are to be avoided if any alternative attack is possible.

The argument leading to the steady-state theory is one such line of attack. Already the old requirement that the expansion of the Universe be imposed as a starting condition has been disposed of, but many problems remain—the average size of clusters of galaxies and the large scale uniformity of the Universe are two of them.

How far the present attack will go is difficult to say. My impression is that it will go a considerable way but that a complete success is not to be expected. More penetrating developments seem necessary, for the theory must surely be related to the properties of individual particles in a more significant way than anything that is understood at present. We have spoken of material originating as hydrogen and there is now strong evidence that this view is correct. Why does the

351

material of the Universe originate as hydrogen? Hydrogen is certainly the simplest of the elements, but an argument based on simplicity is scarcely an entirely satisfactory one. There must it seems be a clear-cut reason why it is hydrogen that originates and not other elements. What this reason is we do not know. Nor can the reason apparently be supplied within the framework of any of the theories that are being considered at the moment. Yet unless a reason can be given we are once again faced with an arbitrary situation. Even if all the projects outlined above turn out successfully the theory must still be judged incomplete until it has explained why it is only hydrogen that can originate and not other elements. And we can scarcely imagine that such an explanation can be forthcoming until a connection with the detailed theories of nuclear physics has been established.

In the first chapter we spoke of the fourth revolution in physics, the revolution that has only just started, and we said that so far it is not known how this revolution may come to affect our conceptions of the Universe. It is difficult to resist the impression that we have now reached the stage of our argument where a connection with the fourth revolution of physics is likely to take place. At the moment man's investigation of the ultra-small ends in mystery and his investigation of the ultra-large ends in mystery. It is not a very far-fetched hope that the two mysteries will turn out to be closely connected. We spoke in the first chapter of the range of size of the phenomena examined by physics, the size of the ultra-large being greater than the size of the ultra-small by the huge number 10,000,000,000,000,000,000,000,000,000,000,000,000,000. The hope is that the two ends of this enormous span will become tightly connected and that physics instead of being entirely contained in the ultra-small will come to be considered over a whole connected circle of argument.

There are some extremely curious numerical similarities that give support to this view. If we take the ratio of the electrical force between a proton and an electron to the gravitational force between them we again obtain an enormous number, and it turns out to be close to the enormous number written down above. Is this just a chance coincidence? If we put it down to chance, then what do we make of the fact that if we take the square root of the number of hydrogen atoms within the Olbers limit we obtain another extremely large number, a number that is again very close to the one written down in the previous paragraph. Is this just another coincidence? If we take the ratio of the density in the central region of a supernova to the average density of material in the Universe we again obtain a number that is similar to the one of the previous paragraph. Is this a coincidence once more? Unless we are willing to answer that all are coincidences, we are obliged to suppose that the laws of physics as we know them today are substantially incomplete and that so far unperceived connections must exist between the physics of the ultra-small and the physics of the ultra-large.

The only really serious attempt to discover what these curious relations may be was made by Eddington. Yet Eddington's work in this respect has passed without much regard, not because physicists doubt that relations exist, but because it is very seriously doubted whether enough is yet known to allow any useful insight to be gained into the problem. Eddington's attempt was made within the terms of reference of what we have called the third revolution of physics. It is generally felt that physics was then too incomplete, and that the hoped-for understanding will only be forthcoming in the course of the fourth revolution.

One further remark must be made about the steady-state theory of the Universe. It is not a point in support of this theory that it contains conclusions for which we might happen to have an emotional preference. Herbert Dingle has quite correctly warned us recently against promoting a theory simply because we happen to like it. The grounds for the acceptance of a theory are its agreement with observation. The grounds for a serious discussion of a theory lie in the possibility of subjecting it to observational test. This condition the steady-state theory fulfils in good measure, as we saw in the previous chapter. The steady-state theory must always be more subject to observational check than its rivals because by disposing of arbitrary starting conditions it removes a whole series of hypotheses that from their very nature are beyond test.

The weakness of the superdense theory for instance is that it puts most of the important observational features of the Universe into its starting conditions—the reason for the expansion of the Universe, for its large scale uniformity, for the condensation of the galaxies, are put into the theory in a manner that cannot be tested. This is to miss what seems to be the whole point of a scientific theory, that its value depends on the possibility of disproving it: Gold has expressed this most aptly by saying that 'for a theory to be of any value it must be vulnerable'. Vulnerability supplies the conditions for success or failure in accordance with observational tests, and it is on this that science, and indeed all rational argument, is based. The aim in science is not to build a theory that is so hedged in with protective conditions that nobody can get at it. The aim is to build a theory that is exposed to observational attack in as many directions as possible, and which then manages to survive.

Quite apart from its attempt to eliminate arbitrary starting conditions there is a further reason why the steady-state theory must be more vulnerable to observational attack than any other cosmological theory. In the steady-state theory all observable features must be consequences of processes that are still happening. In other theories most of the important features of the Universe are consequences of processes that are over and done with. In some cases there may be a possibility of examining the situation at an earlier time by observing light received from great distances (the light having started on its journey at a much earlier time, and therefore giving information about an earlier state of affairs). But this will not always be the case, and indeed no positive observation has so far been made that refers unequivocally to a significantly different epoch from the present. In the steady-state theory all processes must on the other hand still be happening and are therefore susceptible to observation. The steady-state theory therefore places observation on a stronger footing than any other theory, since according to the steady-state theory there is no aspect of cosmology that cannot (at any rate in principle) be directly verified. It is true that we must not accept a theory on the basis of an emotional preference but it is not an emotional preference to attempt to establish a theory that would place us in a position to obtain a complete understanding of the Universe. The stakes are high, and win or lose, are worth playing for.

Index

71 72 73 10 9 8